ORGANIC CHEMISTRY 1 PRIMER 2018

BY RHETT C. SMITH, ANDREW G. TENNYSON, AND TANIA HOUJEIRY

Marketed by Proton Guru

Find additional online resources and guides at protonguru.com, online July 2

There is a lot of online video content to accompany this book at the Proton Guru YouTube Channel! Just go to YouTube and search "Proton Guru Channel" to easily find our content.

Correlating these reactions with your course: The homepage at protonguru.com provides citations to popular text books for further reading on each reaction in this book, so that you can follow along using this book in any course using one of these texts.

Instructors: Free PowerPoint lecture slides to accompany this text can be obtained by emailing IQ@proton.guru from your accredited institution email account. The homepage at protonguru.com provides a link to citations to popular text books for further reading on each Lesson topic in this primer.

Cover photo courtesy of By William C. Dennis, Jr.

Printed in the United States of America

10 9 8 7 6 5 4 3 2 1

ISBN 978-0-9991672-7-4

Organic Chemistry 1 Primer 2018

Rhett C. Smith, Ph.D.

Andrew G. Tennyson, Ph.D.

Tania Houjeiry, Ph.D.

Table of Contents

Purpose of the Primer

This brief, plain language Primer is meant to provide the most basic principles and concepts of organic chemistry as simply as possible. It is meant to be an excellent *primer* to read *before* lecture so that once you get to lecture you will already have some knowledge of what will be discussed. It is also meant to be an excellent pre-exam review. Especially in cases where you are preparing for a final exam – which may be cumulative and cover material that you have not specifically studied for weeks or months – it should be useful as a more compact review than will be offered by a text book or other study guides.

Online Content, Reaction Guide and Practice Problems

There are many resources to support the material covered in this book. Many of these resources are found on protonguru.com (launched in July 2018).

The Proton Guru website site includes:

- Links to video content including solved practice problem videos and lectures for important topics

- References to chapters in popular text books used at universities so that you can use this book and all the associated YouTube video content easily in any course using those text books

- Printable brief study sheets and executive summaries to help you study

- Links to other tutorial websites with even more practice problems and videos

Proton Guru also has a reaction and practice problem guide that can be used with this Primer. It is "Organic Chemistry 1 Reactions and Practice Problems 2018" by Rhett C. Smith and can be found on Amazon.com.

The Reactions and Practice Problems book includes:

- Brief review of each reaction with bullet point lists of key features of each reaction and a quick self test/answers for each reaction

- More extensive Problem Sets for important topics, including multiple choice questions like you might see on standardized exams

- Progress Checks: practice exams with solutions

- A cumulative practice final exam on reactions and introductory concepts in a typical first semester organic chemistry course

PART I. Structure, Stability and Conventions

Lesson I.1 Coulombic Forces and Representation of Structure

Lesson I.2: Polarity, Dipole Moments and Formal Charge

Lesson I.3: Intermolecular Forces, Boiling Point and Melting Point

Lesson I.4: Nucleophiles, Electrophiles and Functional Groups

Lesson I.5: Arrow-Pushing Formalism

Lesson I.6: Hybridization, Sigma and Pi Bonds, Lone Pairs and Bond Geometry

Lesson I.7: Resonance and Delocalization Energy

Lesson I.8: Elementary Steps of Reaction Mechanisms: Applying the Arrow-Pushing Formalism

Lesson I.9: Acids and Bases I: Definitions

Lesson I.10: Acids and Bases II: Relating Structure to the Strength of an Acid or Base

Lesson I.11: Stability of Cations and Radicals

Lesson I.12: Predicting Reaction Spontaneity and Direction of Equilibria

Lesson I.13: Reaction Coordinate Diagrams and Reaction Rate

Lesson I.14: Nomenclature I: Alkanes, Alkyl Halides, Alcohols and Cycloalkanes

Lesson I.15: Isomerism and Conformational Analysis I: Linear Alkanes and Newman Projections

Lesson I.16: Conformational Analysis II: Cycloalkanes and the Chair Conformation of Cyclohexane

Lesson I.17: Stereochemistry I: Chirality and Optical Activity

Lesson I.18: Stereochemistry II: Cahn-Ingold-Prelog Rules and Assigning R- and S- Labels of Configuration

Lesson I.19: Stereochemistry III: Fischer Projections

Lesson I.20: Stereochemistry IV: Enantiomers, Diastereomers and Meso Compounds

Lesson 1.1: Coulombic Forces

Coulombic forces are the forces that exist between charged particles. Particles may be either negatively charged or positively charged. Negative charges repel other negative charges, and positive charges repel other positive charges. Such repulsive forces tend to push like-charged entities away from one another as much as possible. If you hold two like-charged entities in close proximity, you will have to apply force, thus *exerting energy* to keep them close together. This creates a *strain*, and the interaction of like-charged particles is said to be **unfavorable** or **destabilizing.**

Oppositely-charged particles attract one another. This means that if two oppositely-charged particles come in close proximity, they will **spontaneously** pull towards one another; their interaction is said to be **favorable**, and arrangements that maximize such attractive forces are **stabilizing**.

The fundamental particle of negative charge is the electron (sometimes written as "e^-"). The fundamental particle of positive charge is the proton (sometimes written as "H^+"). In the familiar picture of an atom, the positive charge is located in the nucleus while the negatively-charged electrons are held in an "orbit" or "cloud" around the nucleus by attractive Coulombic forces. In an atom, the number of electrons is equal to the number of protons, so that the atom is overall neutral. In general chemistry, you learned that an atom can lose one or more electrons, leaving an excess of positive charge. The resultant species, an ion, is charged. A positively-charged ion is called a **cation** (pronounced "CAT-eye-on"). If an atom gains one electron or more, there is an excess of negative charge, thus forming a negatively-charged ion, which is called an **anion** (pronounced "ANN-eye-on").

Example I.1.1

Provide the charge of the ion formed when each of the following species undergoes the indicated change:

a.   gain one electron
$Cl \longrightarrow$?

b.   gain one electron
$[CH_3]^+ \longrightarrow$?

c.   gain one electron
$O^- \longrightarrow$?

d.   lose one electron
$Br \longrightarrow$?

e.   lose one electron
$O^- \longrightarrow$?

f.   lose one electron
$Cu^+ \longrightarrow$?

Solution I.1.1

Adding an electron (in a-c) leads to one additional unit of negative charge. So, in a. the neutral Cl becomes Cl^-. For b., the +1 charge of the $[CH_3]^+$ cation becomes $(+1-1) = 0$, giving $[CH_3]$. For c., O^- has a -1 charge so after adding another unit of negative charge it becomes O^{-2}. If an electron is removed from a species, it gains one more unit of positive charge. So, in d. the Br becomes Br^+, while in c. the O^- becomes a neutral O atom, and in f. Cu^+ becomes Cu^{+2}.

Lesson I.1.2: Representation of Structure

We learned in general chemistry (or even high school chemistry) how to draw Lewis dot structures to represent molecular structures, and how to interpret these representations. If you do not recall how to write Lewis structures, you will need to review this to succeed in organic chemistry. In the Lewis structures, one can use a dot to represent one electron and a line to represent two electrons. It is vital to your ability to understand organic chemistry that you recognize that a line or a dot represents negatively-charged electrons in the outer shell of an atom (the valence electrons). The atomic symbol (the letter(s) you use for the atom in a structure) represents the positively-charged nucleus, along with any inner-shell electrons (which typically do not interact with other atoms).

In your study of the valence shell electron pair repulsion (VSEPR) theory, you likely also encountered a way to draw bonds in order to represent a three-dimensional shape on a flat surface by using wedge or hashed lines. In this convention, wedges represent bonds coming out of the surface (e.g., chalkboard, whiteboard, paper, computer screen, etc.), hashed lines represent bonds going into the surface, and simple lines represent bonds that lie within the plane of the surface:

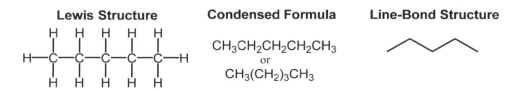

C-X and D-X bonds: in the plane of the page
A-X bond: comes out of page, with A closer to the viewer
B-X bond: goes into the page, with B farther from the viewer

In addition to the familiar Lewis structures and wedge/hashed lines, organic chemists use the *line-bond* notation to represent organic structures. The line-bond notation is especially helpful for organic compounds having multiple carbon atoms in chains or rings. An example of how the line bond is used to abbreviate a five-carbon-long chain is shown below:

Lewis Structure	**Condensed Formula**	**Line-Bond Structure**

$CH_3CH_2CH_2CH_2CH_3$
or
$CH_3(CH_2)_3CH_3$

In the line-bond notation, a line represents a bond, just as it does in the Lewis structure notation. However, in the line-bond notation, each bend in a line, end of a line, or change in the number of parallel lines (e.g., single bond to triple bond) represents a carbon atom. In this notation, one assumes the correct number of H atoms on each carbon for the given charge. A neutral carbon atom has four bonds, so any bonds not explicitly shown in the line-bond notation are assumed to be to H; one does not need to draw out the H atoms on carbon atoms whose symbols are not drawn out as a C. All other non-C atoms, as well as any H atoms attached to non-carbon atoms *must* be shown. Also, if you draw out a 'C' letter for a carbon atom by choice (even though you do not have to), you would need to show all the H atoms on that C, for example:

11

For C₃H₆: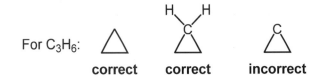

correct   **correct**   **incorrect**

Here are a few examples of compounds shown in both Lewis structure and line-bind notation. One can readily see how the line bond notation can save a lot of time in drawing a structure as well as provide a simplified, compact picture of the molecule:

represents the same molecule as:

represents the same molecule as:

represents the same molecule as:

Example I.1.2

Provide the line-bond structure for each of these Lewis structures:

A)   B)   C)

Solution I.1.2

A)   B)   C)

12

Lesson I.2.1: Polarity

In your prior chemistry courses, you learned about electronegativity and its influence on polarity, dipole moments, etc. We will briefly review how some of these concepts apply specifically to organic chemistry. Electronegativity is the pull an atom exerts on electrons in a bond. A higher value of electronegativity indicates a greater pull for electrons. Electronegativity of an element increases towards the top and towards the right side of the periodic table, with F being the most electronegative element.

In a bond between two atoms of equal electronegativity, the electrons in the bond will be held exactly in between the two nuclei in a symmetric distribution of charge, so there are no regions of unusually high negative or positive charge, and thus the bond is **nonpolar**. If the electronegativity values for two atoms are quite similar, then those bonds are not significantly polar. **An important example of nonpolar bonds in organic chemistry are C–H bonds.**

Examples of Nonpolar Bonds

ALL the bonds in this molecule!

If one of the atoms in a bond has a significantly higher electronegativity, it pulls the electrons more closely towards it, so that there is more negative charge on its end of the bond, and less on the other end from which the electrons were pulled, creating a *polar bond*:

Arrows Point to Polar Bonds in these Examples

In the picture above, you may notice two new symbols. The δ^- symbol indicates **the partial negative charge** present at the negative pole of a **polar bond**, while the δ^+ symbol indicates the **partial positive charge** present at the positive pole of the polar bond. The use of these symbols to indicate what sites on a molecule have an excess of charge will become very important to your ability to solve problems as we move through organic chemistry. The greater the difference in electronegativity between the two bonded atoms, the more polar the bond will be, and thus there will be greater amounts of positive and negative partial charges on each side of the polar bond.

The polarity of a bond may also be represented by a **dipole moment** arrow. These arrows are vector arrows that have a "plus sign" at one end and the arrow head points in the direction in which the electrons are pulled:

Using Dipole Arrows to Indicate Polar Bonds

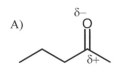

Example I.2.1

Fill in the δ+ and δ– symbols for any polar bonds in the structures below.

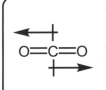

Solution I.2.1

Lesson I.2.2: Dipole Moments of Molecules

One or more polar bonds may be present in a molecule, and each of the polar bonds that is present may pull electrons in a different direction. The sum of all these vectors representing electron-pulling forces in their respective directions is equal to the **dipole moment of that entire molecule**. If there are two bonds of equal polarity, but the two are oriented such that they pull electrons in opposite directions, then the molecule as a whole is not polar. An example is carbon dioxide (CO_2):

O=C=O   The vector arrows have equal magnitude and point in opposite directions. They therefore cancel one another out. This is not a polar <u>molecule</u>, even though there are polar <u>bonds</u> present.

In cases where there are two dipole vectors pointing in non-opposing directions, the sum of the vectors can result in a dipole moment for the molecule that points in a direction in which neither of the polar bonds is pointing. An example is in water:

The small black vector is the dipole moment for the molecule. The larger grey arrows represent the dipole for each bond. The sum of bond vectors is the dipole moment of the molecule.

Example I.2.2

Fill in the molecular dipole moment for each molecule:

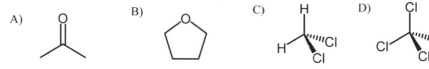

A)   B)   C)   D)

Solution I.2.2

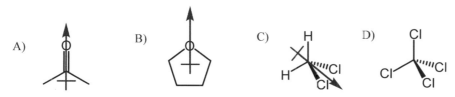

A)   B)   C)   D)

No molecular dipole despite polar bonds; the pull in all four directions cancel out!

15

Lesson I.2.3: Formal Charge

In addition to the partial charges discussed above, some atoms can take on a full positive or negative charge, as you have no doubt seen in ions in your prior courses in chemistry. It is important to know how to assign formal charges in organic chemistry. The formula for formal charge of an atom in a structure can be given as follows:

Formal charge =
[# of valence e^- in neutral atom] – [# nonbonding e^- on the atom] – [number of bonds to that atom]

Consider carbon in several different structures:

(valence – nonbonding electrons – bonds)	(valence – nonbonding electrons – bonds)
(4 – 0 – 4) =	(4 – 0 – 3) =
formal charge of 0 (zero) on C	formal charge of +1 on C
(valence – nonbonding electrons – bonds)	(valence – nonbonding electrons – bonds)
(4 – 2 – 2) =	(4 – 2 – 3) =
formal charge of 0 (zero) on C	formal charge of -1 on C

In the structures above, all the bonds and non-bonding electrons are shown. A neutral carbon atom has four valence electrons. One simply plugs the values into the equation and the formal charge is readily determined. It is vitally important to determine which atoms in a molecule have partial or formal charges, so that we can begin to predict the properties and reactions of molecules as a result of Coulombic attraction or repulsion. Learning the ability to make such predictions forms the majority of an introductory organic chemistry course.

Example I.2.3

Provide all non-zero formal charges for atoms in these structures:

A) 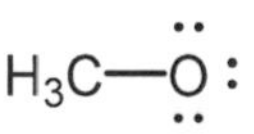 $H_3C-\overset{..}{\underset{..}{O}}:$ B) $HC\equiv C:$ C)    D)

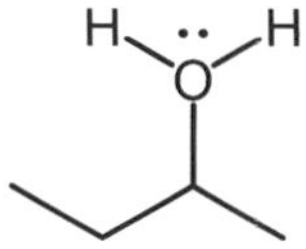

Solution I.2.3

A) 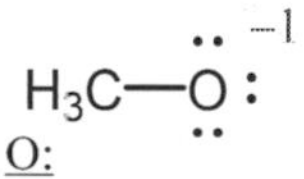 $H_3C-\overset{..}{\underset{..}{O}}:^{-1}$

For O:
6 valence – 6 lone pair electrons – 1 bond
= F.C. of –1

B)  $HC\equiv C:^{-1}$

For C:
4 valence – 2 lone pair electrons – 3 bonds
= F.C. of –1

C) 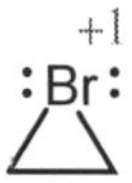 $^{+1}$

For Br:
7 valence – 4 lone pair electrons – 2 bonds
= F.C. of +1

D) 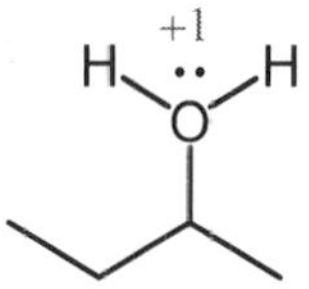 $^{+1}$

For O:
6 valence – 2 lone pair electrons – 3 bonds
= F.C. of +1

17

Lesson I.3.1: Intermolecular Forces

There are three types of intermolecular forces on which we will focus in this book:

    i.   Hydrogen Bonding

    ii.   Dipole–Dipole interactions

    iii.   van der Waals interactions (London dispersion forces).

The **strongest** of these intermolecular forces is **hydrogen bonding** (sometimes abbreviated "H-bonding"). Hydrogen bonding is a specific type of Coulombic attractive force between the partial negative charge of one polar bond and the partial positive charge on an H atom (induced by the H atom being in a very polar bond):

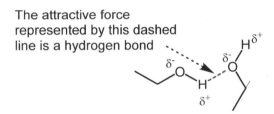

The greater the charges on H and X in the molecule, the greater the Coulombic attraction will be, so the two molecules will be more strongly attracted to one another. The elements with the three highest electronegativity values are F > O > N. Consequently, the most polar H–element bonds occur in molecules in which hydrogen is bonded to one of these elements. Molecules capable of the strongest H-bonds all feature H–F, H–O and H–N bonds. For the purposes of organic chemistry courses, you will typically only see compounds with H–O and H–N bonds engaging in hydrogen bonding.

The **second strongest** of the intermolecular forces we will cover are **dipole–dipole interactions**. Dipole–dipole interactions are simply the attractive forces between a partial positive charge on an atom in one molecule and the partial negative charge on an atom in another molecule. The greater the partial charges, the stronger the Coulombic attraction between the two:

The attractive force represented by the dashed line
is a **dipole-dipole interaction**

The weakest of the intermolecular forces we will cover are van der Waals interactions, sometimes called London Dispersion Forces. The van der Waals interactions arise from temporary dipoles that form in molecules that lack polar bonds. When two such molecules come in close proximity, the electron clouds on the atoms in one molecule repel the electron clouds on the atoms in the other molecule. This will, very briefly, cause a very weak 'induced dipole' on the molecules whose electrons were repelled. These forces, however, are far weaker than either dipole–dipole interactions or H-bonds.

Lesson I.3.2: Using Intermolecular Forces to assess Relative Melting and Boiling Points

In a solid, it is the intermolecular forces that hold molecules close together with enough force to allow the solid to maintain its shape. A solid will only melt into liquid form when the intermolecular forces are disrupted enough to allow the molecules to flow past one another. To disrupt intermolecular forces, one needs to add energy, generally by heating the sample to its melting point. *The stronger the intermolecular forces, the more heat (higher melting point) is needed* to melt the sample. This observation allows us to predict the relative melting points of several samples simply by comparing their structures.

The boiling point of a liquid can be estimated in a similar way. In a liquid, the molecules remain close to one another even though the molecules can flow past one another. When enough energy is added to boil the liquid, the intermolecular forces are completely overcome, allowing the molecules to break free into the gaseous state, whereupon the molecules too far apart to experience intermolecular forces between one other. *The stronger the intermolecular forces, the more heat (higher boiling point) is needed* to boil the sample.

Example I.3.1

List the strongest intermolecular force that is present between molecules in a sample of each of the following and rank the compounds 1–4 in terms of boiling point, 1 being highest.

Solution I.3.1

The strongest intermolecular force in each is:

I: H-bonding (two sites)

II: dipole-dipole

III: van der Waals interactions (London dispersion forces)

IV: H-bonding (one site)

The boiling point increases as the strength of the force increases, and compound I has *two* H-bonding units whereas compound IV only has one. So, the order of boiling point is **I** > **IV** > **II** > **III**, where compound **I** has the highest boiling point.

Lesson I.4.1: Nucleophiles and Electrophiles

Thus far, we have seen that intermolecular forces are capable of influencing properties of a pure compound. However, there can also be attractive forces between two *different* chemical species. If this force is strong enough and circumstances are correct, the two species may undergo a **chemical reaction: a rearrangement of atoms and electrons** (possibly bonding electrons) to create one or more new species. How can we begin to understand the chemical changes we see among organic compounds? How can we predict what reactions might happen between two species? These questions are complex, but understanding Coulombic forces is a good first step in our quest to answer them. To begin this task, it is useful to divide chemical species into two classes: **nucleophiles** and **electrophiles**.

A nucleophile (Greek for "nucleus-loving") will be attracted to positive charges, such as nuclei, cations, or the partial positive-charged end of a polar bond. A nucleophile will thus tend to be something with a full or partial negative charge on it, or it may simply have loosely-held electrons (e.g., lone pairs) that are attracted to an external positive charge. Some examples are shown here:

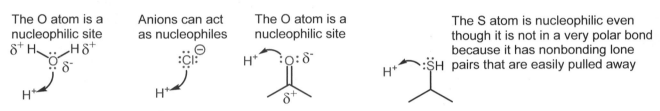

The H nucleus, a proton (H⁺) is used as an example of an electron acceptor
Curved arrows show from what site the electrons would be taken to give them to the acceptor.

An electrophile (Greek for "electron-loving") will be attracted to negative charges such as anions, lone pair electrons, or the partial negative-charged end of a polar bond. An electrophile will thus tend to be something with a full or partial positive charge on it, or something with an atom that has less than an octet of electrons in its valence shell. Some examples are shown here:

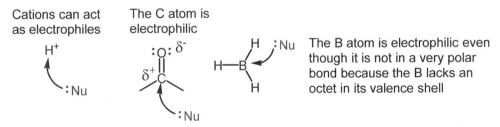

The symbol "Nu" is used to represent a nucleophile.
Curved arrows point to the electrophilic site to which electrons could be donated.

By filling in the partial charges on the atoms in a molecule, we identify the likely sites to which an electrophile or a nucleophile might be attracted. An example of this type of analysis is provided in Example I.4.1. We will do many of these assessments throughout the course.

Example I.4.1

Identify each molecule as a potential nucleophile, electrophile, neither, or both. Draw arrows pointing towards electrophilic sites and draw arrows pointing away from nucleophilic sites.

Solution I.4.1

Each atom with a lone pair may act as a nucleophile. Each atom that is the partial positive end of a polar bond is electrophilic.

Lesson I.4.2: Functional Groups

We now have the ability to identify sites in molecules between which there may be attractive forces, and we have also begun to rationalize how these attractive forces could lead to a chemical reaction. With these skills, we can understand that a C=O bond might generally interact with a nucleophile in a consistent way, regardless of which specific molecule contains that C=O bond. You would expect the partial positive charge on the C of the C=O unit to attract nucleophiles, for example. You might also expect the partial negative on the O in the O–H bond to attract electrophiles, regardless of the molecule on which the OH group resides. We can make generalizations about how a particular **group** of atoms might **function**. Organic chemists have identified specific groups of atoms that do react in predictable manners within a wide range of molecules. These predictably-reacting groups are called **functional groups**. The structures and names of the most important functional groups are shown on the following page. The "R" in these generic structures may be any chain or ring composed of C and H atoms, attached to where the "R" group is placed.

Hydrocarbons

R-C(R)(R)-C(R)(R)-R
Alkane

(R)(R)C=C(R)(R)
Alkene

R-C≡C-R
Alkyne

Aromatics (arenes)

Heteroatom-Containing Compounds

Amine

R—OH
Alcohol

R-O-R'
Ether

R—X
Alkyl halide
(X = F, Cl, Br, I)

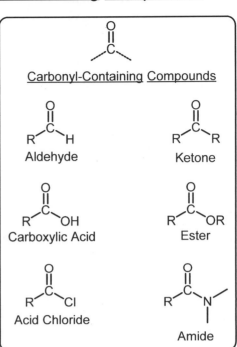

Carbonyl-Containing Compounds

Aldehyde

Ketone

Carboxylic Acid

Ester

Acid Chloride

Amide

C=O is refered to as a carbonyl bond. The functional groups above contain carbonyl subunits, but "carbonyl" is not itself a functional group.

It is important to be able to look at a complex molecule and rapidly identify all such functional groups that are present. Below is an example of an anti-cancer drug with its functional groups labeled:

Taxol (a complex cancer drug) without (left) and with (right) functional groups labeled

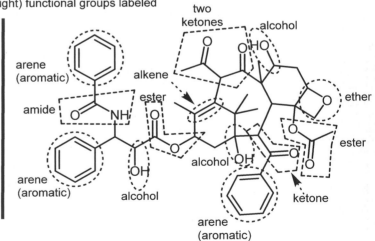

Example I.4.2

Identify all non-alkane functional groups in this molecule by circling them and writing in the group's name beside each.

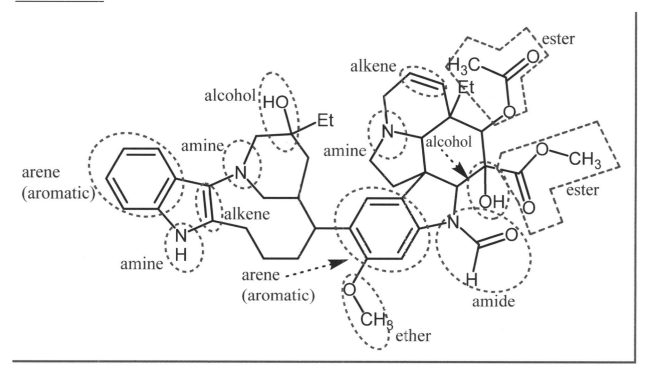

Vincristine

Solution I.4.2

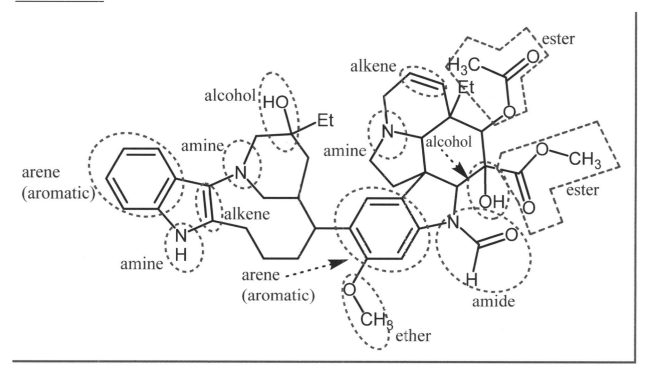

Lesson I.5: Arrow-Pushing Formalism

Lesson I.5.1: Curved Arrows

Each covalent bond is made of two electrons. In a chemical reaction, bonds are broken and/or made. Sometimes several bonds are broken/made simultaneously, such that a complex rearrangement of atoms and electrons takes place all at once. To represent these rearrangements, chemists have developed the **Curved Arrow Formalism**. In this convention, one uses arrows to point to where the electrons go. Most reactions in organic chemistry involve the movement of pairs of electrons. A curved arrow thus represents movement of a pair of electrons to wherever the arrow points. These arrows must be curved, to distinguish them from the straight arrows used in chemical equations (e.g., A + B → C + D). Here are a few examples of how the curved arrow formalism is used:

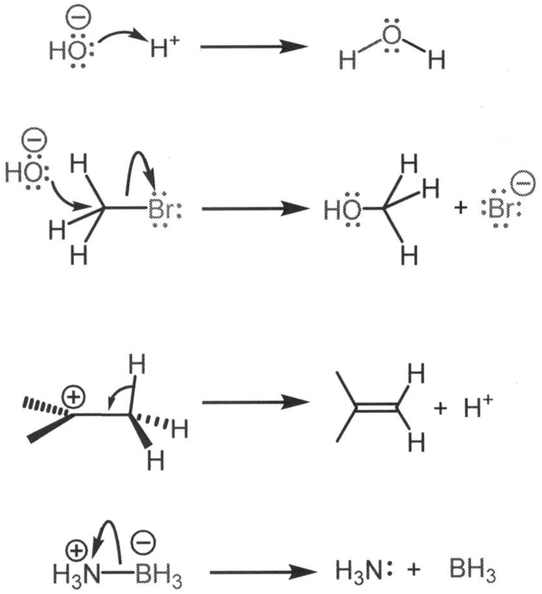

If only one electron moves, we instead use a "fishhook arrow", which has only half an arrow head to point to where the electron goes. Here are a couple examples using this fishhook arrow notation:

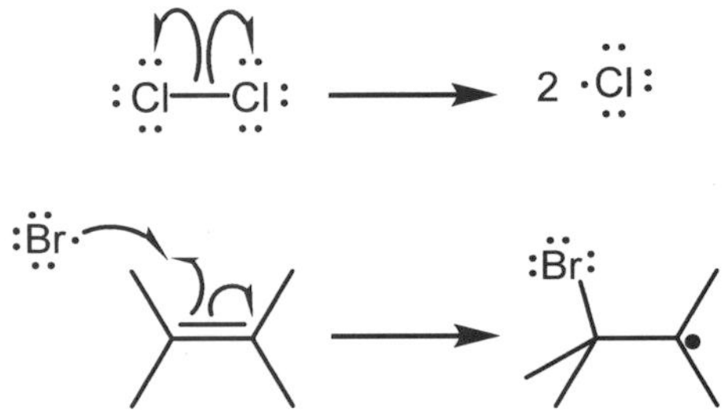

Soon, we will study specific patterns for electron movement and eventually be able to make predictions about what reactions happen. For now, focus on understanding how the arrows work.

Lesson I.5.2: Representing Reactions

We now have a considerable amount of knowledge that we can put together:

1) the curved arrow formalism allows us to represent movement of electrons

2) the ability to assign partial charges and formal charges allows us to identify sites to which electrons might be attracted and from what sites they may be pulled

3) we can identify species as being electrophilic (pull electrons towards them) or nucleophiles (they give electrons away)

Consider the observation that an acid, represented as H^+, and a base, represented as HO^-, react with one another to form water. Here are the Lewis structures of the reactants and the product:

We see that the product of this reaction is a combination of the OH and the H, with the new bond between the O and the H. The positive charge on H^+ tells us that it is electrophilic and will pull electrons towards it (our curved arrow should point to it). Conversely, the negative charge on HO^- suggests that it is nucleophilic and will donate electrons. The movement of electrons in the reaction is represented as:

From the above representation of the reaction, we can say that the proton (H^+) acts as an electrophile, accepting electrons from the nucleophilic hydroxide (HO^-). When the O atom of the nucleophile shares electrons with the H atom in the electrophile, a new covalent bond between O and H results. The formal charges on the O (–1 in the reactant) and the proton (+1 in the reactant) change to 0 in the.

For the more complex example shown below, we again start by identifying the bonds made/broken:

Bonds made: HO to H (to get water), second bond between two carbons.
Bonds broken: H–C bond (left side), C–I bond.
Next, evaluate changes in charge. The O in HO^- starts negative and ends neutral, so it must donate electrons away. The iodine begins neutral and ends negative, so electrons must be pushed onto it. The most reasonable way to accomplish all of these things in a single step is to move the electrons as follows:

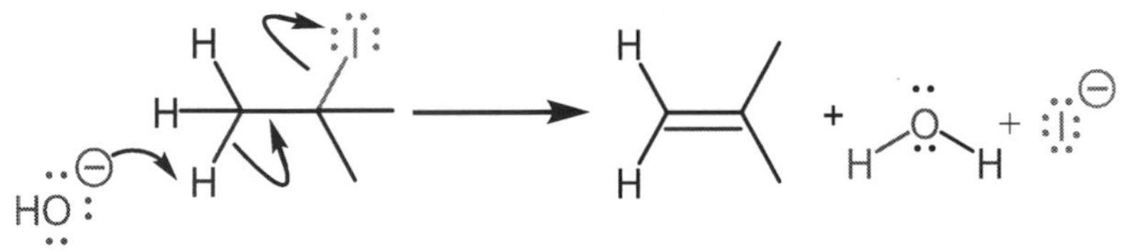

In the two examples above, we were given a set of reactants with a known product, and from that information we determined how the electrons would have to flow in order to accomplish the reaction. We can also predict products if we know how the electrons move. Consider these reactants and the accompanying curved arrows:

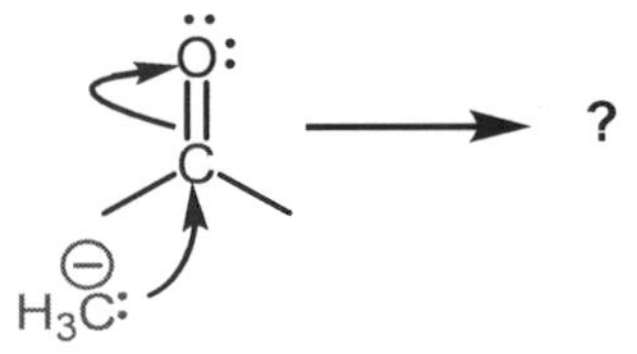

In this case, we can predict the products by filling in any new bonds formed, removing any broken bonds, and noting any changes in formal charge. The lower arrow indicates that the CH_3 will share a lone pair with the C of the C=O bond, leading to a new C–C bond. The upper arrow shows that the two electrons in one of the C=O bonds gets localized onto the O, so the O goes from having two lone pairs to three, and it acquires a formal chare of -1:

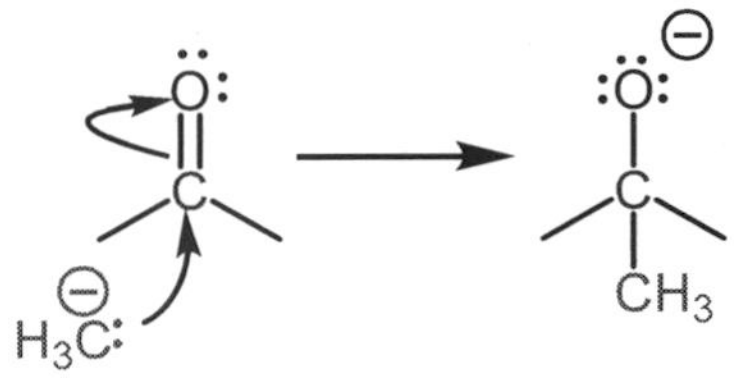

Note that, at this point, we are simply representing how electrons pairs would move about to yield a given molecule or, if we are told how the electrons will move, we can provide the products. We are not yet armed with the tools we need to *predict* what reaction will take place or to decide whether a given hypothetical reaction is reasonable. These skills will come in the following lessons.

Example I.5.1

For 1–5, fill in the missing products of the indicated electron movement. For reactions 6–11, fill in arrows to show the flow of electrons needed to change reactants to the indicated product(s).

Solution I.5.1

Lesson I.6.1: Hybridization

Each element in the second row of the periodic table has one $2s$ orbital and three $2p$ orbitals in its valence shell. The valence shell electrons are the only ones we show in Lewis structures because they are the only ones involved in bonding and chemical reactions. To accomplish the most effective bonding and minimize repulsion between bonding pairs, the s- and p-orbitals present on *individual atoms* mix to form hybrid orbitals in *molecules*. The s orbital is always mixed into hybrid orbitals. The number of p-orbitals that mix with the s-orbital on a given atom depends on the sum of lone pairs and atoms attached to that atom as follows:

If (lone pairs + atoms attached) = 2   **then**   hybridization = sp

If (lone pairs + atoms attached) = 3   **then**   hybridization = sp^2

If (lone pairs + atoms attached) = 4   **then**   hybridization = sp^3

Note that the total number of orbitals ($s + p$) that mix to form the hybrid orbitals is equal to (lone pairs + atoms attached).

An sp-hybridized atom has two sp-orbitals on it. To minimize repulsion between the electrons in these orbitals, the orbitals are oriented 180° apart, in a linear geometry:

The two p-orbitals that were not incorporated into the hybrid are still on the C:

The hybrid orbitals may hold lone pairs or form bonds. The type of bond formed by a hybrid orbital involves electron density directly between the two atoms involved in the bond. These are called σ-bonds (σ is the lowercase Greek letter "sigma"). There can be no more than one sigma bond between any two given atoms, and each single bond is a σ bond.

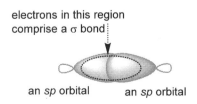

electrons in this region comprise a σ bond

an *sp* orbital   an *sp* orbital

28

Each *p*-orbitals that does not mix into the hybrid orbital may interact with a *p*-orbital on an adjacent atom, forming a bond with electron density above and below the internuclear axis. Such a bond is called a π-bond (π is the lowercase Greek letter "pi"). Each bond beyond the first bond between two atoms (which is a σ bond) is a π bond. So, a double bond is made of one σ- and one π-bond

One π bond:
Two total e⁻ spread over the whole area
above/below internuclear axis (dashed line)

The *sp*-hybridized atom in particular has two *p*-orbitals on it, so it can make two π-bonds.

Molecules with sp hybridized atoms (bold):

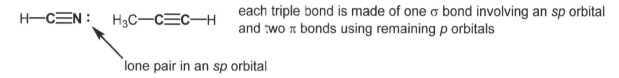

each triple bond is made of one σ bond involving an *sp* orbital and two π bonds using remaining *p* orbitals

lone pair in an *sp* orbital

It is important to know whether electrons are in a lone pair, σ-bond or π-bond because, for a given atom, lone pair electrons are held less strongly (attraction to only one nucleus) than bonding electrons (attracted to two nuclei). Furthermore, the π-bond electrons are held less tightly than the σ-bonding electrons. This knowledge will help us predict which electrons might be the easiest to pull away from a molecule to interact with an electrophile. Thus, for a given atom, lone pair electrons would be easiest to pull away, followed by π-bonding electrons, and σ-bonding electrons would be most difficult to remove. We would therefore predict that, if H⁺ (an electrophile) interacts with an alcohol, it would most likely interact with the lone pair electrons on O. If H⁺ interacted with an alkene, the electrophile would pull the π-bond electrons from the alkene. If H⁺ interacted with an alkane, the σ-bond electrons might be too tightly held to be pulled away by the H⁺. These simple predictions all turn out to be true!

An sp^2-hybridized carbon atom has three sp^2-orbitals on it. To minimize repulsion between electrons in these orbitals, the orbitals are 120° apart, in a trigonal planar geometry:

There will be one unhybridized *p*-orbital, so an sp^2-hybridized atom can make three σ-bonds and one π-bond. Here are some examples of molecules which incorporate sp^2-hybridized atoms:

Molecules with sp^2 hybridized atoms (bold):

H₂C=C(CH₃)H structure, O=C, C⁺ structures

each double bond is made of one σ bond involving an sp^2 orbital and one π bond using the unhybridized p orbital

lone pairs on O are in sp^2 orbitals

cation has an empty p orbital

An sp^3-hybridized carbon atom has four sp^3-orbitals on it. To minimize repulsion between the electrons in each orbital, the orbitals are 109.5° apart, in a tetrahedral geometry:

There are no unhybridized p-orbitals on an sp^3-hybridized atom, so it cannot form any π-bonds. Example I.6.1 illustrates how atom hybridization states are identified in more complex molecules.

Example I.6.1:

Identify the hybridization for each atom to which an arrow is pointing:

Solution I.6.1:

Nitrogen atom (a) has a lone pair and is bound to one other atom; (lone pairs + atoms attached) = 2, so hybridization = sp.
Carbon atom (b) is bound to two other atoms and has no lone pairs; (lone pairs + atoms attached) = 2, so hybridization = sp.
Carbon atom (c) is bound to three other atoms and has no lone pairs; (lone pairs + atoms attached) = 3, so hybridization = sp^2
Carbon atom (d) is bound to four other atoms and has no lone pairs; (lone pairs + atoms attached) = 4, so hybridization = sp^3
Oxygen atom (e) is bound to one other atom and has two lone pairs; (lone pairs + atoms attached) = 3, so hybridization = sp^2

Note that lone pairs are not always shown on atoms. Likewise, the H atoms on C are not always shown in the line-bond notation. The structure of the molecule given in Example I.6.1 could also have been provided as:

In such a case, you would be expected to use the periodic table and your knowledge of formal charge to fill in the proper number of electrons and H atoms, much like you would if you were trying to draw a Lewis structure from scratch.

Lesson I.6.2: Influence of Hybridization on Electronegativity

We know that electronegativity increases towards the top of the periodic table, where the electrons are in orbitals closer to the nucleus and thus have a stronger attraction to the nucleus. We also know that electrons in an *s*-orbital are closer to the nucleus than electrons in a *p*-orbital, and this is why the *s*-orbital is filled first in the electronic configuration of an atom. These facts make it clear that the orbital holding electrons influences how strongly the nucleus pulls on those electrons. The electronegativity of an atom in a molecule is thus influenced by what orbitals hold the electrons in its valence shell. A hybrid orbital has some fraction of *s*-orbital and some fraction of *p*-orbital. An *sp*-orbital is made of an *s*-orbital and a *p*-orbital, so this hybrid orbital has 50% *s*-character. Only one of the three orbitals mixed to make an *sp²*-orbital is *s*, so it has 33% *s*-character. Only one of the four orbitals comprising the *sp³*-orbital is *s*, so an *sp³*-orbital has 25% *s*-character. Because *s*-orbitals are closer to the nucleus, the greater the "*s*-character", the closer the electrons in that hybrid orbital are to the nucleus, and the more electronegative that atom will be. A good rule of thumb is that an *sp*-hybridized C is similar in electronegativity to an *sp³*-hybridized N. We will study the influence of this effect in Part III.

Lesson I.7.1: Representing Resonance using Curved Arrows

Some molecules can be drawn with two or more valid Lewis dot structures, in which the atoms are all connected in the same arrangement, with only the placement of electrons differing. These different forms of the same molecule are called *resonance forms* or *resonance contributors*. As an example, consider the task of drawing a Lewis structure for the anion, $[C_2H_3O]^-$. You could come up with two possible structures in which each non-H atom has its octet filled, the proper number of electrons has been placed, and the necessary overall charge is –1 has been reached:

Note that the double-headed arrow used in the above graphic is only used to represent interconversion between two resonance forms of the same structure. This is *not* a chemical reaction, and it is *not* an equilibrium (which is represented using *two* half-headed arrows, each one pointing in opposite directions). Note, also, that the σ-bond framework remains the same in both structures: *only non-bonding and π-bonding electrons can be changed between resonance forms. No σ-bonds break when resonance forms interconvert.* We can use the curved arrow formalism to represent how these two resonance forms can interconvert:

Lesson I.7.2: Resonance Hybrids and Delocalization Energy

So, which of the two possible resonance contributors for this anion is correct? Well, the actual structure of this anion will be some combination of both resonance contributors. The negative charge is spread out (i.e., *delocalized*) over more than one atom in this anion. The real structure is better represented by what is called a *resonance hybrid* of all of the contributors. To draw a resonance hybrid, you have to represent a blend of all possible contributors. To illustrate how this is done, consider the properties of the two contributors for this anion:

i.   The σ-bonding skeleton is the same in both contributors, so this skeleton will be the same in the hybrid, and that is what we draw first:

σ bond framework only

32

ii. In addition to the σ-bond between C and O, there is a π-bond in contributor on the right. In the hybrid, we *use a dashed line to represent the π-bond that is only in some, but not all, of the resonance contributors* to indicate a partial bond in that position:

first partial π bond added

iii. In addition to the σ-bond between C and C, there is a π-bond in the contributor on the left, so in hybrid, we again use a dashed line to indicate partial multiple bonding:

second partial π bond added

iv. Finally, in one contributor the negative charge is on the C and in the other contributor the negative charge is on the O. We therefore use the δ– symbol to show the *partial* occupancy of the negative Coulombic charge on each atom:

partial charges added;
RESONANCE HYBRID

v. This is one way to represent the *resonance hybrid* of this anion. You may also see resonance hybrids drawn with a curved line drawn near all the atoms involved in the "spread-out" multiple bonding, with the net charge drawn near the center of the curved line. The resonance hybrid for this anion could thus also be drawn like this:

alternative representation of
the same resonance hybrid

This delocalization provides additional stability to a molecule by lowering repulsive forces and/or increasing attractive forces. A pair of electrons that is localized within a smaller volume experiences more Coulombic repulsion than a pair of electrons that is delocalized over a larger volume. The extra stability that is afforded to molecules that have multiple resonance forms is called the *delocalization energy* or *resonance energy*. We will see specific examples of this stabilization in lessons on anion, cation and radical stability later in this book.

Example I.7.1:

Provide TWO additional resonance contributors and the resonance hybrid structure for this cation:

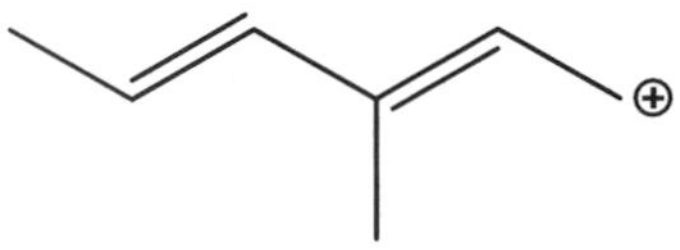

Solution I.7.1:

The resonance contributors (starting with the given structure) are:

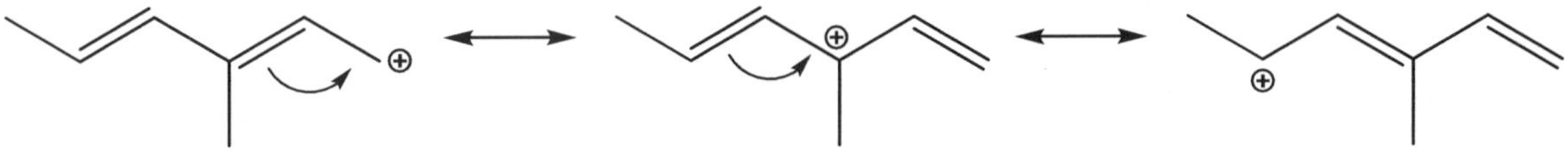

The hybrid will have partial positive charge at each site where there is positive charge in a contributor. Likewise, the hybrid will have π-bond character wherever there is a π-bond in any of the contributors. So, the resonance hybrid will be:

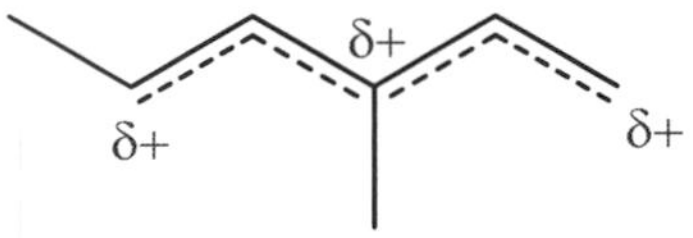

Lesson I.7.3: Influence of Resonance on Hybridization

We now know that, although lone pair electrons generally occupy hybrid orbitals, an exception occurs when a lone pair participates in the resonance delocalization of a π-system. In the case of such delocalization, the lone pair electrons are better represented as occupying an unhybridized *p*-orbital. This will change the assignment of hybridization in some cases. Consider the N atom in ammonia versus the N atom in vinyl amine:

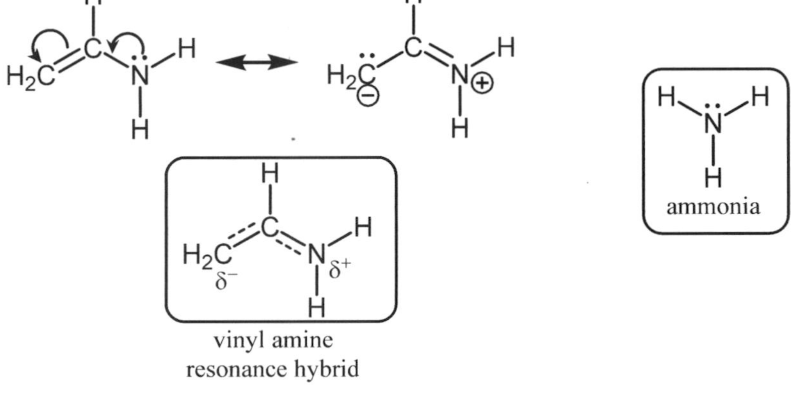

vinyl amine
resonance hybrid

ammonia

In ammonia, the three pairs of electrons comprising the σ-bonds and the lone pair each occupy a hybrid orbital. There are four pairs of electrons, so four orbitals must hybridize together. The N in ammonia is thus sp^3-hybridized. The contribution of the N lone pair to resonance delocalization into the π-bond in vinyl amine, however, means that these lone pair electrons must occupy an unhybridized p-orbital (otherwise they could not be used to make a π-bond!). As a result, only the three pairs of electrons comprising the N–H and N–C bonds will reside in hybrid orbitals, and **the N in vinyl amine is thus better represented as sp^2-hybridized**. From this example, you can see that you must consider possible resonance contributions to the "real" structure prior to doing something as "simple" as assigning hybridization.

Example I.7.2:

Label each C atom in this structure as being sp, sp^2 or sp^3-hybridized.

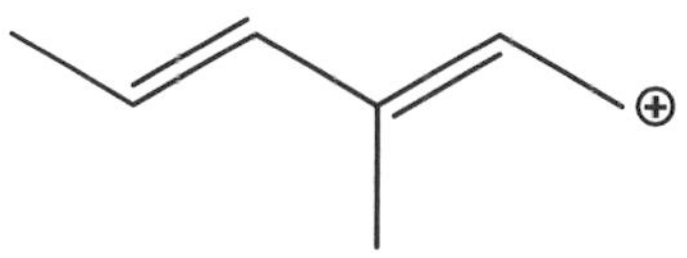

Solution I.7.2:

If we refer back to the solution to Example I.7.2, we will see that the resonance hybrid structure is:

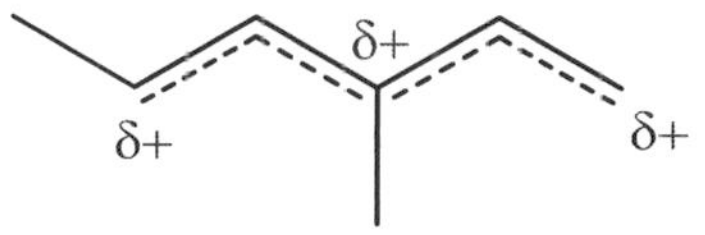

A carbon atom that has exactly three (lone pairs plus σ bonds) is sp^2-hybridized. A carbon atom that exactly two (σ bonds plus lone pairs) is sp-hybridized. A carbon atom with exactly four (σ bonds plus lone pairs) is sp^3-hybridized. This analysis leads us to the following assignments:

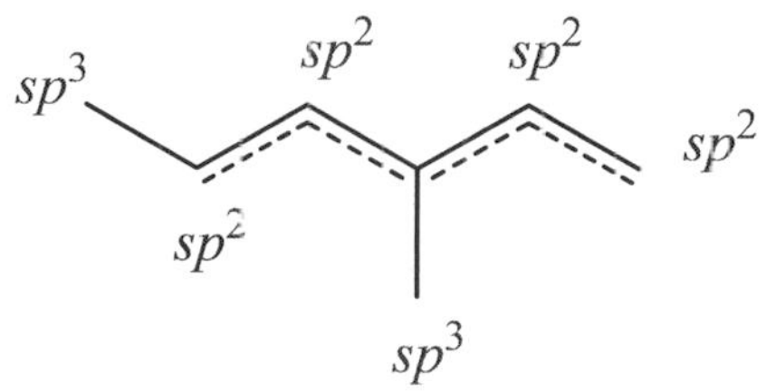

Lesson I.8.1: Common Elementary Steps of Organic Reactions

   With our understanding of chemical structure, the curved arrow formalism, and the types of bonds found in typical organic molecules, we are now equipped to investigate chemical reactions in more detail. Organic reactions can involve many arrow-pushing steps along the path from starting materials to products and may include multiple intermediates along the way. Fortunately, a great many organic reactions, even those that occur over many steps, typically involve only a handful of elementary steps. Most such steps can take place either in the forward or reverse direction. As we continue our studies, we will begin to learn how to identify the conditions under which a given step is favored and likely to occur. In this lesson, however, we have only two goals: 1) introduce the names for the most common elementary steps, and 2) acquire the ability to identify when one of these steps is occurring.

   Six of the basic steps of many organic reactions in introductory organic classes are as follows:

Lesson I.8.2: Identifying Elementary Steps in Multi-Step Mechanistic Pathways

Now that we have a list of some important elementary steps of organic reactions, our next goal is to gain the ability to identify which of these steps is occurring given a reaction scheme. It is helpful to tabulate the types of reagents needed to accomplish each step, as well as the type and number of bonds made/broken in the course of each elementary step. The table below summarizes these observations.

Step	Bonds Broken		Bonds Made		Notes
	σ	π	σ	π	
Coordination	0	0	1	0	One atom shares a pair of electrons with another to form a single bond
Heterolysis	1	0	0	0	Both electrons from the bond go to one atom
Carbocation Rearrangement	1	0	1	0	It must be a carbocation both before and after this step. Only one species involved.
Electrophilic Addition	0	1	1	0	Electrons are pulled **from** the π-bond **towards** an electrophile
Electrophilic Elimination	1	0	0	1	Electrons to make the π-bond come from a σ-bond
E2	2	0	1	1	Three simultaneous curved arrows required!
S_N2	1	0	1	0	Make and break σ-bond simultaneously
Nucleophilic Addition	0	1	1	0	Electrons are pushed **towards** the π-bonded atom **from** a nucleophile
Nucleophilic Elimination	1	0	0	1	Electrons to make the π-bond come from a lone pair, the broken σ-bond electrons push onto a leaving group

Example I.8.1

Identify which elementary step is represented in each of the following reactions:

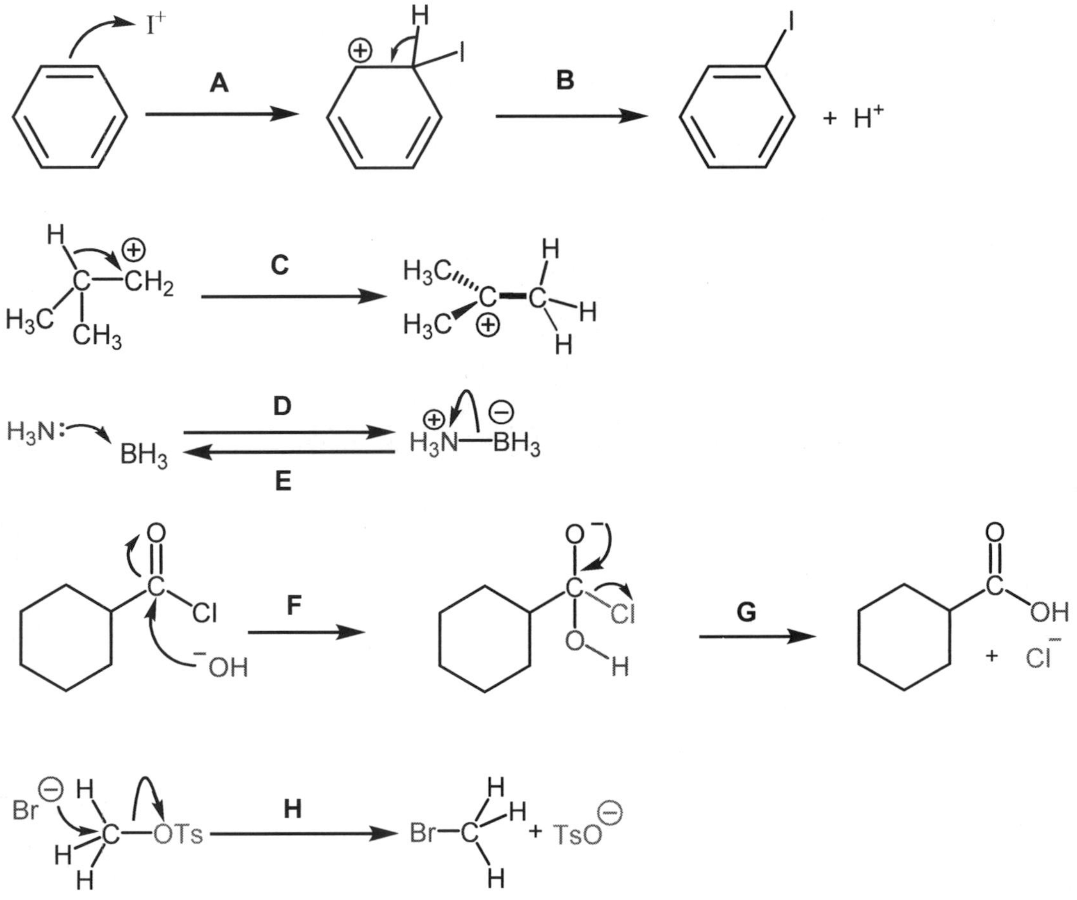

Solution I.8.1

Additional help from "Organic Chemistry 1 Reactions and Practice Problems 2018" (Smith):

- Further reading and more examples of each elementary step, see Reactions A1-7

- After finishing Lesson I.8, you will be ready for Problem Set 1 in the companion book. This Problem Set covers material from Primer Lessons I.1-8

Lesson I.9.1: Arrhenius and Brønsted-Lowry Definitions

There are several definitions of acids and bases used by chemists, and you have undoubtedly studied some of these in prior classes. We will briefly review some of those definitions here. The **Arrhenius definition** is that an acid is a substance that produces H^+ when dissolved in water. We know that H^+ in water is, in reality, the hydronium ion, H_3O^+, so you may see either H^+ or H_3O^+ written, where they are meant to represent the same thing. Examples of Arrhenius acids could be acetic acid (CH_3COOH), HCl, H_2SO_4, etc. The Arrhenius definition is that a base is a compound that makes hydroxide (HO^-) when dissolved in water. Examples of Arrhenius bases are NaOH, [NH4][OH], etc.

The **Brønsted-Lowry definition** considers an acid to be a proton donor – similar to the Arrhenius definition – but expanded upon the definition of what could be a base. In the Brønsted-Lowry definition, a base is a proton acceptor. All of the hydroxide-producing species defined as bases under the Arrhenius definition are still bases under the Brønsted-Lowry definition, because HO^- reacts with H^+ to make H_2O. However, the Brønsted-Lowry definition incorporates species other than HO^- that likewise react with H^+. For example, ammonia, pyridine and methoxide are all bases under the Brønsted-Lowry definition:

Regardless of the type of acid, scientists use pK_a values to quantify acid strength. A lower pK_a value corresponds to a stronger acid. We also know from prior courses that a stronger acid has a weaker conjugate base and that a stronger base has a weaker conjugate acid. This is because chemical reactions are more favorable when more thermodynamically stable species are produced, a theme that we will use to predict reactions throughout organic chemistry. We can conclude that **the more stable the conjugate base anion, the stronger the acid**. Conversely, **the less stable the conjugate base anion the stronger a base it is** because there is greater favorability for it to be neutralized by an acid.

The final definition of acids and bases we will cover is the **Lewis definition**. In this definition, an acid is an electron pair acceptor and a base is an electron pair donor. In the Lewis definition, H^+ is still an acid and HO^- is still as a base, which is apparent in the following mechanism:

Likewise, ammonia fits the definition of a base, much as it did in the Brønsted-Lowry definition:

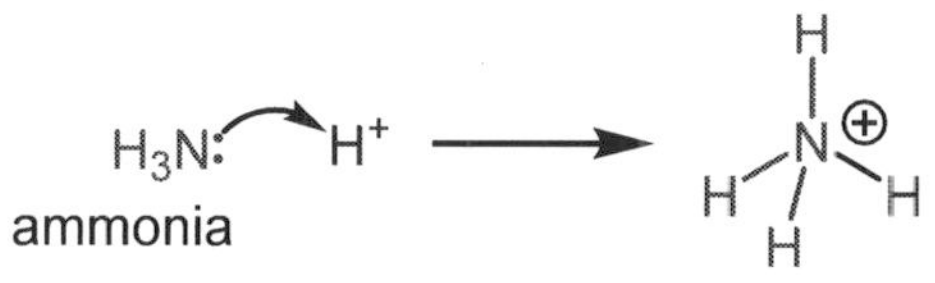

Unlike the Arrhenius or Brønsted-Lowry definitions, however, the Lewis definition allows for species other than H^+ donors to be acids. This is logical, because if we think of an acid as something that neutralizes a base, and we know that things other than H^+ can neutralize base, then these other base-neutralizing species are clearly functioning as acids! A classic example is borane (BH_3), which is a good electron pair acceptor because the B atom has only six valence electrons and accepting a pair of electrons allows it to achieve an octet. Borane is a good Lewis acid that can react with any of the bases we have seen in this lesson:

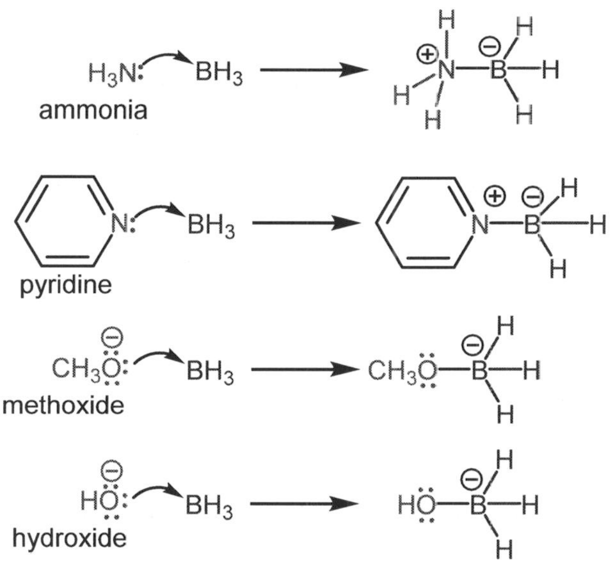

In Lesson I.8, we learned the coordination elementary reaction step. This is a Lewis acid–base reaction because one of the two species donates an electron pair (the base) and the other accepts this electron pair (the acid), and no other electron pair movements occur.

Lesson I.10: Acids and Bases II: Relating Structure to the Strength of an Acid or Base

In the previous lesson, we observed that the more stable the conjugate base anion, the stronger the acid that produces it. The focus of this lesson is to use the chemical structure of a compound to *make relative predictions about acid strength.* We will consider each structural effect individually, in the order of generally most influential to least influential on stability.

Lesson I.10.1: Influence of Conjugate Base Resonance Stabilization on Acidity

One factor that increases anion stability is decreasing the repulsion between electrons in the anion. Repulsion can be alleviated when the negative charge is allowed to spread out over a larger volume. In Lesson I.7, we learned that charge can be spread out (delocalized) through resonance.

If the conjugate base anion is more stable, the acid producing that anion is a stronger acid. We conclude that, all else being equal, the stronger acid in a pair of molecules will be the one that has more resonance delocalization of the negative charge on the conjugate base anion.

Example I.10.1

Which is the stronger acid?

water   acetic acid

Solution I.9.1

The way to answer these types of questions is to draw the conjugate bases. We note that the conjugate base for acetic acid has resonance stabilization. We conclude that it is the more stable (weaker) conjugate base. We therefore conclude that acetic acid is the stronger acid.

water

acetic acid

Lesson I.10.2: Influence of Deprotonated Atom's Size on Acidity

As we saw in Lesson I.10.1, allowing electrons to spread out over a larger volume via resonance alleviated Coulombic repulsion. For the same reason, **when the negative charge is on a larger atom, the anion is more stable** than an analogous species featuring the negative charge on a smaller atom. If the conjugate base anion is more stable, the acid producing that anion is a stronger acid. We conclude that, all else being equal, the stronger acid in a pair of molecules is the one in which the negative charge produced upon deprotonation resides on a larger atom. Consider H_2O vs. H_2S. If H_2O acts as an acid by losing H^+, a negative charge is on O in the conjugate base ($^-$OH). If H_2S acts as an acid by losing H^+, a negative charge is on a much larger S atom in the conjugate base ($^-$SH). We would predict that $^-$SH is more stable than $^-$OH, which would mean that H_2S is a stronger acid than H_2O. The pK_a values confirm our prediction.

water
$pK_a = 14$

hydrogen sulfide
$pK_a = 7$

To assess anion stability, we do not look at the size of the entire molecule, just the size of the atom bearing the formal negative charge in the conjugate base. Larger atoms in the same molecule are irrelevant to anion stability if they never acquire any negative charge following deprotonation.

Lesson I.10.3: Influence of Deprotonated Atom's Electronegativity on Acidity

Another factor leading to increased anion stability is increased attraction between the electrons of the negative charge and the nucleus of the atom. This occurs when the positive charge on the nucleus increases, while the distance from the nucleus to the electrons remains relatively constant.

Atoms in the same row of the periodic table have the same valence orbitals, and consequently have *roughly similar sizes* (the small differences are unimportant to anion stability). Two atoms of the same size have the same distance between the valence electron and the nucleus. So, within a row of the periodic table, the attraction of the electrons to the nucleus increases as the charge on the nucleus increases. In fact, this trend gives rise to the electronegativity differences among the elements within a row of the periodic table. Going from left to right in the second row of the periodic table (i.e., B, C, N, O, F), for example, the charge on the nucleus increases and so does the electronegativity.

When we compare two anions, each of which has a formal negative charge on an atom in the same row, such as HO^- and H_2N^-, we see that **the stability of the anion increases as the electronegativity of the anionic atom increases**. In terms of relating this observation to acidity, we can state that **the stronger acid is the one that leads to deprotonation of the more electronegative atom** if those two atoms are in the same row. It is also important at this point to recall the effect of hybridization on electronegativity (Lesson I.6).

The effect of electronegativity is generally not as influential as the ability to spread charge out via resonance delocalization or atom size. Therefore, it is best to check first for resonance and consider the size of the atom being deprotonated, and then, only if the two possible deprotonation sites are atoms in the same row of the periodic table which have no possibility for resonance, to check the electronegativity.

Example I.10.1

Which is the strongest acid?

A   B   C

Solution I.10.1

First, we identify the atom to be deprotonated in each case. In A, it will be the O because it is more electronegative than C. In B, it is S because S is larger than C. In C, we do not have a choice because only carbon atoms have protons in this case. Thus, B is the strongest acid and C is the weakest acid.

Lesson I.10.4: Influence of Inductive Effects on Acidity

"Inductive effect" is a general term for any effect *induced* by *nearby* groups. Inductive effects can be divided into two types: **stabilizing** and **destabilizing**. In the context of anion stability, stabilizing inductive effects are observed when groups *near* the anionic atom have some attraction for the negative charge. Conversely, destabilizing inductive effects are observed when some nearby group has a repulsive interaction with the anionic atom's negative charge. Furthermore, the magnitude of the effect, whether stabilizing or destabilizing, is greater the closer the attractive/repulsive unit is to the anionic atom. An example of a stabilizing inductive effect is an attractive force between the anionic atom and a nearby partial positive end of a polar bond:

Dashed line = attractive inductive force

An example of a destabilizing inductive effect would result from repulsion between the negative charge and electrons in nearby bonds:

Curved lines = repulsive inductive force

Inductive effects generally have less influence on stability than do the effects of resonance, size and electronegativity.

Example I.10.2

Which is the strongest acid?

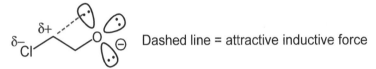

A   B   C

Solution I.10.2

All of these species will be deprotonated at the OH group to leave a negative charge on O. In B, there are no strong attractive or repulsive forces between the methyl group and the O. In contrast, the larger cyclohexyl group in A will have an inductive repulsion for a negatively-charged O. So, A is a weaker acid than is B. This leaves us with C. The conjugate base of C will experience an attractive inductive force:

$\delta-$ $\delta+$ Cl

Dashed line = attractive inductive force

For these reasons, C is the strongest acid, followed by B, and A is the weakest acid.

Lesson I.11.1: Influence of Resonance/Inductive Effects on Cation Stability

In Lesson I.10, we examined how various structural features influence the stability of anions. We will now study how such structural features influence the stability of cations. We will, however, limit our discussion to carbocations (cations having the positive charge on C):

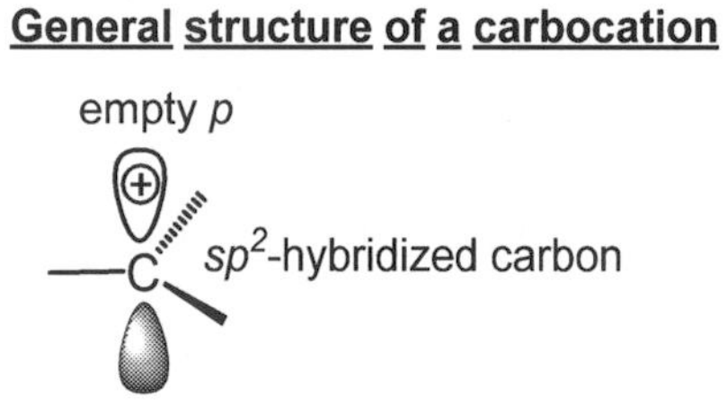

General structure of a carbocation

empty *p*

sp^2-hybridized carbon

Because we are limiting our discussion to species with a positive charge on C, we do not need to consider size or electronegativity effects like we did in Lesson I.10. We will only consider inductive effects and resonance.

For most carbocations encountered in first-semester organic chemistry, the inductive effect trend comes into play. In the Lesson I.10, we saw that σ-bonding electron pairs repel negative charge, so having more "branches" near an anion was destabilizing. Because electrons *attract* positive charge, a σ-bonding electron pair will be attracted to the empty *p*-orbital on the carbocation, which is a *stabilizing* interaction. This specific interaction is called **hyperconjugation.**

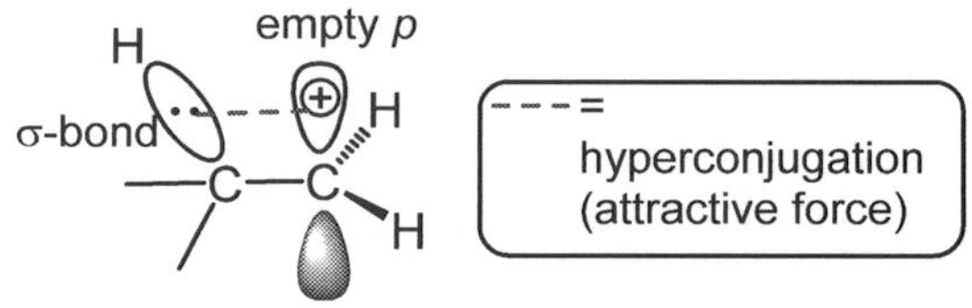

empty *p*

σ-bond

┌─────────────┐
│ - - - =   │
│ hyperconjugation │
│ (attractive force) │
└─────────────┘

Due to hyperconjugation, the more non-H substituents on the cationic C, the more stable it is. For convenience, chemists refer to a carbocation in which the positively-charged **carbon makes bonds to one carbon as a primary (1°) carbocation, with two carbons as secondary (2°), and with three carbons as tertiary (3°):**

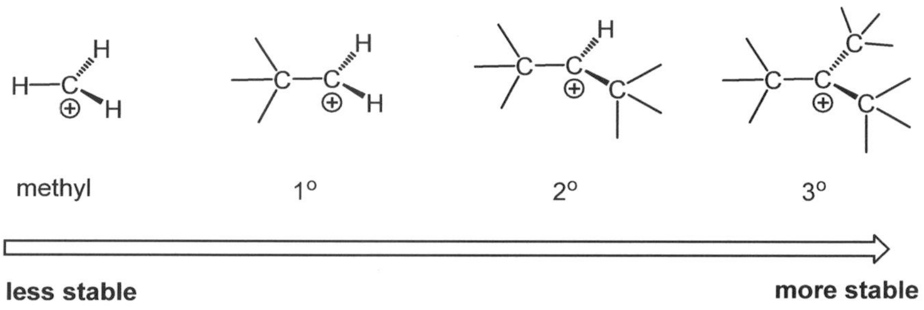

methyl   1°   2°   3°

less stable   more stable

46

Resonance can also stabilize a cation by allowing the positive charge to spread out over a larger volume. A good rule of thumb is that stabilization afforded by the presence of additional resonance contributors is equivalent to having one additional alkyl chain. The trend in carbocation stability, with resonance factored in, is as follows:

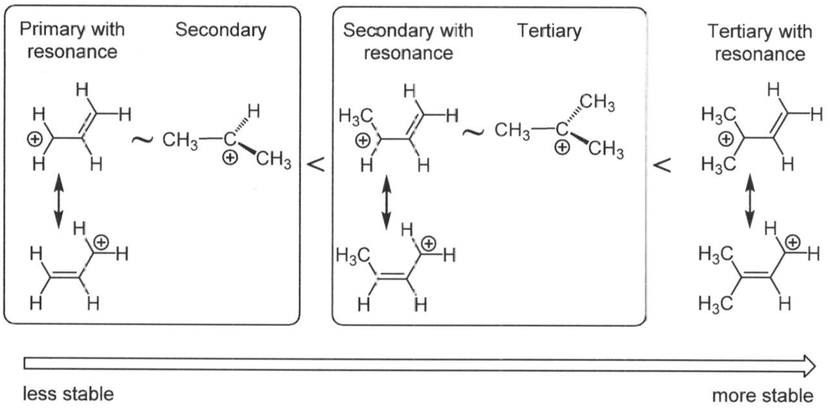

less stable   more stable

Lesson I.11.2: Definition of a Radical and the Influence of Resonance/Inductive Effects on Radical Stability

A radical is a species having an unpaired electron. As with cations, we will limit the current discussion to carbon-centered radicals. Like carbocations, carbon-centered radicals feature an sp^2-hybridized carbon atom, in which the C does not have an octet, so it will have an affinity for electrons:

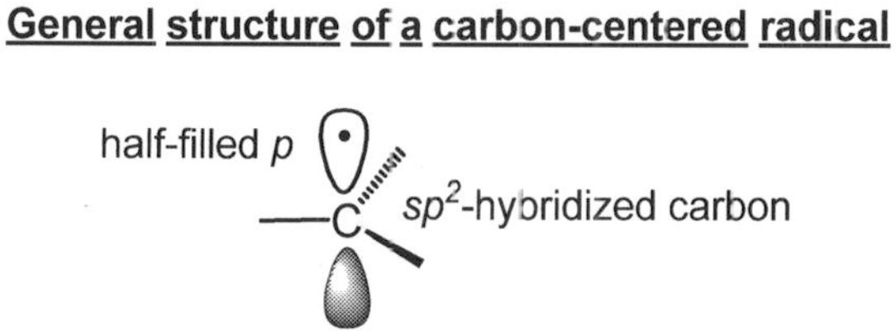

General structure of a carbon-centered radical

Carbon-centered radicals are similar in electronic structure to carbocations (both lack a complete octet), therefore the trend in radical stability is roughly similar to that for carbocations, but resonance exerts an even higher stabilizing effect in radicals. The stability trends can thus be summarized here:

47

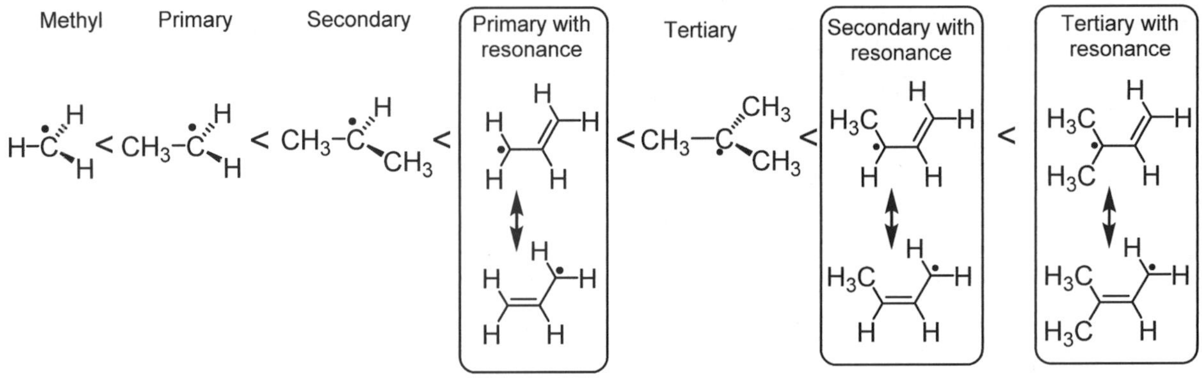

Methyl, Primary, Secondary, Primary with resonance, Tertiary, Secondary with resonance, Tertiary with resonance

---

Example I.11.1

Which is the more stable species within each pair of molecules shown?

A)

C)

B)

Solution I.11.1

A.

A) 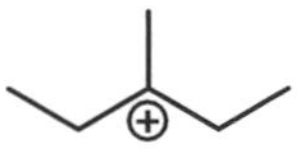 Tertiary is more stable

B) 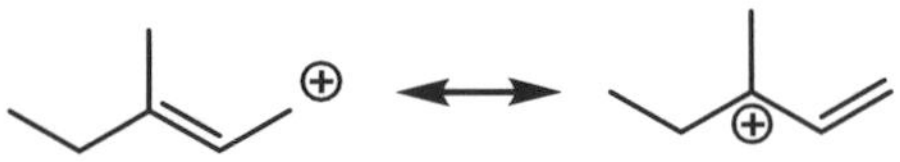 ⟷ Consider both resonance contributors. Tertiary with resonance even to primary is more stable than tertiary with no resonance

C)  Tertiary is more stable

---

Lesson I.11.3: Alkene Stability and Heats of Hydrogenation

Hydrogenation of an alkene leads to addition of an H atom to each C atom in the C=C bond:

Hydrogenation

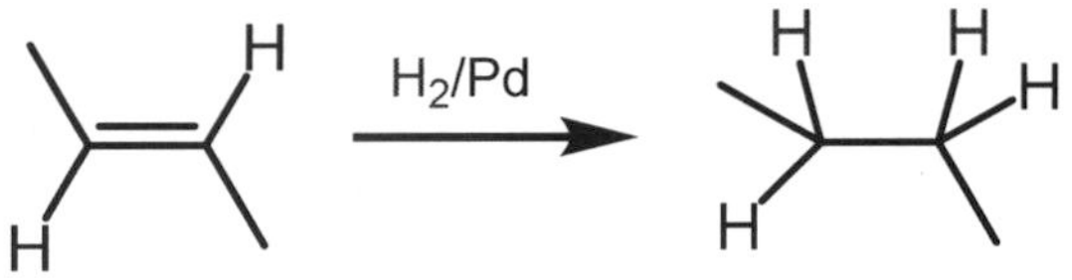

H_2/Pd

The resulting σ-bonds are stronger than the π-bond that was replaced. As a result, hydrogenation of an alkene to an alkane will be exothermic (i.e., give off heat), and this is referred to as the "heat of hydrogenation". Scientists have observed that, as the sp^2-hybridized carbons in the alkene become more electron deficient, the alkene will become less stable with respect to the alkane, and thus a greater heat of hydrogenation (ΔH_h) will be observed upon converting the alkene to the alkane.

In Lesson I.6, we saw that an sp^2-hybridized C (like the C atoms in a C=C bond) is more electronegative than is an sp^3 hybridized C. In Lesson I.11 we learned that a carbon atom that has a pull for electrons (for example a carbocation) is stabilized by electron donation from sp^3-hybridized substituents. In an analogous fashion, each alkyl branch on an alkene stabilizes it further by electron donation. Thus, the ranking of stability of simple alkenes is tetrasubstituted > trisubstituted > disubstituted > monosubstituted > ethylene. Ethylene is the least stable of the alkenes (i.e., highest in energy), so it will give off the most energy upon hydrogenation. As an alkene becomes progressively more stable, it will give off progressively less energy upon hydrogenation.

Degree of substitution:	none	mono	di			tri	tetra
	$H_2C{=}CH_2$		cis-	geminal	trans-		
ΔH_h: (kcal/mol)	−32.8	−30.1	−28.7	−28.5	−27.5	−27.0	−26.6

Disubstituted alkenes can have both substituents on the same carbon of the C=C (labeled *geminal* in the table above), the substituents may both point to the same side of the C=C unit, one off each C of the C=C (called the *cis*-isomer) or the substituents may point in opposite directions, one off each C of the C=C (called the *trans*-isomer). *cis-* > *geminal* > *trans-*. The reason that the *cis*-isomer is less stable than the *trans*-isomer is that the *cis*-isomer has unfavorable steric repulsions:

cis-isomer

It is not sterics that makes the geminal isomer higher in energy than the *trans*-isomer. Instead, it is an electronic reason. Remember from Lesson I.6.2 that the sp^2-hybridized C is more electronegative than an sp^3-hybridized C, so the C atoms in the C=C unit are stabilized by sp^3-carbon donors. One side of the C=C in 2-methylpropene has no donor groups, but both sides of the C=C bond have electron donors in the *trans*- isomer, making it more stable. The general trend for the heats of hydrogenation for alkenes is, in descending order: $CH_2{=}CH_2$ > monosubstituted > external disubstituted ~ *cis*-isomer of internal disubstituted > *trans*-isomer of internal substituted > trisubstituted > tetrasubstituted.

<u>Example I.11.2</u>

Which of the following alkenes would have the higher heat of hydrogenation?

<u>Solution I.11.2</u>

Both molecules are disubstituted alkenes, but in **A** the double bond has *cis* stereochemistry, whereas **B** has *trans* stereochemistry. **A** is less stable (i.e., higher in energy) than **B** due to steric interactions, and will thus release more energy upon hydrogenation of the C=C bond. **A** will have the higher heat of hydrogenation.

Lesson I.12.1: Favorable Reactions

In Lesson I.10, we saw that the acidity of a species increases as the stability of the deprotonated species (conjugate base anion) increases. In acid–base reactions, and in all chemical reaction, **the formation of a more stable species is more favorable than the formation of a less stable species**. In the same line of reasoning, **consumption of less stable species is more favorable**. When chemists refer to something as being more favorable, they mean more energetically favorable (more thermodynamically favorable). A more favorable reaction will require less energy to carry out. Indeed, a **spontaneous reaction** is in which the products are more stable than the reactants. Such reactions typically give off heat as a result of reaction. An example would be burning gasoline. You do have to put in a small initial bit of energy (e.g., a spark), but overall you will get much more energy out upon combustion of the gasoline than you put in. So how can we predict when a reaction will occur spontaneously?

In Lessons I.10 and I.11, we discussed how to evaluate the attractive/repulsive Coulombic forces present within anions, cations and radicals and, by doing so, assess their relative stability. Now we can use these skills to predict relative spontaneity of a reaction. The questions "which is the more spontaneous reaction", "which is more thermodynamically favorable", "which is more energetically favorable", or simply "which is more favorable" are all asking the same thing: *which reaction consumes the less stable starting materials or produces the more stable products?*

Example I.12.1

Assuming that each process is mechanistically allowed, use your knowledge of stability trends to predict whether formation of product would be thermodynamically favorable (spontaneous):

Solution I.12.1

In reaction A) the reactant is a 2° carbocation and the product is a 3° carbocation. We know from the Lesson I.11 that a 3° carbocation is more stable than a 2°, due to hyperconjugation. Reaction A) is therefore spontaneous.

A)

secondary carbocation
less stable

tertiary carbocation
more stable

In reaction B) there are two reactants, one anion and one neutral species. There are likewise two products, also an anion and a neutral species. Which species do we focus on in our analysis of stability? Unless a neutral species has some significant strain (we will learn about these later), which is not present in reaction B), ionic species have the greatest contribution to stability/instability, because they have formal Coulombic charge. For reaction B), this means we compare HO^- to $[C_4H_9NH]^-$. From Lesson I.9, we know that an anion having the negative charge on a more electronegative atom (i.e., oxygen) is more stable than an anion having the negative charge on a less electronegative atom (i.e., nitrogen). So, in reaction B), the reactant anion is more stable than the product anion. The reaction is therefore **not** thermodynamically favorable in the forward direction.

B) OH^- +

more stable
anion

H_2O +

less stable
anion

In reaction C), we again compare the anions. From Lesson I.9, we know that an anion having the negative charge on a larger, more electronegative atom like N (as in the product anion) is more stable than an anion having the negative charge on a smaller, less electronegative atom like H (as in the reactant anion). So, in reaction C), the reactant anion is less stable than the product anion. The reaction is thermodynamically favorable in the forward direction.

C) H^- +

less stable
anion

H_2 +

more stable
anion

Lesson I.12.2: Equilibria

A state of equilibrium occurs when the rates of the forward and reverse reactions are identical so that the concentration of all species remains constant. The side of an equilibrium that has more stable species is the side that is favored. The product side is favored in cases where the products are more stable than the starting materials and vice versa. If the products and reactants are equally stable, then neither side is favored, which leads to an equal abundance of products and reactants. The equilibrium constant (K_{eq}) for any equilibrium (regardless of reactant/product stability) is given by:

$$K_{eq} = [\text{products}]/[\text{reactants}]$$

We can conclude that, for a favorable reaction, the equilibrium constant is greater than one – there will be a higher concentration of products than reactants, because the products are more stable. For an unfavorable reaction, the equilibrium constant will be less than one. In general, **the greater the value of the equilibrium constant, the more thermodynamically favorable the reaction is**. This fact allows us to quantify the relative spontaneity of reactions and, by extension, the relative stabilities of different species.

Lesson I.13.1: Parts of a Reaction Coordinate Diagram

In Lesson I.12, we learned how to predict relative favorability of a reaction by comparing the relative stability of reactants and products across multiple reactions. It is often helpful to have a pictorial representation of the energy changes involved in a reaction. For this purpose, chemists use what is called a **reaction coordinate diagram**. A reaction coordinate diagram has energy on the *y*-axis and reaction progress (time) on the *x*-axis. Here is an example:

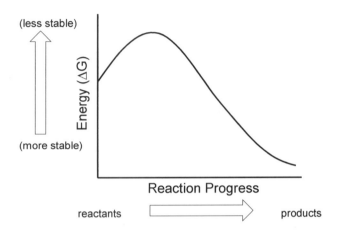

There are several critical pieces of information that we can gain from a simple analysis of a reaction coordinate diagram. First, we can tell whether the reaction is thermodynamically favorable or not:

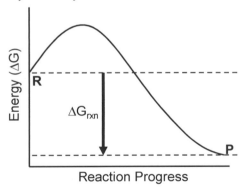

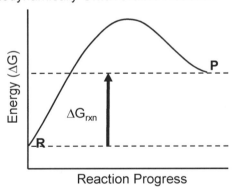

In a spontaneous reaction, the energy of products (**P**) will be lower in energy (i.e., more stable) than the reactants (**R**).

We can also tell how many steps, intermediates, and transition states are in the mechanistic path from reactants to products. Each peak represents a transition state (**T**) for each reaction step. Transition states are not isolable species, and only transiently exist at local energy maxima. Each valley (local

54

energy minimum) corresponds to an intermediate (I). An intermediate is an isolable species, which serves as the starting point for another step. Consider the reaction coordinate diagrams below:

A) Reaction Coordinate Diagram for a Spontaneous, Concerted (one step) Reaction

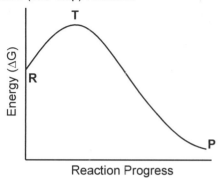

B) Reaction Coordinate Diagram for a Spontaneous, Two-Step Reaction

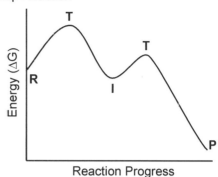

Note the obvious difference between the observed energy changes for a reaction that takes place via one mechanistic step (single step reactions are called **concerted** reactions) and one that takes place via two steps. If one records the energy changes during a reaction, mechanistic information can be found.

Example I.13.1

A scientist does a reaction and observes energy changes shown in this reaction coordinate diagram:

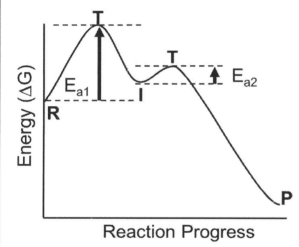

Which of the following mechanisms is consistent with this observation?

E1 reaction

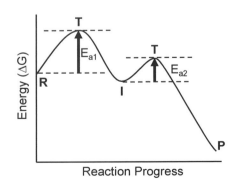

$$heterolysis \quad\quad electrophilic \;\; elimination$$

LG

H

LG$^{\ominus}$

$\oplus$

H

H$^+$

E2 reaction

LG

HO$^{\ominus}$

H

+ H$_2$O + LG$^{\ominus}$

<u>Solution I.13.1</u>

Reaction coordinate B) indicates that there are two steps in the mechanism. The E2 reaction choice shows only one step (an E2 step that we learned in Lesson I.8), which is consistent with reaction coordinate A), but not B) as is asked in this question. The E1 reaction, however, consists of two elementary steps, heterolysis followed by electrophilic elimination (also from Lesson I.8). The E1 mechanism is consistent with the observed energy changes represented in reaction coordinate diagram B).

The rate of a reaction can also be determined from a feature in the reaction coordinate diagram. You may recall from General Chemistry that the rate constant (k) for a reaction is proportional to the energy of activation (E_a) of a reaction, as outlined in the Arrhenius equation:

$$k = Ae^{-(E_a/RT)}$$

(A = Arrhenius constant, R = gas constant, T = temperature)

We are not going to use the equation here, but we can conclude **that a higher energy of activation leads to a slower reaction.** The energy of activation is shown on a reaction coordinate diagram below: it is the amount of energy needed to get "over the hump" of any given step of a reaction.

Energies of Activation for Step 1 (E_{a1}) and two (E_{a2})

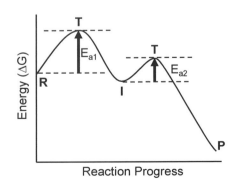

In the reaction coordinate diagram above, the first step has a higher energy of activation than does the second step, so the first step will be slower. This leads to another piece of information that we can gain from the diagram. The slowest step of a reaction is termed the **rate-limiting step**. Knowing the rate-limiting step helps one make predictions about reaction trends and products, as well as practical laboratory or production plant considerations, such as solvent selection or the amount of heat that must be supplied for a reaction. We will see examples of this throughout the book.

Lesson I.14.1: Linear Alkanes and Substituents

In Lesson I.4, we saw examples of the functional groups typically covered in introductory organic chemistry. Alkanes are molecules consisting of only carbon and hydrogen atoms, with all the carbons interconnected by only single bonds. There is an infinite number of ways that C and H atoms could combine to form alkanes, so it is important to develop a naming system (a nomenclature convention) for alkanes to use in our studies. **Linear alkanes** have all carbons attached in a linear chain, with no C-containing branches or other **substituents** coming off of the chain other than hydrogen. Below are shown the linear alkanes, up to ten carbon atoms in length, along with their names. On the right is the name for substituent chains having the same number of C atoms as the corresponding linear alkane on the left. In addition to these alkyl substituents, halide substituents (fluoro for -F, chloro for Cl-, bromo for Br- and iodo for I-) can be used in naming alkyl halides following the same rules in Lesson I.14.2 for alkanes.

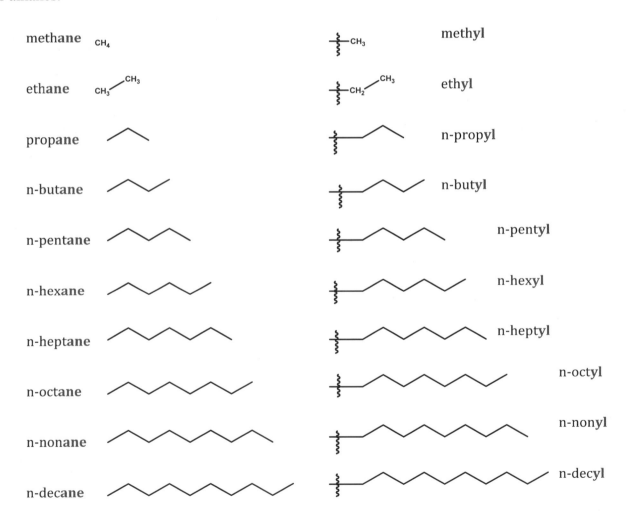

Note that some of the linear chains have an "n-" in front of their names. This 'n-' stands for "normal", and it is sometimes left off of the name and we assume that it is a "normal" linear chain. On the other hand, some arrangement of hydrocarbon chains that are placed as substituents have specific names that use other designators in front of the part of the word telling us how many C are present. The more common ones are provided below for reference.

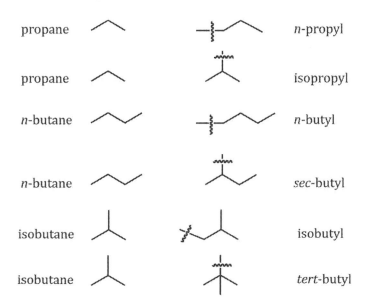

There are also different ways that the same set of carbon atoms can be arranged for a given molecular formula. If two molecules have identical molecular formulae but differ in their bond connectivity, we term these **constitutional isomers**. As an example, the possible constitutional isomers the formula C_5H_{12} are provided below:

Lesson I.14.2: Naming Branched Alkanes and Alkyl Halides

We will now use a series of examples to illustrate how to use the following six-step guide for naming alkanes. Note that, for most alkanes, you will only need some of these rules.

1) Find the longest chain. This is the 'parent chain'; the other things coming off of the parent chain are its substituents.
2) Number the carbon atoms in the 'parent chain' in the way that gives the lowest number to the substituent closest to an end of the parent chain.
3) If more than one type of substituent is present, name in alphabetical order.

4) If more than one of the same substituent are present on your parent chain, use di, tri, tetra, etc., prefixes to denote this (these prefixes do not count when alphabetizing, though; neither do the *n-*, *sec-*, or *tert-* prefixes; however, the *iso* prefix DOES count)

5) If numbering leads to the same lowest number substituent in either direction, the correct numbering gives the lowest number to the substituent that is first alphabetically.

6) If you find two different possible parent chains of the same length, you choose the one with more substituents coming off of it.

Consider the molecule on the left. The longest chain (step 1) has five carbons, so the parent chain is pentane (highlighted on the right).

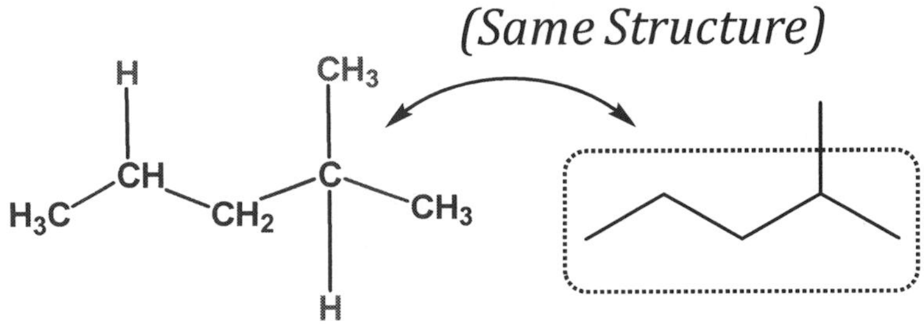

(Same Structure)

Having identified the parent chain, we move on to step 2, numbering the carbon atoms in the parent chain such that the substituent (here a methyl) has the lowest number:

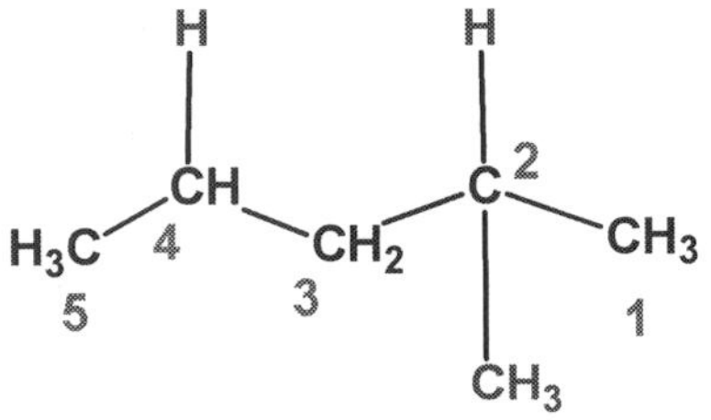

This molecule is thus called **2-methylpentane**. Note that there is always a dash between a numeral and the substituent to which it refers. Consider another example, in which we have already applied rules 1 and 2, and have found a heptane chain having a methyl substituent at position 2 and an ethyl substituent at position 4:

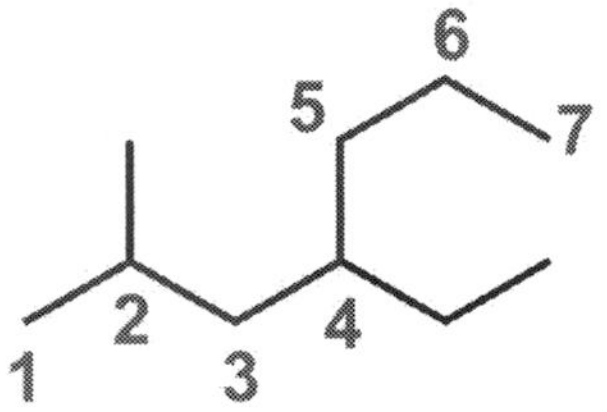

We now need to apply rule 3 (list substituents alphabetically) to compose the final name of **4-ethyl-2-methylheptane**.

In a case in which a parent is substituted by more than one of the same substituent, for example:

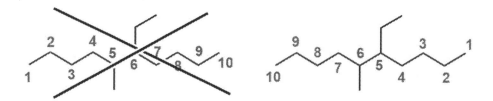

We will need rule 4 involving use of di-, tri-, etc. prefixes. The molecule above is thus properly called **2,4-dimethylheptane**.

If we encounter a case like this:

In which there are two possible ways to number the parent chain, we need to apply the fifth rule. This rule tells us that in a tie, give the alphabetically first substituent the lower number, as shown on the right, above. This approach allows us to properly name the molecule as **5-ethyl-6-methyldecane**.

We may encounter a molecule in which two possible longest parent chains are identified, as in the example below.

In these cases, rule 6 tells us to choose the parent chain having more substituents (the one on the left), so this molecule is properly called **2,4,6-trimethyl-5-propyloctane**.

Alkyl halides are named using the same set of rules as are alkanes, as illustrated by the example below:

4-bromo-3-chloro-2-methylhexane

Lesson I.14.3: Naming Substituted Cycloalkanes/ cis- and trans- Isomers

Alkanes that have a cyclic structure, rather than linear, are called **cycloalkanes**. The structures and names for the most common unsubstituted cycloalkanes are provided below.

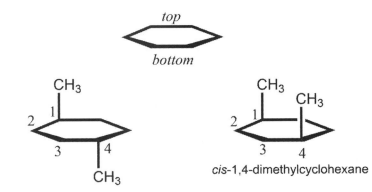

cyclopropane   cyclobutane   cyclopentane   cyclohexane

cycloheptane   cyclooctane

A cycloalkane may be substituted just as a linear alkane may be substituted. The cycloalkane can also be the parent chain, if it is the longest contiguous chain of carbon atoms in the molecule. A parent chain may be composed *either* of C atoms in a cycloalkane *or* C atoms in a linear chain. One may not mix C atoms from both types of alkanes to form a parent chain, so:

4-cyclopentyl-2,3-dimethylhexane   1-ethylcyclohexane

The rules for naming linear alkanes also apply to cycloalkanes. There is one additional consideration when naming cycloalkanes, however. A ring of atoms has a "top" face and a "bottom" face, as indicated in the picture below.

top

bottom

trans-1,4-dimethylcyclohexane

cis-1,4-dimethylcyclohexane

62

Because there are two faces of the ring, we will need to provide a prefix in front of the name of a disubstituted cycloalkane to indicate whether one group is oriented a face opposite of the other (we use the *trans-* prefix for this) or if the two groups are oriented on the same face (we use the *cis-* prefix in such cases). The two examples above illustrate this convention. The *trans-* and *cis-* forms of a disubstituted cycloalkane are examples of **configurational isomers**. Configurational isomers have the same constitution (all atoms are attached to the same atoms in both cases) and differ only in directions that the groups point off of the structure. Configurational isomers also **cannot interconvert without σ-bond breakage**: if we wanted to change the *cis-* into the *trans-* isomer, we would have to break the σ-bond to the Me substituent and switch its position, for example. We will cover other types of configurational isomers in more detail throughout the rest of this text.

Lesson 14.4: Naming Alcohols

For alcohols, use the rules for naming alkanes and cycloalkanes as a starting point, with the following adjustments: Replace the "e" at the end of the alkane name with "ol".

1) The alcohol is always given the lowest possible number. Note that this means that the alcohol is always given the "1" position in cycloalkanes (so there is no need to add a number, because it is always 1).
2) Place the number indicating the position of the alcohol directly before the parent chain name (which now ends in "ol").

Again, we will illustrate how the rules are applied with examples:

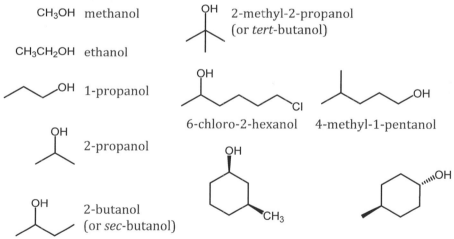

Additional help from "Organic Chemistry 1 Reactions and Practice Problems 2018" (Smith):

- After finishing Lesson I.14, you will be ready for Problem Set 2 in the companion book. This Problem Set covers material from Primer Lessons I.4 and I.14

Lesson I.15: Isomerism and Conformational Analysis I: Linear Alkanes and Newman Projections

Lesson I.15.1: Newman Projections and Conformational Isomers of Ethane

Now that we have a strong foundation in analyzing attractive and repulsive forces in molecules, we can begin to evaluate how these forces can influence the geometries of molecules and the relative spatial orientation of their bonds. Consider a simple molecule like ethane. We can draw ethane in several possible ways, two of which are illustrated below:

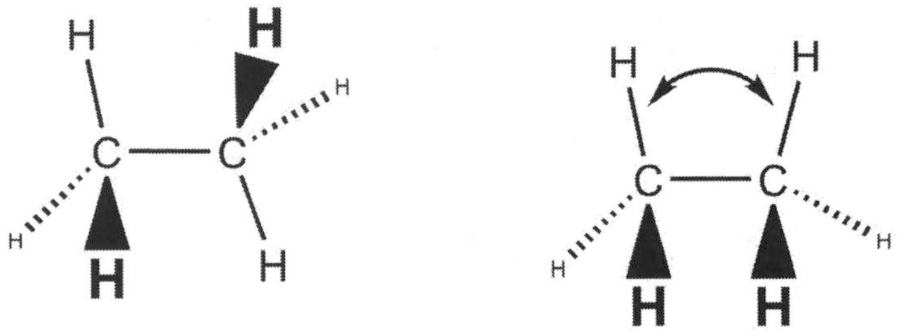

The only difference between these two representations of ethane is how the H atoms on one C are rotated relative to the H atoms on the other C. Structures that differ only by the angle of rotation about a σ-bond are called **conformational isomers**. Unlike the configurational isomers discussed in Lesson I.14, conformational isomers can be interconverted by simple bond rotation, so we do not need to add a prefix in front of the name to distinguish these separate species (because they interconvert easily). Both of the conformations shown in the picture are simple called "ethane" as a molecular name. Note, however, that the two conformations do not have the same stability. As indicated by the double headed arrow in the structure on the right, the C–H bonds are pointed in the same way on each of the two carbons. Remembering that a bond comprises two electrons and that electrons repel one another, placing the C–H bonds close together like this will be a less stable arrangement than the conformation on the left, in which the bonds are staggered and thus farther apart from one another. This is easier to see if we take a look at the molecule from a perspective looking down the C–C bond:

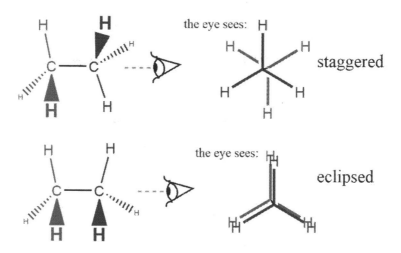

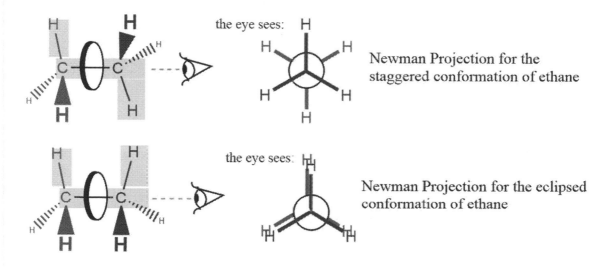

Note that it is somewhat difficult to discern which H atoms are attached to which C in the drawings on the right, so chemists use what are called **Newman Projections** for a clearer view of attachment:

We can easily see from the Newman Projections on the right that the eclipsed conformation of ethane places the electrons in the C–H bonds on the front C closer to the C–H bonding electrons on the back carbon, whereas the staggered conformation minimizes this by placing these C–H bonds as far apart as possible. A staggered conformation along a bond is thus more stable than the eclipsed and is the conformation that most ethane molecules will have in a given sample.

Lesson I.15.2: Conformational Isomers of Butane

We can carry out the same type of analysis for more complex molecules as we did for ethane. When we undertake such conformational analysis of linear alkanes, we need to keep in mind two basic principles:

1) Eclipsed bonding pairs have more repulsion than do staggered bonding pairs
2) The larger the groups, the greater will be the repulsion

If we start off an analysis of butane, we will find that we can draw it in four unique staggered or eclipsed Newman Projections along the C(2)–C(3) bond:

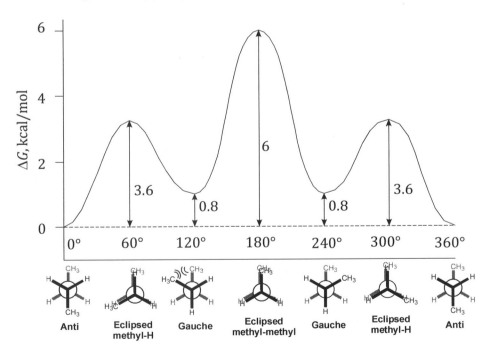

We can easily determine the relative stability of these structures by applying two principles. First, each of the two staggered conformations (Anti and Gauche) are more stable than either of the eclipsed conformations (Eclipsed methyl–H or Eclipsed methyl–methyl). Secondly, the Gauche conformation is less stable than the Anti conformation because the Gauche has the two methyl groups close enough to one another to induce some repulsion (called a **Gauche interaction**). Although not nearly as destabilizing as are eclipsing interactions, the Gauche interaction still makes the Gauche conformation less stable than the Anti by about 0.8 kcal/mol.

By a similar line of reasoning, it is evident that the Eclipsed methyl–methyl conformation is less stable than is the eclipsed methyl–H conformation because the eclipsed methyl–methyl places the two largest groups closest to one another. On the basis of the foregoing discussion, we can rationalize the diagram below, which is a plot of C(2)–C(3) σ-bond rotation angle versus energy:

We can apply this type of analysis to any number of organic compounds to rationalize and predict stability trends, which we will do specifically for cycloalkanes in the next lesson.

Lesson I.16.1: Strain in Cycloalkanes

Cycloalkanes can be subject to constrained geometries that lead to deviations from ideal bond angles. For example, cyclopropane with equal C–C bond angles will be an equilateral triangle, with angles of 60°. This angle differs from the ideal angle of 109.5° for an sp^3-hybridized C atom. The 'ideal' angle is the angle that gives the strongest bond, thus holding the molecule together most tightly (i.e., making it most stable). Deviating from the ideal angle thus leads to weaker bonds and less stable molecules. The decreased stability that results from the bonds being strained from the ideal angle is called **angle strain**. The angles that would be present in the planar forms of some cycloalkanes are provided here:

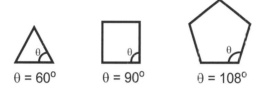

$$\theta = 60° \qquad \theta = 90° \qquad \theta = 108°$$

We saw in the previous lesson that certain conformations of molecules, specifically those in which there are eclipsing interactions, are less stable than are staggered conformations. When atoms are constrained in a ring, there is not free rotation about a C–C bond (we could not, for example, rotate 360°), so it is sometimes impossible to alleviate eclipsing interactions in the way we did with ethane and butane. For this reason, there is can also be some steric strain induced in cycloalkanes. The sum of all steric and angle strains together is often referred to as **ring strain**.

An example of steric stain is induced by molecular geometry is in cyclopropane. Cyclopropane is locked in a conformation in which every H is eclipsing two others (the Newman Projection below shows the perspective down one C–C bond in the right-hand image):

eclipsed!

eclipsed!

eclipsed!

eclipsed!

If cyclobutane were planar, it would suffer from the same destabilizing forces (left image, below). As ring size increases, however, the flexibility of the ring also increases. This flexibility allows the cyclobutane to "pucker" a bit (i.e., slight bond rotations occur) in response to eclipsing interactions to alleviate some of the steric strain (right image, below):

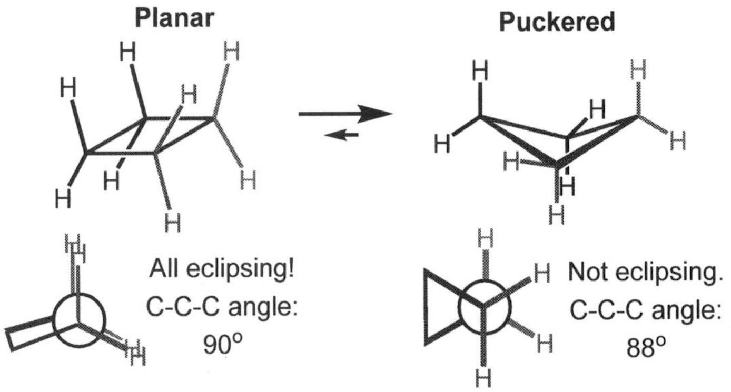

Planar

Puckered

All eclipsing!
C-C-C angle:
90°

Not eclipsing.
C-C-C angle:
88°

Similarly, cyclopentane distorts from a planar conformation to an envelope conformation, which is the actual form found in solution, via what is known as an **envelope distortion** (right image):

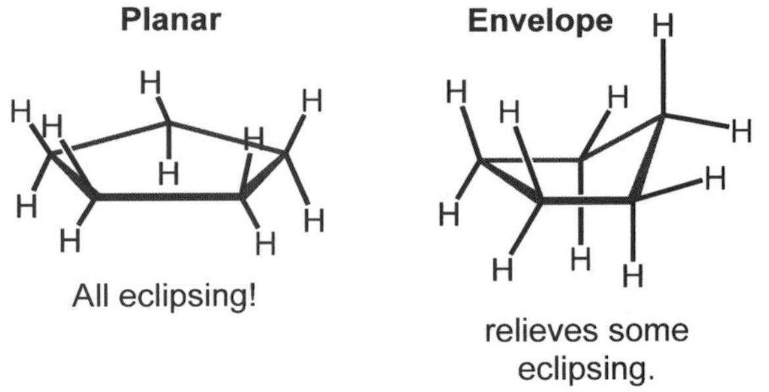

Planar

Envelope

All eclipsing!

relieves some
eclipsing.

The relative strain per CH_2 unit in cycloalkanes trends in the order cyclopentane < cyclobutene < cyclopropane because flexibility increases as the ring size increases (which allows greater C–C bond rotation), thus allowing greater ability to alleviate steric strain. This effect becomes dramatic in the case of cyclohexane, as detailed in the next section.

Lesson I.16.2: The Chair Conformation of Cyclohexane

In cyclohexane, the flexibility of the ring allows two envelope distortions to occur (one up and one down) to produce what is called the **chair conformation** of cyclohexane:

fold flap up

'envelope-like'
distortion 1

'envelope-like'
distortion 2

fold flap
down

**Chair conformation
of cyclohexane**

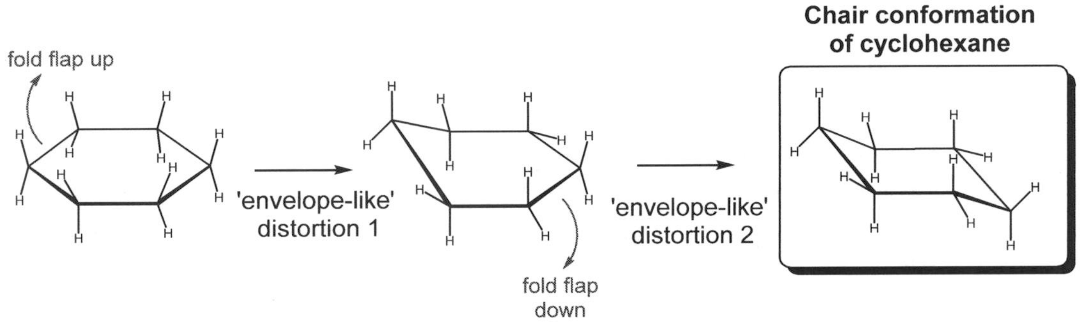

In the chair conformation, all bond angles are ideal, so there is no angle strain. Additionally, there are no eclipsing steric strains. Thus, **the chair conformation of cyclohexane thus has ~0 ring strain:**

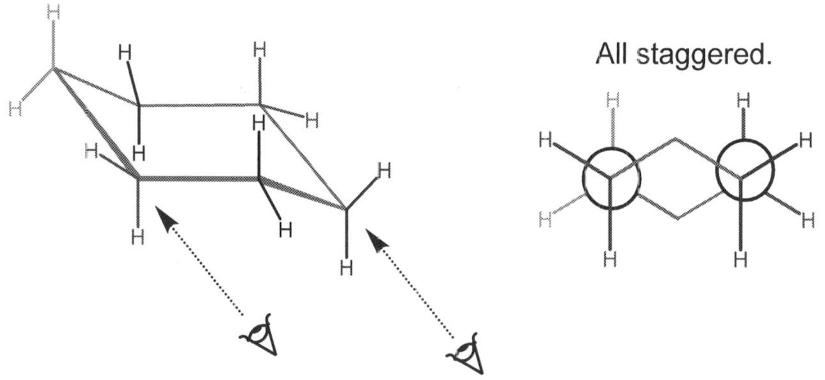

All staggered.

One notable feature of the chair conformation that becomes important when we start adding substituents is that there are two types of sites with H atoms: those that point straight up or straight down around are at **axial** sites, those that project horizontally from the ring are at **equatorial** sites:

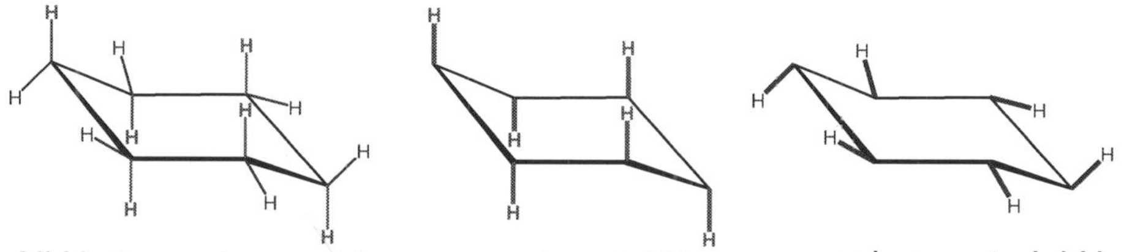

All H atoms drawn out   only axial H   only equatorial H

If there is enough thermal energy (i.e., at sufficiently high temperatures), the cyclohexane molecule can undergo a **ring flip**, where a conformation in which the "left tip" is up and the "right tip" points down interconverts with a conformation in which these "tips" are inverted:

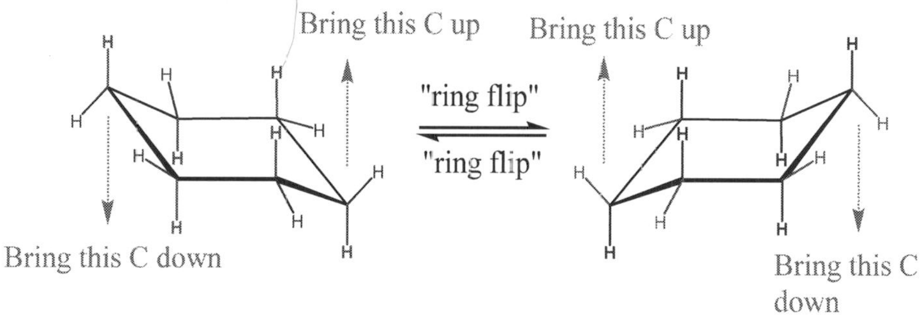

Ring flips are common at room temperature and at reaction temperatures, and later in this text we will encounter cases in which the flip is required to accommodate a reaction process. Note that each C has an axial and an equatorial site. Each C also has one 'up' and one 'down' site. When substituents are added, the ring flip may become more energetically unfavorable, as we will discuss in the next section.

Lesson I.16.3: Substituted Cyclohexane

Now that we have a good grasp of the parent chair cyclohexane, we can examine the extent to which substituents may influence stability of the ring. If we place anything larger than an H atom on one of the axial sites of cyclohexane, it will introduce a destabilizing Gauche interaction to the structure similar to what we saw in butane:

Gauche

Methylcyclohexane

If two larger-than-H groups are placed at axial sites on the same face of the ring, the two may even be able to undergo some steric repulsion known as a 1,3-diaxial interaction:

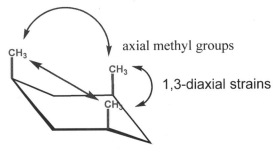

1,3,5-trimethylcyclohexane

If, however, the larger-than-H substituents are at equatorial sites, then a fully-staggered, Gauche-free conformation is maintained, because the equatorial substituent is *anti* to the ring on the adjacent C:

Anti to one another

The overarching lesson we learn from these observations is that the more stable conformation is the one in which the larger substituent is in the equatorial position.

<u>Example I.16.3</u>

Draw the most stable conformation of *cis*-1-*t*-butyl-4-ethylcyclohexane.

<u>Solution I.16.3</u>

Start by placing the largest substituent in the equatorial site so that its steric strain is minimized:

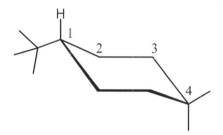

Next, use the information in the name of the molecule to place the ethyl group. The ethyl group is at position 4, and it is cis- to the *t*-butyl group. We placed the *t*-butyl group pointing down, and *cis*- indicates that the two groups must point the same direction, so the ethyl group must also point down. We have only one choice for its placement:

<u>Additional help from "Organic Chemistry 1 Reactions and Practice Problems 2018" (Smith):</u>

- After finishing Lesson I.16, you will be ready for Problem Set 3 in the companion book. This Problem Set covers material from Primer Lessons I.15-16

- You will also be ready for Progress Check 1 in the companion book. Progress Check 1 is a practice exam covering materials from all of the Primer Lessons so far (Lessons I.1-16).

Lesson I.17.1: Chirality and Configurational Isomerism

We saw in Lesson I.14 that isomers that have the same constitution but cannot be interconverted without bond breakage are called configurational isomers. The configurational isomers that we discussed were the *cis-* and *trans*-isomers of cycloalkanes. We will now discuss another type of conformational isomerism. A molecule that has "handedness" is said to be chiral. To identify what molecules have "handedness", it might be helpful to think about what makes a right hand and a left hand different. After all, both hands have four fingers and a thumb attached to a palm. No matter how we rotate a right hand, however, it is not superimposable (not identical) with a left hand. They are mirror images of each other. If we think of a hand has being four surfaces, it may help. A hand has 1) a palm, 2) a backhand, 3) a thumb side and 4) a little finger side. If the hand was the same on front and back or if the hand was symmetric on the front (like a cartoon hand with three fingers), then we could superimpose them. However, because all four 'sides' are different, the hands have what we have come to call "handedness". For molecules, we use the term "**chirality**" in place of "handedness". A molecule that possesses chirality is said to be **chiral**. A tetrahedral C atom has four substituents much as a hand has four "sides". If all four substituents coming off the tetrahedral C are different, we say the C atom is a **chiral center** (alternatively known as a **chirality center**, **stereocenter**, or **stereogenic center**, in various books). If any two substituents coming off of the C are identical, the C is not a chiral center. We indicate stereocenters in a molecule with an asterisk (*).

Example I.17.1

Which carbon atoms in these structures are stereocenters?

Solution I.17.1

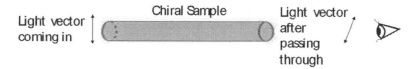

None   Br   OH

None

Lesson I.17.2: Properties of Stereoisomers

A chiral molecule and its mirror image share many of the same chemical properties: the two will have the same stability, solubility, boiling point, and melting point, for example. How, then, do we tell the two apart, and why does chirality even matter? One property of chiral molecules that differs between the two mirror images is the direction in which they rotate plane polarized light. For this reason, a chiral molecule is also said to be **optically active**. An instrument called a polarimeter is used to measure the angle by which plane polarized light is rotated by a given sample (units in °, positive values for clockwise rotations, negative values for counter-clockwise rotations). A simplified drawing of a polarimeter is provided here:

Light vector coming in   Chiral Sample   Light vector after passing through

A chiral molecule that causes clockwise rotation of the plane polarized light vector is called a **dextrorotatory** molecule, and a "(+)-" symbol is placed in front of that molecule's name. If the mirror image of this dextrorotatory isomer is measured at the same concentration, we would instead observe a counterclockwise rotation of the light vector by the same angle. The mirror image of dextrorotatory is **levorotatory**, and a "(–)-" symbol is placed in front of a molecule's name to indicate it is a levorotatory molecule. A sample of **achiral** (not chiral) molecules will not cause the plane polarized light vector to rotate at all, and such samples are said to be **optically inactive**. Because the dextrorotatory and levorotatory isomers rotate the vector by the same angle but with opposite signs (i.e., in opposite directions), a sample containing dextrorotatory and levorotatory isomers in equal amounts will exhibit no optical activity (the + and – cancel out). A 1:1 mix of dextrorotatory and levorotatory isomers is termed a **racemic mixture** (or **racemate**) to distinguish it from samples of achiral molecules.

Lesson I.18: Stereochemistry II: Cahn-Ingold-Prelog Rules and Assigning *R*- and *S*- Labels of Configuration

Lesson I.18.1: The Cahn-Ingold-Prelog Rules

In the previous lesson, we observed that the dextrorotatory and levorotatory isomers of a molecule rotate plane polarized light in different directions. The direction of light rotation, however, does not correlate with molecular structure in a predictable way. For this reason, scientists have come up with a system to identify chiral molecules that does not involve rotation of plane polarized light. The naming system is based on the relative spatial orientation of different substituents in order of priority about the chiral center. To name chiral molecules, then, we must first learn the convention for assigning priority to the substituents coming off a stereogenic atom, which is called the **Cahn-Ingold-Prelog** (CIP) rules. Consider this hypothetical structure to illustrate how these rules work:

Cahn-Ingold-Prelog (CIP) rules:

1) First look at the atoms directly attached to the stereogenic atom. Higher atomic number = higher priority (A, B, C and D in the figure above).
2) If same atomic number, higher mass = higher priority (Deuterium > H, ^{13}C > ^{12}C, etc.)
3) If atoms A and B are identical, move to highest priority atom attached to A and B until a break in the tie is found (first compare A1 to B1 priority. If tie, compare A2 to B2. If tie, compare A3 to B3, etc.)

Example I.18.1

Prioritize the substituents on the stereogenic atom in the structure below (1 for highest priority to 4 for lowest priority).

The directly-attached atoms are O, H, C and C. The OH substituent is the highest priority (1), the H is the lowest (4), and the two C-attached substituents are tied, so we move out:

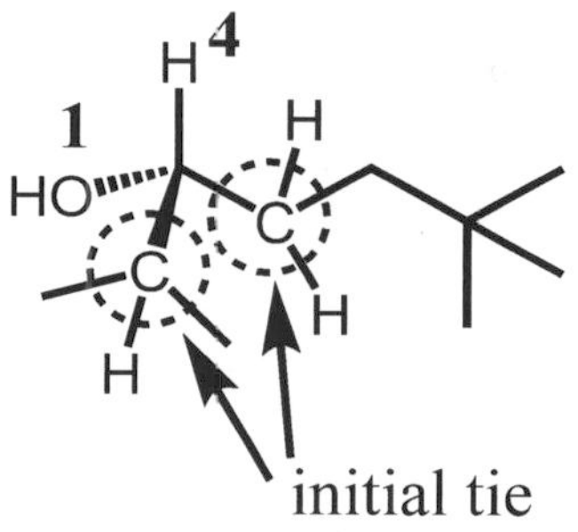

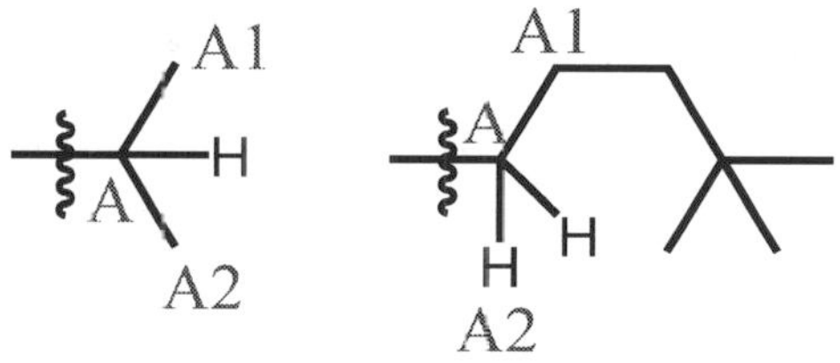

comparison of two initially-tied groups

We still have a tie upon comparing the "A1" atoms (both C), so we compare "A2" atoms. Finally, the tie is broken because the isopropyl substituent has a C at "A2", whereas the other substituent has an H. Our final prioritization is thus:

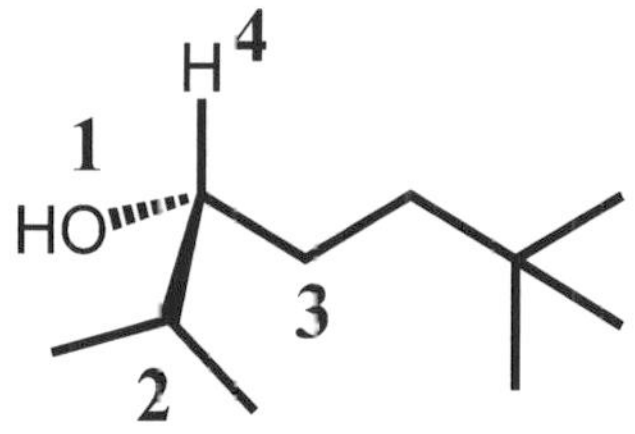

Cahn-Ingold-Prelog (CIP) rules (cont'd):

4) If a substituent is doubly or triply bonded to another atom, use the 'break and duplicate' strategy to create 'false atoms' as a visual aid to prioritize:

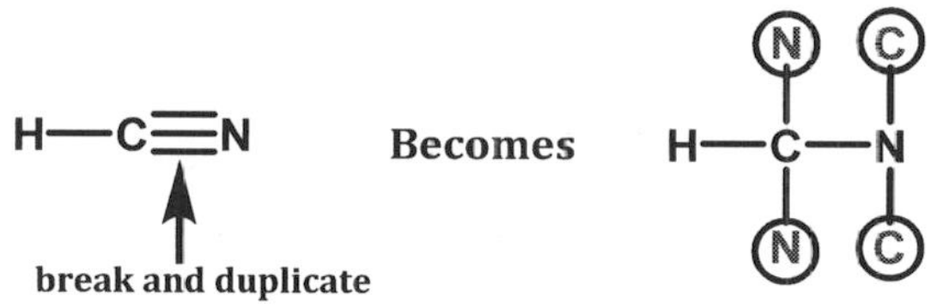

In the previous section, we learned the CIP rules to prioritize substituents as a first step to naming chiral molecules from their structures. We will now learn how to name the chiral molecules. When we label hands, we use the terms "right" and "left" as indicators of the handedness. When naming molecules, we use the Latin terms for right (*rectus*) and left (*sinister*) to indicate molecular handedness. We place a label of configuration in front of the molecule's name (i.e., a stereochemical prefix) so the reader knows to which isomer the name refers: "(*R*)-" for "rectus" and "(*S*)-" for sinister.

To determine whether an isomer is (*R*)- or (*S*)-, we follow these steps:
1) Assign priorities to the four groups (using CIP rules)
2) Point the **lowest** priority group (4th place) away from you
3) Determine the direction of procession from **1**→**2**→**3** priorities. If the procession is clockwise, that chiral center has an "(*R*)-" configuration. If the procession is in the counterclockwise direction, that chiral center has an "(*S*)-" configuration.

Example I.18.2

Assign a configurational label to this molecule:

Solution I.18.2

First assign priorities for each of the substituents:

Here, the 4th place substituent is already pointing away from you, so simply draw an arc from 1 to 2 to 3, ignoring the 4th place substituent:

Here, the arc goes in a counterclockwise direction, so this molecule is in the (*S*)- configuration. Its full name would be written as (*S*)-2-butanol.

If the lowest priority substituent is not initially pointing back, you will need to rotate the molecule to point the 4th substituent back. You can do this by building a model and physically turning it or, as you become more proficient with these problems, mentally picturing the molecule and rotating it. One alternative strategy to consider is, if the lowest priority atom is pointing towards you (opposite of what you want), you can instead count $3\rightarrow2\rightarrow1$ (opposite of normal counting), and you will still attain the correct configuration. If the lowest priority substituent is in the plane of the page, however, this alternate strategy cannot be used, and you will have to reorient the molecule. In the next lesson, we will learn a convenient representation of chiral molecules drawn such that all substituents are pointed either towards or away from the viewer. Helpful video examples for manipulating 3D structures to determine configuration are provided on the Proton Guru YouTube channel (search "Proton Guru Channel" on youtube.com to find the channel).

Lesson I.19: Stereochemistry III: Fischer Projections

Lesson I.19.1: Fischer Projections

Our study of stereochemistry and chirality has made the importance of three-dimensional shapes of molecules evident. The **Fischer Projection** is another way to represent the three-dimensional structure of chiral molecules. In this convention, each stereogenic atom is placed at the intersection of orthogonal lines. The groups on the horizontal lines are understood to represent substituents pointing towards the viewer from the chiral center, with groups on the vertical lines representing substituents pointing away from the viewer from the chiral center.

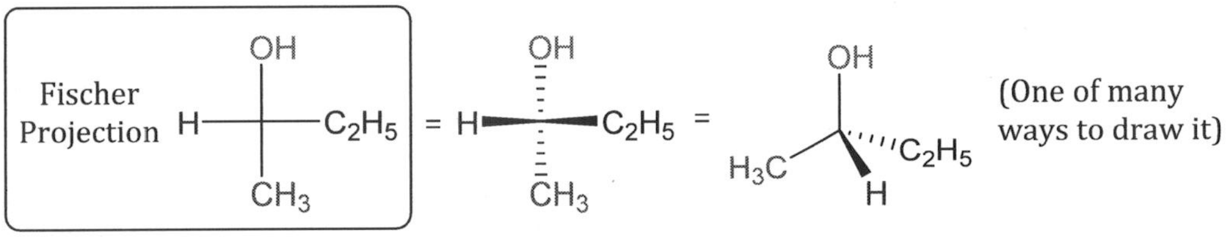

Example I.19.1

Assign the configuration of the chiral center in the Fischer Projection shown below:

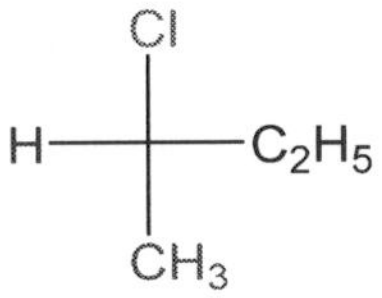

Solution I.19.1

First, prioritize the substituents:

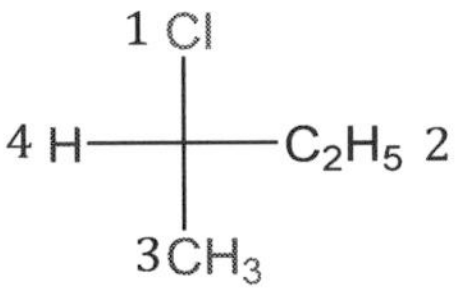

We see that the 4th place substituent (H) is towards us in the Fischer Projection convention. This is a "backwards" molecule, so we count 3→2→1, instead of 1→2→3 (see Lesson I.18.2):

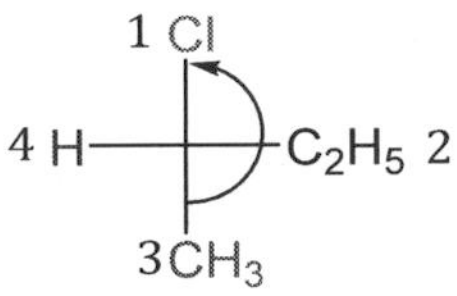

We see a counterclockwise precession from 3→2→1, corresponding to the (*S*)-configuration.

Lesson I.20.1: Enantiomers

A molecule may have only one chiral center or it may have many stereocenters. Each stereocenter in a molecule may be in the (R)- or (S)- configuration, so a molecule with "n" stereocenters can have up to 2^n stereoisomers. As an example, a molecule with two stereocenters at carbons 1 and 2 can have up to 2^2, or 4, stereoisomers: the "(1R,2R)-" isomer, the "(1S,2S)-" isomer, the "(1R,2S)-" isomer, and the "(1S,2R)-" isomer. Some vocabulary is needed to delineate the relationship between these isomers. Two chiral molecules that are non-superimposable mirror images are referred to as **enantiomers** and form an **enantiomeric pair**. A molecule and its enantiomer will have opposite configurations at *every* stereocenter in the molecule. If a molecule has a "(1R,2R)-" configuration, its enantiomer will have a "(1S,2S)-" configuration. Likewise, the enantiomer of a "(1R,2S)-" isomer is a "(1S,2R)-" isomer.

Lesson I.20.2: Diastereomers

Stereoisomers that are not mirror images are known as **diastereomers**. In contrast to enantiomers, two diastereomers do not necessarily have the same stability, solubility, melting point, boiling point, etc. Consequently, it is possible to separate diastereomers by distillation, recrystallization, etc., much easier than for enantiomers. Referring back to the example in Lesson I.20.1, a "(1R,2R)-" isomer will be a diastereomer of both the "(1R,2S)-" and the "(1S,2R)-" isomers.

Example I.20.1

Provide the stereochemical relationships between the compounds shown below:

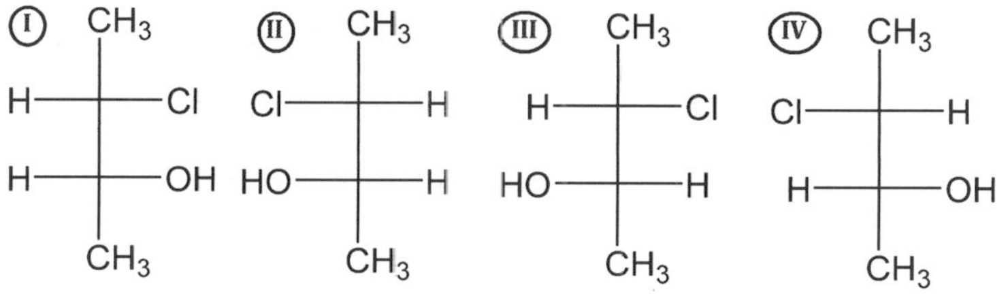

Solution I.20.1

We can see that I and II are mirror images of one another and are non-superimposable, so I and II form an enantiomeric pair. Likewise, III and IV are enantiomers. All other pairs we compare are diastereomers (I+III, I+IV, II+III, II+IV).

Lesson I.20.3: Meso Compounds

It is possible for a molecule to contain stereogenic *atoms* in its structure, but that the *molecule as a whole* is achiral. This condition occurs when one half of a molecule is the mirror image of the other half (i.e., has a plane of symmetry). Remember, a symmetric object cannot be chiral. Molecules that have stereogenic atoms but which are achiral molecules are called **meso compounds**.

Example I.20.2

Which of the following are meso compounds?

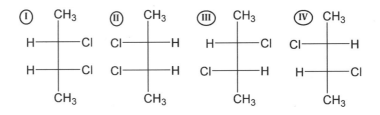

Solution I.20.3

Compounds I and II each possess a plane of symmetry (represented by the dashed lines) and are thus achiral, despite the fact that carbons 2 and 3 are stereocenters. Compounds I and II are therefore meso compounds. In fact, they are identical.

Additional help from "Organic Chemistry 1 Reactions and Practice Problems 2018" (Smith):

- After finishing Lesson I.20, you will be ready for Problem Set 4 in the companion book. This Problem Set covers material from Primer Lessons I.17-20

PART II. Substitution, Elimination and Oxidation

Lesson II.1: Stereochemistry V: Tracking Stereocenters in Reactions

Lesson II.2: Nucleophilicity versus Basicity

Lesson II.3: Substitution Reactions of RX I: The S_N1 Mechanism

Lesson II.4: Substitution Reactions of RX II: The S_N2 Mechanism

Lesson II.5: Substitution Reactions of RX III: Stereochemistry of Substitution Reactions

Lesson II.6: Elimination Reactions of RX I: The E1 Mechanism

Lesson II.7: Elimination Reactions of RX II: The E2 Mechanism

Lesson II.8: Stereoelectronic Effects in the E2 reaction

Lesson II.9: Factors Leading to Non-Zaitsev Products in the E2 Reaction: Hofmann Elimination

Lesson II.10: Competition Among Substitution and Elimination Reactions of RX: Predicting Pathways

Lesson II.11: Reactions of Alcohols I: Substitution and Elimination

Lesson II.12: Oxidation and Reduction: Definitions

Lesson II.13: Reactions of Alcohols II: Oxidation

Lesson II.14: Acid Cleavage of Ethers

Lesson II.15: Ring-Opening of Epoxides: Steric versus Electronic Effects on Product Distribution

Lesson II.1: Stereochemistry V: Tracking Stereocenters in Reactions

Lesson II.1.1: Stereocenters Formed in the Course of Reaction

In Lesson I.9, we learned that more stable products often form more rapidly because they often have lower activation barriers. As a result, the most stable product possible is often the product formed in highest yield. In Lesson I.20, we learned that two enantiomers have the same stability as one another. It follows that, *if an achiral starting material undergoes a reaction leading to two enantiomers as products, the two enantiomers will be produced in equal amounts.*

Example II.1.1

A reaction between an alkene and H_2O in the presence of catalytic acid is observed to produce 2-butanol as shown:

Draw the major products of this reaction, indicating stereochemistry where relevant.

Solution II.1.1

We recognize that a stereocenter has been generated and we have labeled it with an asterisk. Two enantiomers of equal stability are possible products. We thus draw both structures and label them with the labels of configuration "(R)-" or "(S)-". The product will be a racemic mixture of the two enantiomers.

(R)-2-butanol   (S)-2-butanol

What if *two* stereocenters are present in a product generated from an achiral starting material? For example, consider the reaction of HBr/H_2O_2 with an alkene to form an alkyl bromide:

In this case, up to four products might be produced:

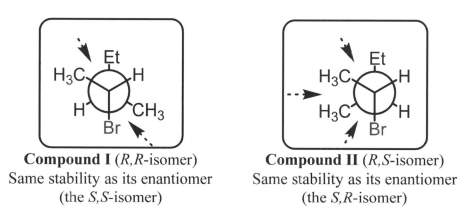

Compounds I and IV form one enantiomeric pair; compounds II and III form another. All other pairings represent diastereomers. We know that two enantiomers have the same stability and that two diastereomers have different stability. We will take two diastereomers and determine which is more stable; for this purpose, we choose I and II. Compounds I and II are configurational isomers, so all of the bond types are the same, thus any difference in stability must be caused by sterics. By drawing the Newman projections of I and II, we can identify any destabilizing interactions:

Compound I (*R,R*-isomer)
Same stability as its enantiomer
(the *S,S*-isomer)

Compound II (*R,S*-isomer)
Same stability as its enantiomer
(the *S,R*-isomer)

The arrows in the above diagram show destabilizing *gauche interactions* between non-H groups. There are fewer of these repulsive steric forces in compound I, so we predict that it is the more stable of the diastereomers. Consequently, the major product would be predicted to be a racemic mixture of I and IV.

Lesson II.1.2: Stereocenters Present Before a Reaction Occurs

If a starting material has stereocenters in it prior to a reaction, there are several considerations one must take into account. The first question is whether this reaction affects the bonds to the stereogenic atom in question. If not, then the configuration of that stereogenic atom does not change. If bonds to the chiral atom are affected during a reaction, its configuration may be inverted, it may be retained, or it may be scrambled to a mixture of *R*- and *S*- configurations. Which of these occurs depends on what arrow-pushing steps occur between the starting material and product. You will learn how to predict which steps occur and how those steps impact stereocenters as you continue your study of organic chemistry. For now, consider these three illustrative examples (only substitution products are shown):

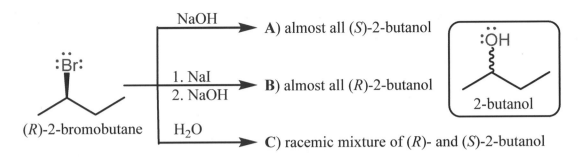

In pathway A, the arrow-pushing mechanism involved to change the starting material into the product involves one S_N2 step. Later, you will learn that an S_N2 step inverts configuration, so by doing one S_N2 step the configuration is inverted from R- to S- in this case.

Pathway B requires two S_N2 steps in succession. The first step inverts R- to S-, then the second step inverts that S- back to R-, and you end up with net retention of stereochemistry.

Pathway C involves heterolysis followed by coordination (a sequence known as the S_N1 reaction, which we will see later on):

Details for Pathway C

Note that the carbocation formed by heterolysis of the C–Br bond is planar, and therefore achiral. The final product has a chiral center, so we apply the concepts discussed in the prior section. The two enantiomers are of equal stability and are thus formed in equal amounts (a racemic mixture).

One final point to consider: if there is already a chiral center present in a molecule, it may exert an influence on what products form, even if none of the bonds to the chiral atom are changed during the reaction. One example is the reaction of this chiral alkene to form the cycloalkane:

To predict the way that all of the squiggly (as-yet-undefined stereochemistry) lines will point, we need to know two things about the reaction mechanism:

84

1) The two D atoms added must both point to the same face of the ring (both wedge bonds or both hashed line bonds)
2) The π-bond in the starting material must get close to the D atoms at the surface of the Pd metal for the reaction to proceed

We can now consider a simplified drawing that incorporates these requirements to help determine to which face of the alkene the D atoms will more readily add:

Armed with our knowledge of the mechanistic requirements of the reaction, we can see that addition of D atoms to the face opposite the isopropyl group is far more energetically accessible. The major product is thus:

This is a good illustration of how to combine mechanistic information with fundamental concepts to rationalize why a particular product predominates or, in this case, even to predict what the major product will be before we even do a reaction. It also demonstrates the effect that can be exerted by a chiral center even if none of the bonds to the chiral atom are made or broken during the reaction.

Lesson II.2: Nucleophilicity versus Basicity

Lesson II.2.1: Basicity is a Measure of Thermodynamic Stability

We know that acid strength is measured by pK_a values, which is calculated from the equilibrium constant (K_a) of the acid dissociation reaction (Lesson I.9). Equilibrium constants are thermodynamic parameters, with $\Delta G = -RT \ln K$. As a result, acid and base strengths do not tell us whether the reaction to add/remove H^+ is fast or slow, just whether that reaction is favorable/unfavorable. In the current lesson, we will focus on base strength: *A less stable anion is a stronger base*. The first strong base typically taught in chemistry is hydroxide (^-OH). Knowing that ^-OH is a strong base, and therefore anything less stable than ^-OH will also be a strong base, we can make a generalization to help us quickly identify strong bases: **an anion with negative charge that is (1) located on H, O, N, or C and (2) is not stabilized by resonance delocalization will be a strong base**.

To identify which reagents could produce basic anions in solution, we must recall that only ionic compounds dissociate into cations and anions in solution. Covalent compounds do not dissociate into ions and will thus never produce anions that could be strong bases. An ionic compound must have a counter-cation associated with the anion, most commonly a proton, a group I/II metal (Li, Na, K, Mg, Ca) or an ammonium ($[NH_4]^+$) cation. Here are some examples of covalent and ionic reagents that are commonly used in introductory organic chemistry:

Covalent	Ionic	
CH_3OH	$NaOH$	$[NH_4][O_2CCH_3]$
H_2O	$KOCH_3$	HBr
NH_3	$LiNH_2$	NaH

None of the covalent reagents will dissociate into ions in solution, so none can function as strong bases. All the ionic compounds will dissociate into ions upon dissolution. The only ionic compounds that do not yield strongly basic anions are HBr (negative charge on Br) and $[NH_4][O_2CCH_3]$ (negative charge stabilized by resonance, which is easier to see if you draw out its Lewis structure).

Lesson II.2.2: Nucleophilicity is a Measure of Reaction Rate (Kinetics)

It is easy to confuse nucleophilicity with basicity because bases and nucleophiles both function as electron donors. The key difference is that basicity is a measure of *stability*, whereas nucleophilicity is a measure of *reaction rate*. **The faster a species donates its electron pair to an electrophile, the better a nucleophile it is**. Note the difference in terminology as well: bases are referred to as being 'strong' or 'weak', whereas nucleophiles are classified as 'good' or 'poor'. A given anion may be a strong base + good nucleophile, a strong base + poor nucleophile, a weak base + good nucleophile, or a weak base + poor nucleophile. Let us begin with identifying anions that are good nucleophiles.

Because nucleophilicity is not tied to stability in the way that basicity is, many more anions are good nucleophiles than are strong bases. What factors might make an anion a poor nucleophile? One factor is electronegativity. Fluorine is the most electronegative element, so it is slow to give up its electrons, making fluoride a poor nucleophile. The steric bulk of a nucleophile also influences its ability to rapidly give electrons to an electrophile. Consider the difference between the nucleophile approach by the small HO⁻ vs. the bulky t-BuO⁻ to the partial positive charge of ethyl chloride:

It is not difficult to see that the bulkier t-BuO⁻ must overcome a greater a steric repulsive force (a higher energy of activation) than the smaller HO⁻. In general, **bulky anions are poor nucleophiles**. "Bulky" in this context means that the sites adjacent to the anionic atom have three or more non-H branches (t-BuO⁻ has three methyl branches, for example). To summarize: **non-bulky anions other than fluoride are mostly good nucleophiles**. Now consider neutral compounds. Most common neutral compounds are significantly more stable than the hydroxide anion (our prototypical strong base), so there are few *strong* neutral bases. Nucleophilicity, however, only requires rapid donation of electrons. Large atoms (3rd row of periodic table or lower, e.g., P and S) with lone pairs can thus serve as good nucleophiles. These atoms are not as electronegative as are the second-row atoms like O and N, so there is a lower activation barrier for pulling electrons from such species.

To summarize our evaluation of nucleophiles:

Bases and nucleophiles must both donate electron pairs in the course of their usual reactivity, so any factors that hinder electron pair donation will diminish their basicity and nucleophilicity. One way that the ability to donate an electron pair is diminished is by strong attraction of solvent molecules for the lone pair or negative charge. The strongest type of interactions that can occur between a neutral solvent molecule and an anion (whether it is a base or a nucleophile) is hydrogen bonding (see Lesson I.3 for a review of intermolecular forces). It is easy to see how the **solvent cage** surrounding an anion could influence its basicity and/or nucleophilicity. Consider A^- solvated by water

The pull of the $H^{\delta+}$ in the H_2O molecules makes the anion less basic and less nucleophilic, as can be visualized in the simplified reactions below, in which B^- is a base and Nu^- is a nucleophile:

The weakening of basicity/nucleophilicity is most pronounced in H-bonding solvents, which are often referred to as **polar protic solvents**. Common polar protic solvents include water and alcohols.

Polar solvents that cannot engage in H-bonding of bases/nucleophiles are called **polar aprotic solvents**. Common polar aprotic solvents include acetone ($CH_3C(O)CH_3$), acetonitrile (CH_3CN), *N,N*-dimethylformamide ($HC(O)N(CH_3)_2$, DMF) and dimethylsulfoxide ($CH_3S(O)CH_3$, DMSO). Although polar aprotic solvents are incapable of H-bonding, they can engage in dipole–ion interactions with the anion. Dipole–ion interactions are weaker than H-bonding, so attenuation of basicity/nucleophilicity is not as pronounced in polar aprotic solvents as it is in polar protic solvents.

Nonpolar solvents (like alkanes) do not engage in strong intermolecular interactions with anions, so basicity and nucleophilicity are highest in these solvents. The general trend is:

nonpolar solvent   <   polar aprotic solvent   <   polar protic solvent
(most basic/nucleophilic)   (least basic/nucleophilic)

From a practical standpoint, very polar species that typically dissociate into ions upon dissolution (i.e., ionic salts) are usually insoluble in nonpolar solvents. For this reason, chemists most often do reactions requiring a strong base or a good nucleophile in a polar aprotic solvent to optimize reactivity while maintaining the solubility of their reagents.

Lesson II.3: Substitution Reactions of RX I: The SN1 Mechanism

Lesson II.3.1: SN1 is Heterolysis then Coordination

In Lesson I.8, we saw some of the elementary steps of organic reactions. We are now going to learn our first reaction mechanism that involves more than one of these steps: the SN1 reaction. The SN1 reaction involves: 1) heterolysis to form a carbocation, then 2) coordination of a nucleophile to the carbocation:

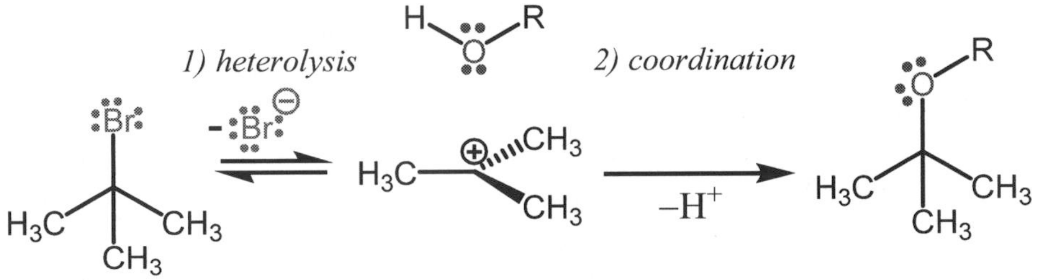

Note that the carbocation to which the nucleophile coordinates is very reactive, so that even a weak nucleophile – like the neutral alcohol in the example above – will suffice for this reaction.

Here are some examples of net SN1 reactions, without showing the mechanistic steps:

General:

$$R{-}LG + H{-}Nu \longrightarrow R{-}Nu + H^+ + LG^-$$

$$R{-}LG + Nu^- \longrightarrow R{-}Nu + LG^-$$

Br^- as LG
H-OH as H-Nu

**note that H^+ comes off of the H_2O after H_2O adds so that the O will be neutral*

H_2O as LG
Br^- as Nu^-

**note that NaBr dissociates in solution to form Na^+ and Br^- and that the LG in this case is a neutral molecule*

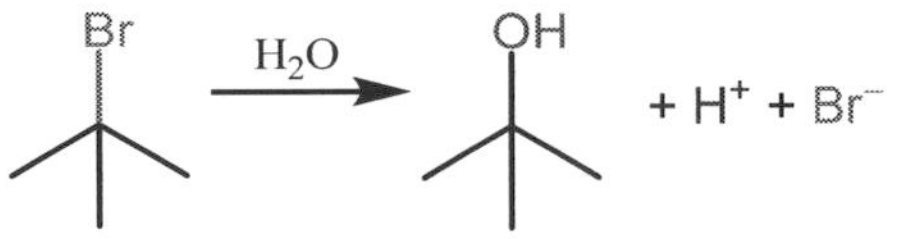

The net result is that the *leaving group* (LG) – the group removed from C in the heterolysis step – is substituted by the nucleophile. The "S" in SN1 stands for substitution and the subscript "N" stands for nucleophilic. The "1" indicates that the kinetics of the reaction are *unimolecular*: the reaction rate only depends on the concentration of *one* species. In this case, we look at the mechanism and see that the carbocation is the least stable species formed on the way to the product, so this step is *rate-limiting*. A qualitative reaction coordinate diagram for a thermodynamically-favorable SN1 reaction might look like this:

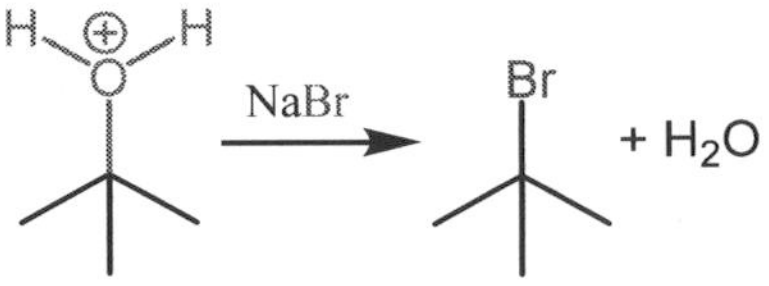

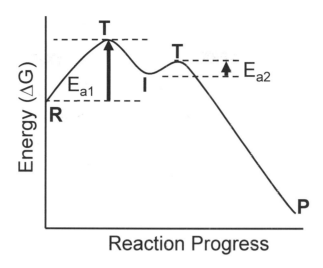

Where **R** is the reactant, **I** is the carbocation intermediate, the peaks **T** are transition states, and **P** is the product. The first 'hill' represents the activation barrier for heterolysis and the second 'hill' represents the activation barrier for coordination.

The rate of the overall two-step process is governed by the high E_a of the heterolysis step, so the rate is only dependent on the concentration of the starting material (the substrate, R–LG), so

$$\text{Rate} = k[\text{R–LG}]$$

Note that, since the nucleophile does not show up in the rate law expression, its concentration does not influence the rate. If we double the nucleophile concentration, the reaction rate is unchanged. If we double the concentration of the substrate (R–LG), which *is* a term in the rate law, the reaction rate will double.

The rate of the S$_N$1 reaction can also be influenced by the leaving group identity, substrate substitution degree, and reaction solvent. The better the leaving group (the more stable the species displaced from the substrate), the faster the reaction will be because there is a lower activation barrier to leaving group departure.

In the S$_N$1 mechanism, carbocation formation is rate-limiting, and more stable carbocations form faster. So, in terms of S$_N$1 reaction rate: methyl halide < 1° alkyl halide < 2° alkyl halide < 3° alkyl halide (fastest). Indeed, **the carbocations that would form from methyl and 1° alkyl halides would be so unstable that methyl and 1° halides will never undergo S$_N$1 reactions.**

Because the solvent influences the stability of ions, we must choose a solvent that best stabilizes the carbocation and the leaving group that are formed in the rate-limiting step. As discussed in Lesson II.2, polar protic solvents have the strongest intermolecular interactions with ions. For this reason, the **S$_N$1 reaction is fastest in polar protic solvents**.

Lesson II.3.2: Carbocation Rearrangement

In Lesson I.12, we learned that we can predict reaction spontaneity by comparing reactant stability and product stability. A carbocation is capable of rearrangement (elementary step 2 in Lesson I.8), and **if this rearrangement affords a more stable carbocation, then carbocation rearrangement will happen spontaneously and rapidly** (see carbocation stability in Lesson I.11). In fact, this rearrangement happens so quickly that the major product of a reaction which proceeds through a carbocation will always be derived from the rearranged, most stable carbocation.

Below are two examples of spontaneous carbocation rearrangement reactions, in which a hydride (H with a pair of electrons) or an alkyl group shift from one carbon to an adjacent carbocation:

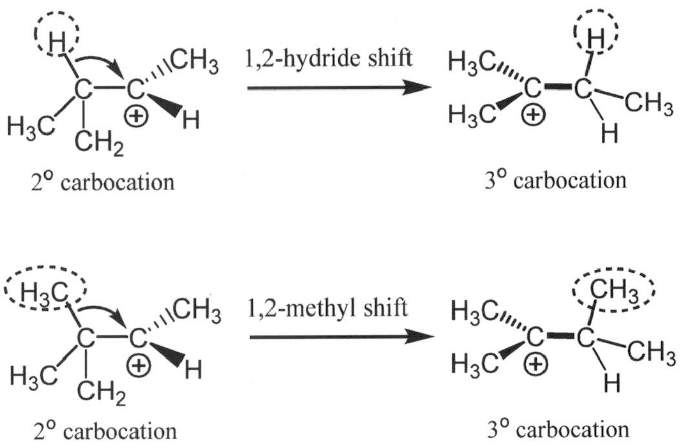

Generally, a hydride shift occurs selectively when it is possible, and an alkyl group will only shift if a hydride is not present to shift, or under other special circumstances.

Example II.3.1

Provide the major product(s) of this S$_N$1 reaction:

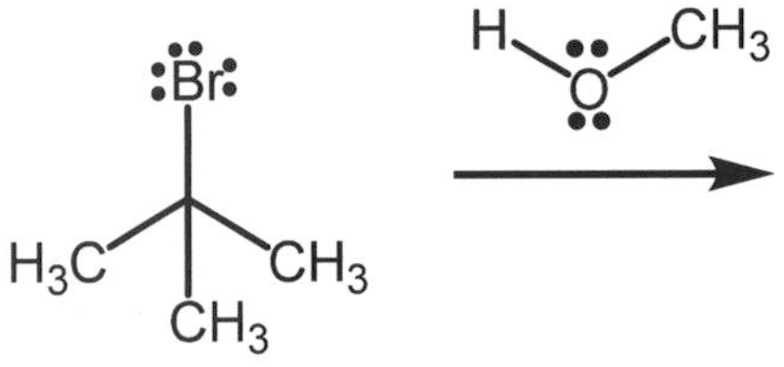

Solution II.3.1

As with all S$_N$1 reactions, the sequence it 1) heterolysis of LG then 2) coordination of nucleophile.

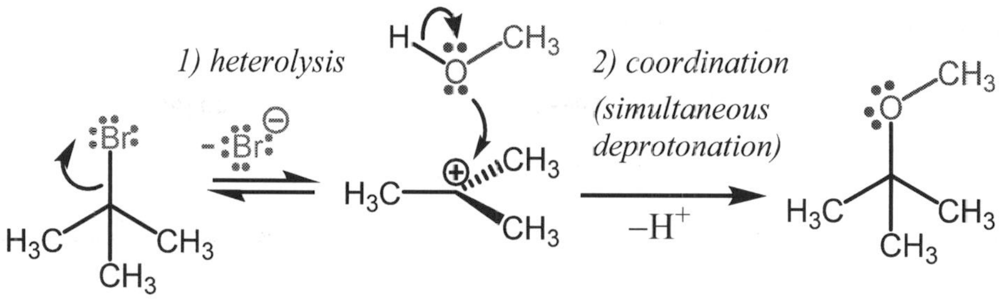

1) *heterolysis*

2) *coordination*
(simultaneous
deprotonation)

$-$:Br: $^{\ominus}$

$-H^+$

93

Lesson II.4.1: S$_N$2 is a Concerted Elementary Step

In Lesson I.8, we saw that the S$_N$2 reaction is an important elementary step in many organic reaction mechanisms:

In contrast to the S$_N$1 reaction (Lesson II.3), in which a nucleophile coordinates to a carbocation, a nucleophile in the S$_N$2 reaction is attracted to the partial positive charge on an sp^3-hybridized carbon atom. Because the partial positively-charged C is a poorer electrophile than a carbocation, **a good nucleophile is required for the S$_N$2 reaction** (see Lesson II.2 for how to identify good nucleophiles).

In S$_N$2, everything happens in a single concerted step, so the rate law is easy to determine. Two species come together to facilitate this reaction, so it is a **bimolecular reaction**, with the rate law:

$$\text{Rate} = k[\text{R–LG}][\text{Nu}^-]$$

Both the substrate and the nucleophile concentrations appear in the rate expression. If we double the concentration of the nucleophile, the rate will double. Likewise, if we double the concentration of the nucleophile, the rate will double. If we double the concentration of *both* the substrate and the nucleophile, the reaction is four times faster.

The rate of the S$_N$2 reaction can also be influenced by the leaving group identity, substrate substitution degree, nucleophile strength, and reaction solvent. The better the leaving group (the more stable the species displaced from the substrate), the faster the reaction will be because there is a lower activation barrier to leaving group departure.

In the S$_N$2 mechanism, the nucleophile must pass between any branches at the attached C before it can form a bond to it. The more non-H branches on the electrophilic C, the slower the reaction rate will be, due to the greater activation barrier caused by steric repulsion during nucleophile approach. So, in terms of rate: methyl halide > 1° alkyl halide > 2° alkyl halide > 3° alkyl halide (slowest). Indeed, **the 3° alkyl halides are so sterically hindered that they will never undergo S$_N$2 reactions**. Even the presence of a β-branch (a branch off of the parent chain at a site *beside* the C with the leaving-group) will slow down the reaction:

Recall that nucleophilicity is by definition a measure of how quickly a species donates electrons to an electrophile. This definition tells us that **the S$_N$2 reaction is faster with better nucleophiles**. Because the solvent influences nucleophile strength (Lesson II.2), we must choose a solvent that does not diminishing the nucleophile strength. As discussed in Lesson II.2, this means that **the S$_N$2 rate is fastest in polar aprotic solvents**.

Example II.4.1

Provide the major substitution products for these reactions:

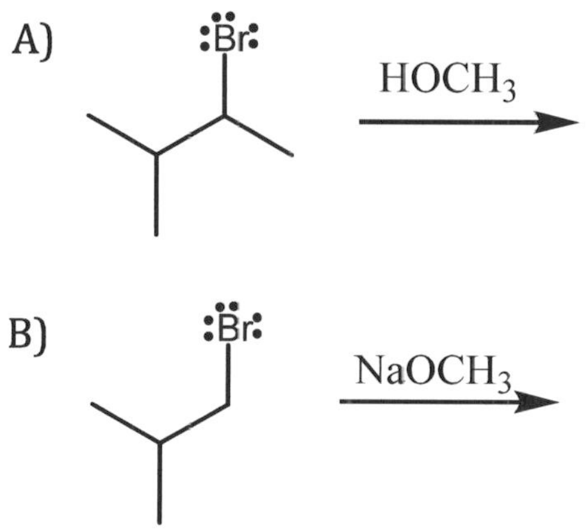

A)

$HOCH_3$

B)

$NaOCH_3$

Solution II.4.1

For reaction A, there is no good nucleophile (methanol is a covalent compound and will not make ions in solution), so this will have to undergo substitution via S$_N$1:

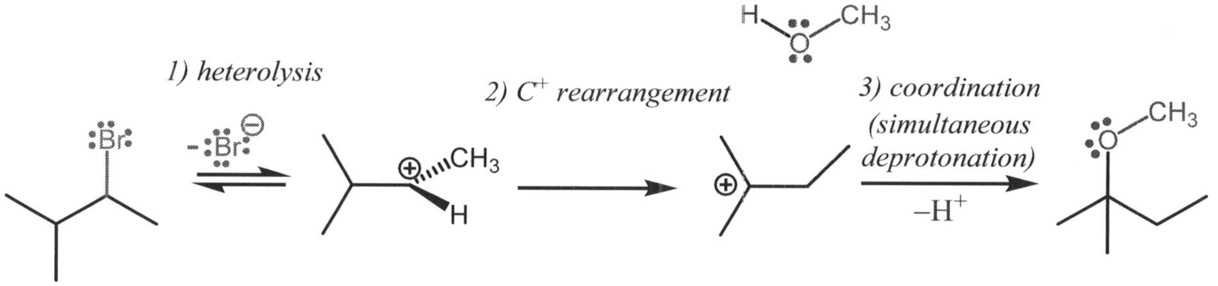

1) heterolysis   *2) C$^+$ rearrangement*   *3) coordination (simultaneous deprotonation)* $-H^+$

For reaction B, there is a good nucleophile (NaOCH$_3$ will dissociate to make methoxide anion) and the primary substrate is appropriate for S$_N$2 reaction:

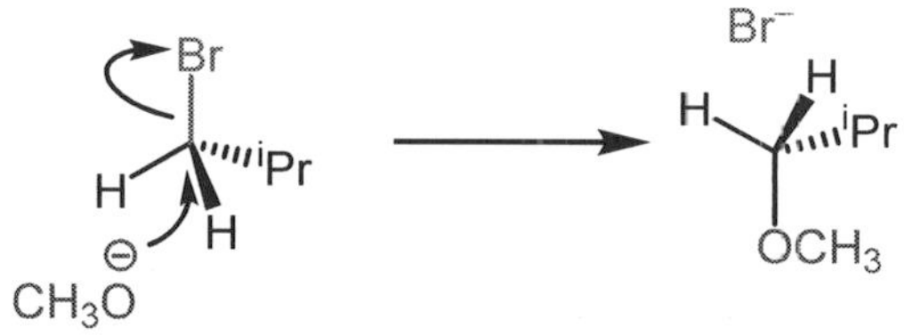

Lesson II.5: Substitution Reactions of RX III: Stereochemistry of Substitution Reactions

Lesson II.5.1: The S_N1 *Reaction is Stereorandom*

Recall from Lesson II.1 that a single chiral product cannot be obtained from an achiral starting material for any step of a reaction sequence. Consider a chiral alkyl halide reacting via an S_N1 pathway:

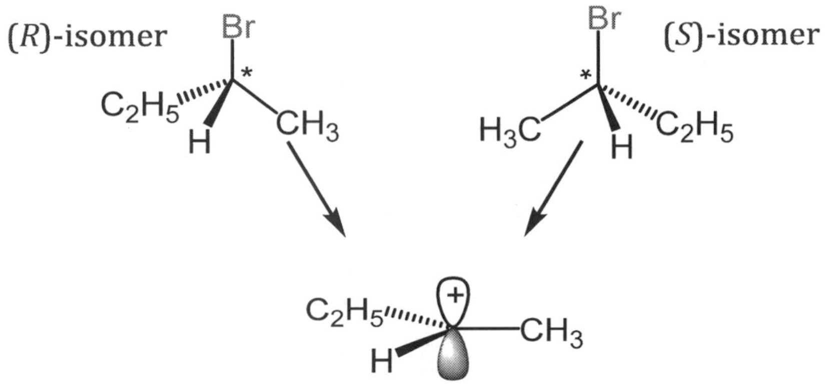

After heterolysis, chirality is lost: the carbocation has trigonal planar geometry and is therefore achiral. We cannot even tell from which of the two isomers this cation was formed. The nucleophile (H_2O in this case) may attack either face of the carbocation plane with equal probability to afford two alcohol product stereoisomers:

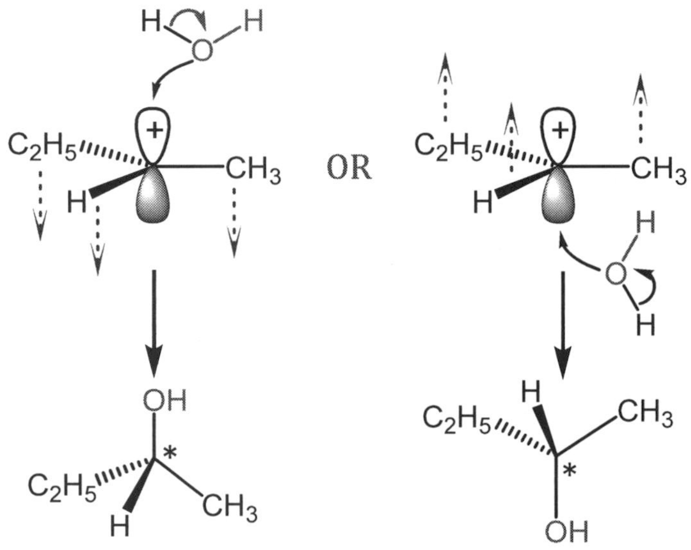

Each of the two enantiomers has the same stability, so we would expect them to be formed in equal amounts in this reaction. We can now see that, regardless of whether we start with the *R*- or *S*-configuration of the alkyl bromide, we will always end with a 50:50 mixture of the two enantiomeric products (a racemic mixture). For this reason, the S_N1 reaction is a stereorandom reaction.

Lesson II.5.2: Backside Attack and Walden Inversion in the S$_N$2 Reaction

The S$_N$2 reaction is concerted, and the nucleophile must attack to form a bond to the carbon 180° apart from where the leaving group is attached. This is sometimes referred to as **backside attack**. One consequence of this concerted, backside attack by the nucleophile is that, if a nucleophile attacks a stereogenic site, a single chiral compound will be produced:

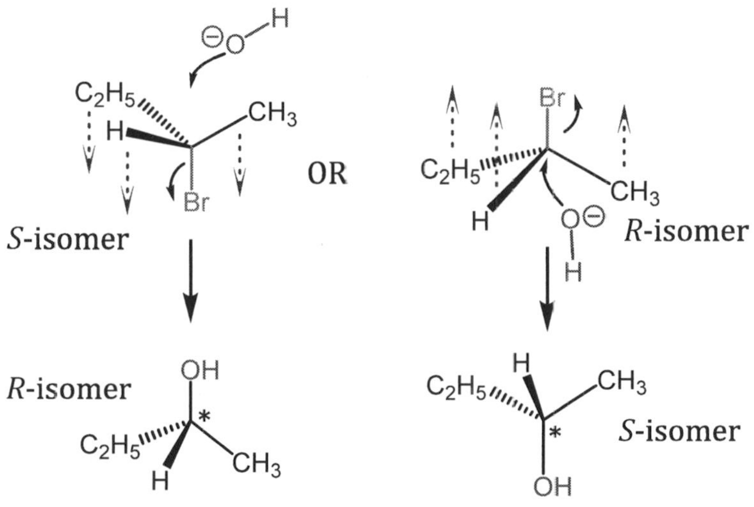

Note that the bonds from the stereogenic C to the three non-leaving groups will be repelled by the electrons on the hydroxide nucleophile in this example, pushing them in the opposite direction to reestablish the tetrahedron. The resulting change of configuration is referred to as **Walden inversion**. Walden inversion means that **the S$_N$2 reaction is a stereospecific reaction**.

Example II.5.1

Provide the major substitution products for these reactions:

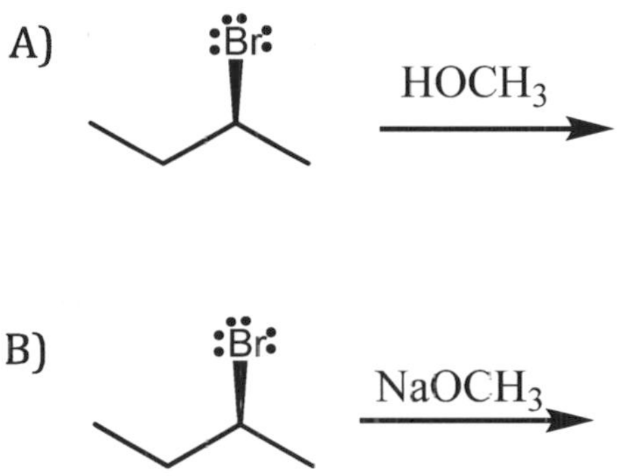

A)

B)

For reaction A, there is no good nucleophile (methanol is covalent), so this has to undergo S_N1. The coordination to the achiral carbocation leads to a stereorandom product.

For reaction B, there is a good nucleophile (NaOCH₃ will dissociate to make methoxide anion) and the primary substrate is appropriate for S_N2 reaction, leading to inversion of configuration:

Additional help from "Organic Chemistry 1 Reactions and Practice Problems 2018" (Smith):

- After finishing Lesson II.5, you may want to review Reactions B.1 and B2 in the companion book. These reaction summaries provide a quick review of key points, mechanism and stereochemistry related to S_N1 and S_N2 reactions.

Lesson II.6.1: E1 is Heterolysis Followed by Electrophilic Elimination

Like the S_N1 reaction, the E1 reaction is a name given to a sequence of two specific elementary steps: 1) heterolysis to form a carbocation, then 2) electrophilic elimination of a proton:

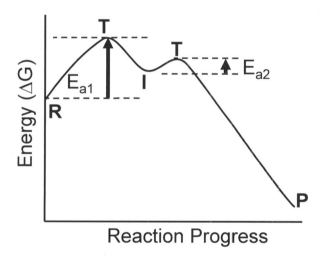

The net result is that the leaving group and an H on the adjacent C are eliminated to give a π-bond between the two C atoms from which the LG and H eliminated. The "E" in E1 stands for elimination and the subscript "N" stands for nucleophile. The "1" indicates that the kinetics of the reaction are *unimolecular*. Only the concentration of *one* species influences the reaction rate. In this case, we look at the mechanism and see that the carbocation is the least stable species formed on the way to the product, so this step is *rate-limiting*. Shown visually, the qualitative reaction coordinate diagram for a thermodynamically-favorable E1 reaction might look like this (the same as for S_N1!):

Where **R** is the reactant, **I** is the carbocation intermediate, the peaks **T** are transition states, and **P** is the product. The first 'hill' represents the activation barrier to heterolysis and the second 'hill' represents the activation barrier to electrophilic elimination.

The rate of the overall two-step process is governed by the high E_a of the heterolysis step, so the rate is only dependent on the concentration of the starting material (the substrate, R–LG), so

$$\text{Rate} = k[\text{R–LG}]$$

If we double the concentration of the substrate (R–LG), the rate is doubled.

The rate of the E1 reaction can also be influenced by the leaving group identity, substrate substitution degree, and the reaction solvent. The better the leaving group (the more stable the species displaced from the substrate), the faster the reaction will be because there is a lower activation barrier to leaving group departure.

In the E1 mechanism, carbocation formation is rate-limiting. More stable carbocations form faster. So, in terms of rate: methyl halide < 1° alkyl halide < 2° alkyl halide < 3° alkyl halide (fastest). Indeed, **the carbocations that would form from methyl and 1° alkyl halides would be so unstable that methyl and 1° halides will never undergo E1 reactions.**

Because the solvent influences the stability of ions, we must choose a solvent that stabilizes both the carbocation and leaving group formed in the rate-limiting step. As discussed in Lesson II.2, polar protic solvents proved the strongest intermolecular forces with ions. For this reason, the **E1 reaction is fastest in polar protic solvents.**

Lesson II.6.2: Zaitsev's Rule for Determining the Major Products of Elimination

Early in the history of elimination reactions, a chemist named Zaitsev noticed that the major product formed by elimination reactions was almost always the most substituted alkene, that is to say, the alkene in which the carbons in a C=C bond had the most non-H substituents. This empirical rule for predicting major products of elimination reactions became known as **Zaitsev's Rule** (sometimes spelled Saytseff's Rule). As we saw in Lesson I.11, this is because the most substituted alkene is typically the most stable. Zaitsev's Rule, then, is essentially telling us that the major product is the most stable product, which we have seen is generally true of many reaction types.

Example II.6.1

Predict the major elimination product of this reaction:

Solution II.6.1

Heterolysis to form the carbocation is the first step:

For the second step, electrophilic elimination, there are two possible sites from which to eliminate the proton:

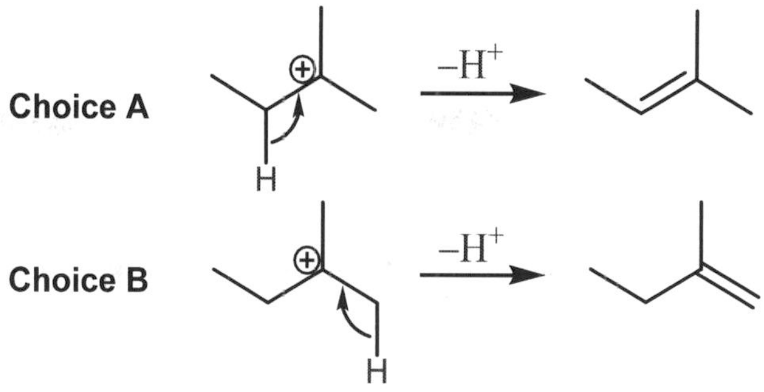

Choice A

Choice B

$-H^+$

Choice A leads to the more substituted, more stable alkene and is the Zaitsev Product. This will be the major elimination product of the reaction.

Additional help from "Organic Chemistry 1 Reactions and Practice Problems 2018" (Smith):

- After finishing Lesson II.6, you may want to review Reaction B.3 in the companion book. This summary provides a quick review of key points, mechanism and stereochemistry related to the E1 reaction.

Lesson II.7.1: E2 is a Concerted Elementary Step

Like the S_N2 reaction, the E2 reaction is one of the elementary steps that we learned in Lesson I.8:

In contrast to the E1 reaction (Lesson II.6), in which H^+ eliminates from a carbocation to yield a more stable neutral alkene, the H^+ in the E2 reaction must be removed from a neutral species. For this reason, **a strong base is necessary for the E2 reaction, to remove this proton** (see Lesson II.2 for help on identifying strong bases).

Everything happens in a single, concerted step, so the rate law is easy to determine. There are two species coming together to facilitate this reaction, so it is a **bimolecular reaction**, with the rate law:

$$\text{Rate} = k[\text{R–LG}][\text{B}^-]$$

Both substrate and base appear in the rate expression. If we double the substrate concentration, the rate will double. Likewise, if we double the concentration of the base, the rate will double. If we double the concentration of *both* the substrate and the base, the reaction is four times faster.

The rate of the E2 reaction can also be influenced by leaving group identity, substrate substitution degree, base strength, and reaction solvent. The better the leaving group (the more stable the species displaced from the substrate), the faster the reaction will be because there is a lower activation barrier to leaving group departure.

Recall that more non-H substituents on the carbons of a C=C bond makes the alkene more stable. Because the C with the halide leaving group on it ends up in the C=C bond, more non-H substituents at that site leads to more stable products. So, **in terms of E2 rate: methyl halide < 1° alkyl halide < 2° alkyl halide < 3° alkyl halide (fastest)**.

A strong base is required for the E2 reaction, and the stronger the base, the faster the E2 reaction. Because the solvent influences base strength (Lesson II.2), we must choose a solvent that solvates the reagents without diminishing the base strength. As discussed in Lesson II.2, this means that **the E2 rate is fastest in polar aprotic solvents**.

Lesson II.7.2: Zaitsev's Rule Applies to Most E2 Reactions

Similar to the E1 reaction (Lesson II.6), the major products of an E2 reaction can generally be predicted by Zaitsev's rule. We will see cases where some mechanistic details can lead to non-Zaitsev products in Lessons II.8 and II.9, but for the examples in this Lesson, the Zaitsev rule works well:

Example II.7.2

Predict the major elimination product of this reaction:

Solution II.7.2

In this concerted reaction, there are two possible sites for deprotonation by $KOC(CH_3)_3$ (a strong base):

Choice A leads to the more substituted, more stable alkene and is the Zaitsev Product. This will be the major elimination product of the reaction.

Lesson II.8: Stereoelectronic Effects in the E2 reaction

Lesson II.8.1: Eliminated Groups must be Antiperiplanar

For an E2 reaction to occur, the H and leaving group (X) that will undergo elimination must be **antiperiplanar**. Antiperiplanar means the two groups are coplanar and in an *anti-* conformation:

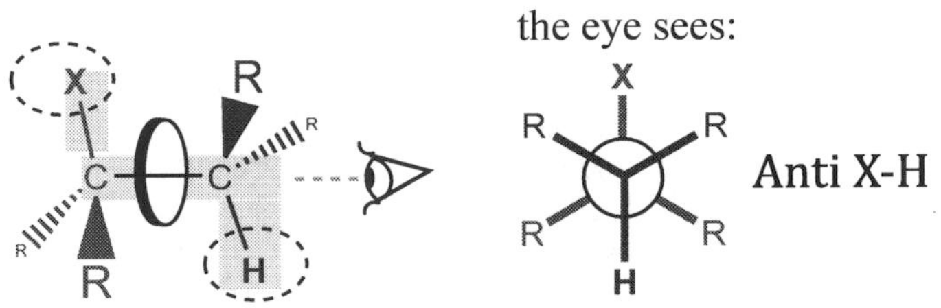

This is what is known as a **stereoelectronic effect**, an effect of the spatial orientation of orbitals (and consequently of the substituents connected via those orbitals). The stereoelectronic requirements of the E2 reaction must be considered when we attempt to predict products of a reaction.

Example II.8.1

Predict the major elimination product of each reaction:

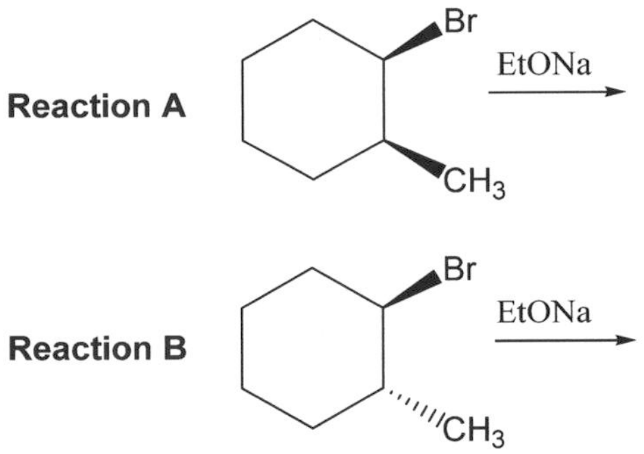

Solution II.8.1

Now that we know that the leaving group (here Br) and the H to be eliminated must be *anti-* to one another, we must be more cautious in selecting the H to be removed by the base. In Lesson I.16, we saw that each C in a cyclohexane ring has an “up” and a “down” position, or in the perspective of this problem a “towards” (wedge) and “away” position. We can fill these H atoms in on the sites adjacent to the leaving group:

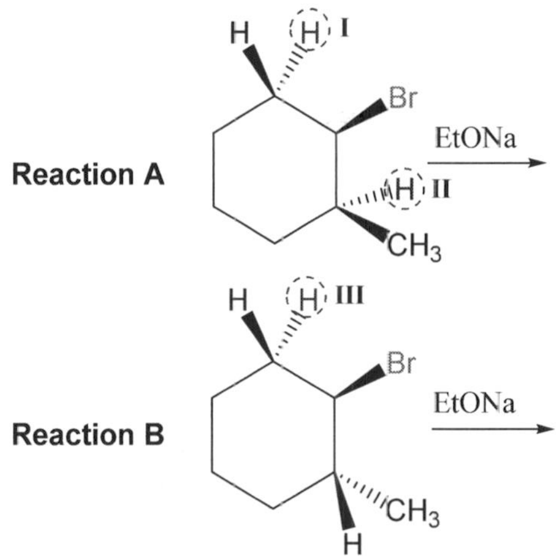

Reaction A (with EtONa)

Reaction B (with EtONa)

Only H atoms pointing in the opposite direction of the Br (i.e., *anti*- to Br) are mechanistically viable reaction sites. These are H atoms I, II and II (circled) in the substrates above.

For reaction A, removal of hydrogen II gives a more substituted product, so the major E2 product is:

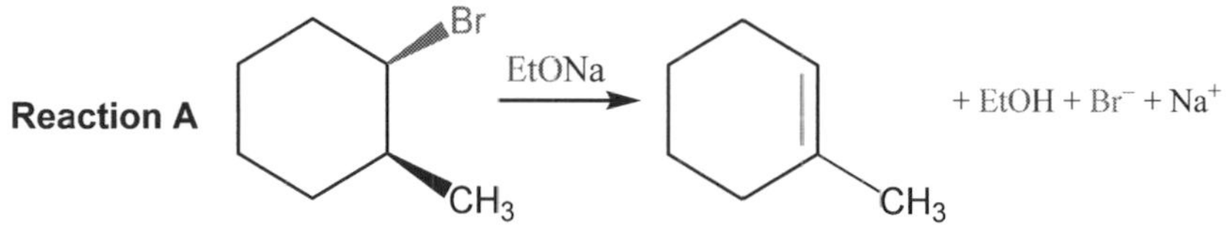

Reaction A

$+ EtOH + Br^- + Na^+$

For Reaction B, there is only one choice (H atom III). Removal of H atom II then gives the major product:

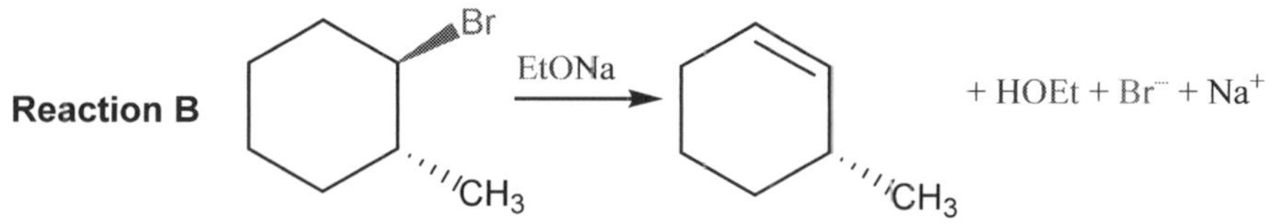

Reaction B

$+ HOEt + Br^- + Na^+$

Note that none of the bonds to the chiral center with the Me substituent changed in Reaction B, so the stereochemical configuration of that Me substituent is retained in the product.

Additional help from "Organic Chemistry 1 Reactions and Practice Problems 2018" (Smith):

- After finishing Lesson II.5, you may want to review Reaction B.4 in the companion book. This reaction summary provides a quick review of key points, mechanism and stereochemistry related to the E2 reaction.

Lesson II.9.1: Steric Hindrance Between Base and Substrate

The more stable/substituted alkene (i.e., the **Zaitsev product**) is the major product in many E2 reactions. There are situations, however, that raise the activation energy of the pathway leading to the Zaitsev product and thus increase the amounts of less substituted, non-Zaitsev products. The non-Zaitsev product is sometimes called the Hofmann product (we will discuss more in Lesson II.10).

Steric hindrance between a bulky base and substrate will generally be greater for deprotonation of a more substituted site (below left) than the less substituted site on the substrate (below right):

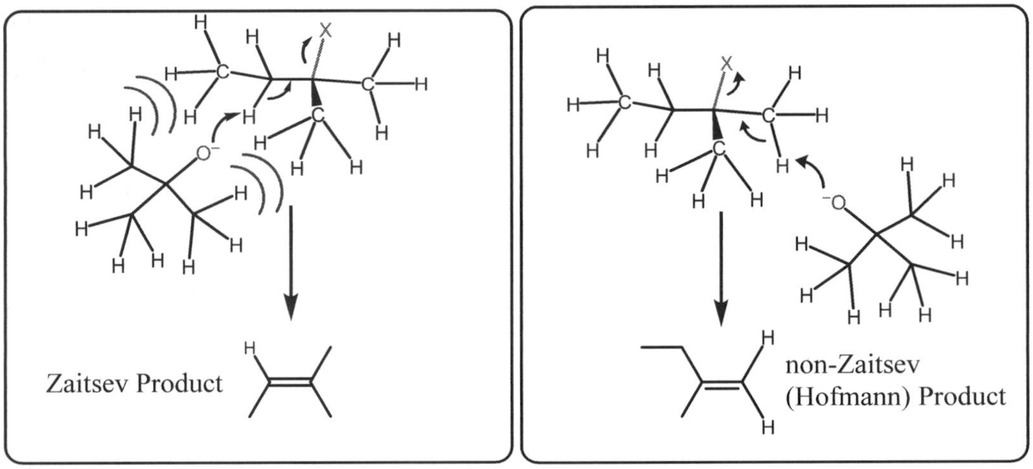

Zaitsev Product

non-Zaitsev (Hofmann) Product

The take home lesson from this is that **as the steric encumbrance of the base increases, we will get a larger percentage of the Hofmann product** in an E2 reaction.

Example II.9.1

Which base will lead to a higher amount of 1-hexene upon reaction with 2-bromohexane: NaOH or $NaOCH(CH_3)_2$ (sodium isopropoxide)?

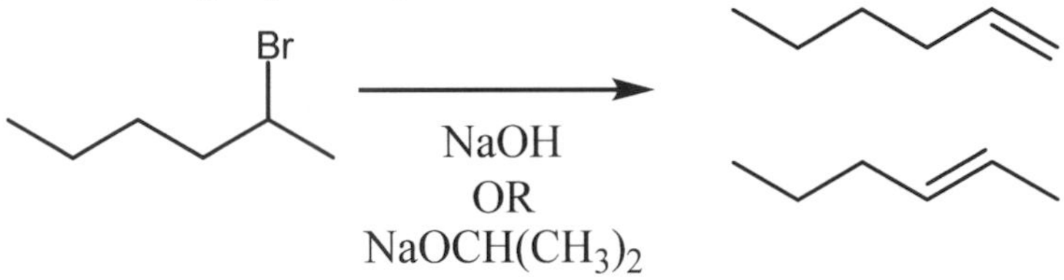

NaOH
OR
$NaOCH(CH_3)_2$

The isopropoxide anion is a much bulkier base than is hydroxide, so it will have a greater steric encumbrance to deprotonate the more substituted site needed to access 2-hexene. A greater yield of the non-Zaitsev product 1-hexene will thus be formed when sodium isopropoxide is added as the base.

Lesson II.9.2: Steric Hindrance in the Substrate can lead to Hofmann Products

There may be cases where the Hofmann product would be our desired product, so we would want this to be the major product. A variation of the E2 reaction called the **Hofmann elimination reaction** was developed and has proven quite useful in this regard. In the Hofmann elimination reaction, the leaving group is an amine, which requires the reactant to contain an ammonium substituent:

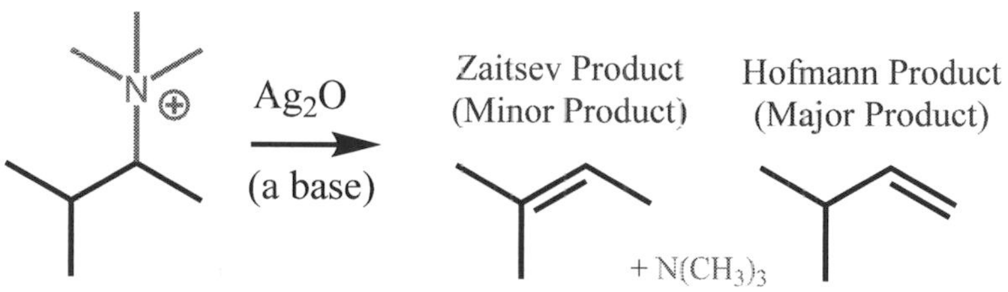

How can we explain the observed products? As with all E2 reactions, Hofmann elimination requires the H and the leaving group to be *antiperiplanar*. It is therefore helpful to compare the relative stabilities of the *anti*-conformation leading to the Zaitsev product vs. the Hofmann product:

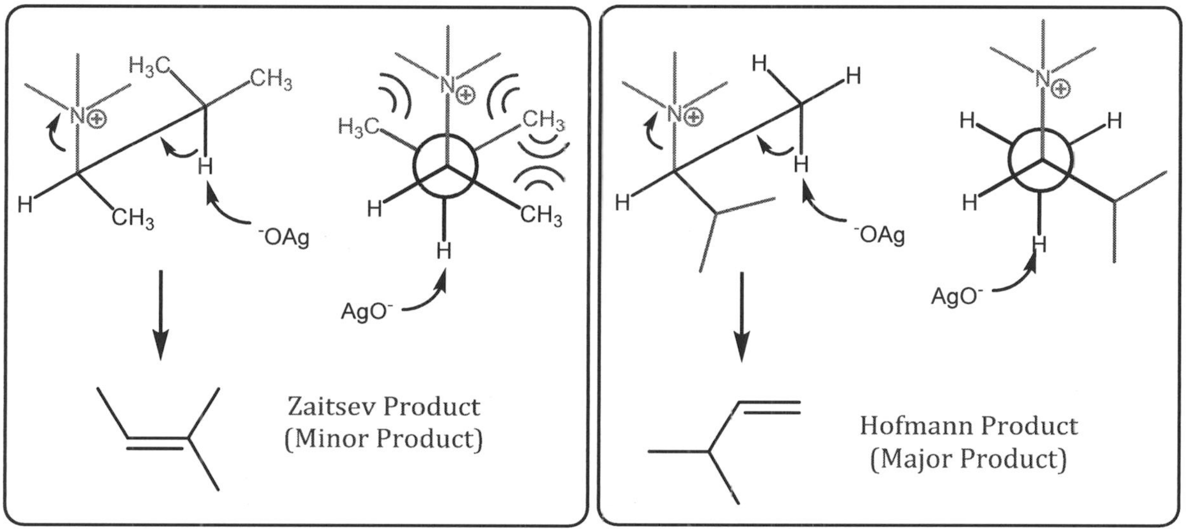

It is evident in the Newman representations that there is significant steric repulsion between the bulky trimethylammonium group and the adjacent Me substituents in the conformation required to produce the Zaitsev product. The conformation required to access the Hofmann product, however, places two small H atoms adjacent to the leaving group. The energy difference between these two conformations is sufficiently great that the Hofmann product forms significantly faster than the Zaitsev product, so it is the major product observed.

Example II.9.2

Provide the major product of this reaction:

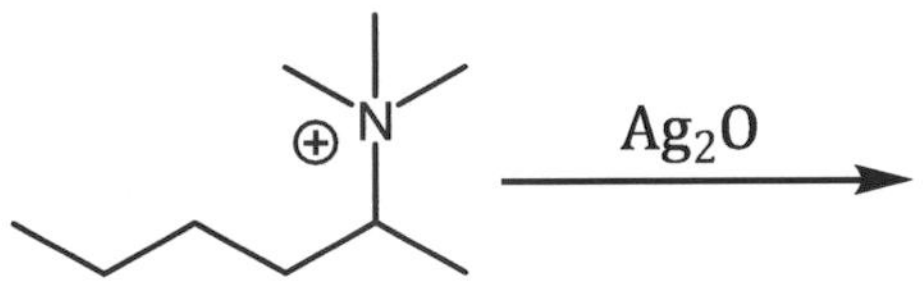

Solution II.9.2

The leaving group hear is a very bulky, 3-branched trimethylammonium unit. The very bulky leaving group favors the conformation analogous to that shown on the previous page, in which the bulky leaving group and the less-substituted (less crowded) carbon are involved in the E2 reaction. Therefore, we will observe the less substituted alkene (non-Zaitsev or Hofmann product):

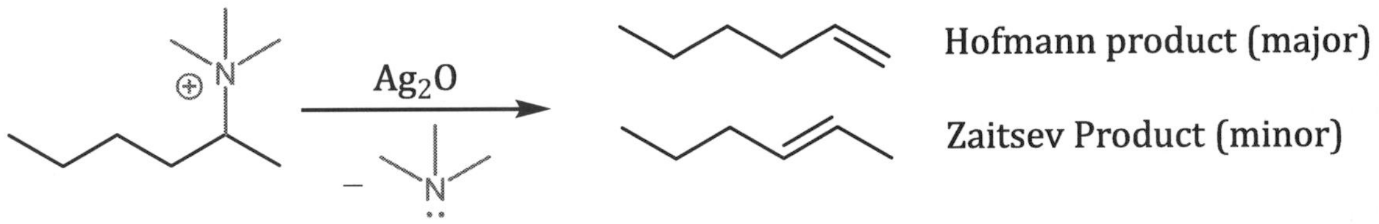

Hofmann product (major)

Zaitsev Product (minor)

Lesson II.10.1: Recapping Factors Influencing Rate of Substitution and Elimination Reactions

If we look back at lessons II.3-7 at all of the factors that influence the rate of the S_N1, S_N2, E1 and E2 reactions, we can summarize these data as follows:

	S_N1 rate	E1 rate	S_N2 rate	E2 Rate
Reagent strength	No effect	No effect	> for better Nu	> for stronger B
Substrate	3°>2°> (1° without resonance)	3°>2°> (1° without resonance)	CH_3>1°>2°> (3°)	3°>2°>1°
Solvent	> in polar protic	> in polar protic	> in polar aprotic	> in polar aprotic

Nu = nucleophile, B = base. **Substrates in parentheses will not work for the indicated reaction. For E1 and S_N1, secondary reacts at a rate similar to that of RX having primary sites with resonance stabilization of the carbocation formed by hydrolysis.**

We can summarize this data more simply if our task is to simply determine which of the pathways will predominate for a given substrate/reagent combination:

Substrate	Reagent			
	Poor Nu/Weak Base	Good Nu/Weak B	Good Nu/Strong B	Poor Nu/Strong B
1° R–X	No reaction!*	Mostly S_N2	Mostly S_N2	Mostly E2
2° R–X	(Slow) S_N1/E1 mix	Mostly S_N2	Mostly E2	Mostly E2
3° R–X	S_N1/E1 mix	Mostly S_N1	Mostly E2	Mostly E2

Nu = nucleophile, B = base.
*If the primary carbocation formed by hydrolysis of RX is resonance stabilized, that RX will undergo a mix of E1 and S_N1.

With these facts in mind, we can design a flowchart to determine which reaction(s) will predominate under a given set of circumstances.

Lesson II.10.2: Flowchart for Predicting Substitution and Elimination Reactions of Alkyl Halides

Below is a flowchart that incorporates all of the information from the above tables:

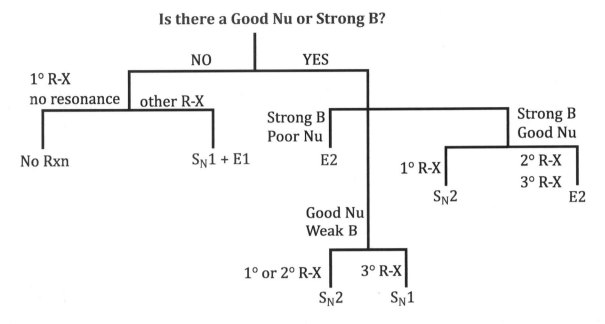

Coupled with our knowledge of what constituted a good nucleophile or a strong base in this context, the flowchart can be an extremely powerful tool for determining which pathway predominates, allowing us to accurately predict the products under a given set of circumstances.

Example II.10.1

Determine the mechanism(s) that predominate for each of these reactions and show the major product(s). Be sure to indicate the proper stereoisomer(s) as necessary.

Solution II.10.1

Good Nu, Strong B; secondary RX = E2 (Zaitsev Product)

Poor Nu, Weak B; secondary RX = S_N1/E1 Carbocation rearranges to tertiary!

Good Nu, Strong E; primary RX = S_N2

Good Nu, Strong B; primary RX = S_N2

Good Nu, Strong B; tertiary RX = E2 (Zaitsev Product)

Additional help from "Organic Chemistry 1 Reactions and Practice Problems 2018" (Smith):

- After finishing Lesson II.10, you will be ready for Problem Set 5 in the companion book. This Problem Set covers material from Primer Lessons II.1-10
- You will also be ready for the brief substitution/elimination Self Test found in section B.4 of the companion book. This Self Test probes your understanding of S_N1, S_N2, E1 and E2 reactions and their competition with one another.

Lesson II.11.1: Activating a Poor Leaving Group with an Acid

In our previous studies on substitution and elimination reactions, we noted that the presence of a good leaving group on the substrate was required for reaction to occur. If we attempt any of these reactions on an unmodified alcohol, our efforts will fail because the leaving group (HO⁻) would be a strong base, and therefore a very poor leaving group. However, there are several ways to activate the OH unit of an alcohol to convert it into a good leaving group. Once this activation has taken place, the substrate is viable for both substitution and elimination reactions.

The first way to activate an alcohol is to protonate the OH group with a strong acid:

(X = Cl, Br, I or HSO_4) **Oxonium Intermediate**

Once protonated, the resultant **oxonium intermediate** has a good leaving group (H_2O). This makes it a viable substrate for both substitution and elimination reactions.

If a reasonably strong nucleophile is present (Cl⁻, Br⁻ or I⁻), a substitution pathway will dominate, with H_2O as the leaving group from the oxonium intermediate. If an S_N2 pathway is viable (methyl, 1° or 2° alcohols), the S_N2 product is the major product. If the S_N2 route is not viable (3° alcohol), then the S_N1 product will be the major product. All of the guiding principles for S_N2 and S_N1 reactions still hold, as they were described in Lessons II.3–II.5, for protonated alcohols.

Example II.11.1

Provide a reasonable mechanistic pathway leading to the major product of the reaction shown:

Solution II.11.1

The first step is protonation of the OH group to form an oxonium intermediate. This is a methyl alcohol, so the 2ⁿᵈ step, substitution, is an S_N2 reaction on the activated substrate:

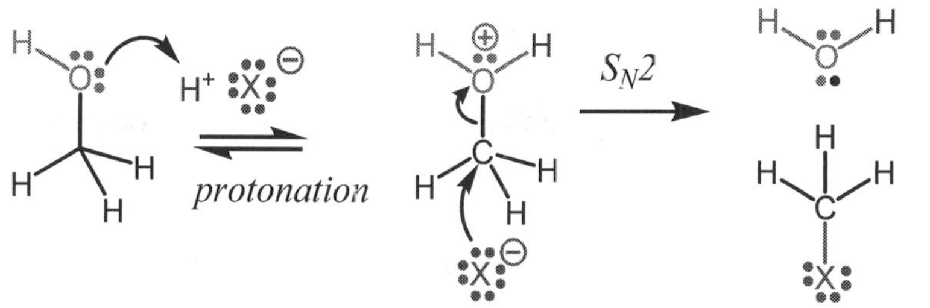

If the conjugate base of the acid used to protonate the alcohol is bulky (as is HSO_3^-, the conjugate base of H_2SO_4), then elimination will dominate. These reactions proceed by an E1 mechanism because E2 requires a strong base, which, of course, could not present when we have added a strong acid!

Example II.11.2

Provide a reasonable mechanistic pathway leading to the major product of the reaction shown:

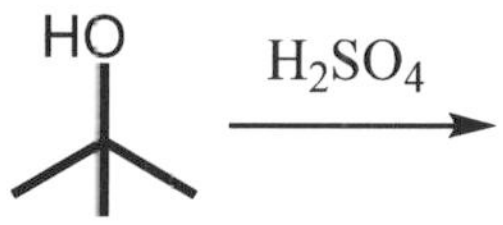

Solution II.11.2

The first step is protonation of the OH group to form the oxonium intermediate. There is no reasonable nucleophile, so an elimination reaction via the E1 pathway follows:

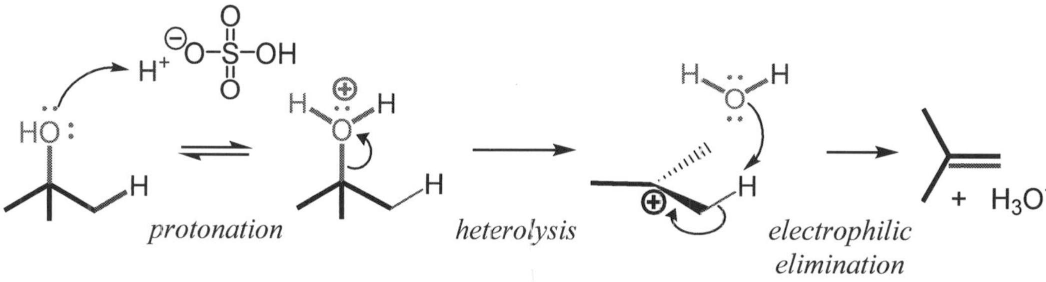

Lesson II.11.2: Activating a Poor Leaving Group with PBr3 or SOCl2

There are ways to activate the OH group of an alcohol for substitution/elimination reactions other than using a strong acid to protonate it. The two alternatives we will cover are thionyl chloride ($SOCl_2$) and phosphorus tribromide (PBr_3). The reaction of an alcohol with PBr_3 proceeds as follows:

113

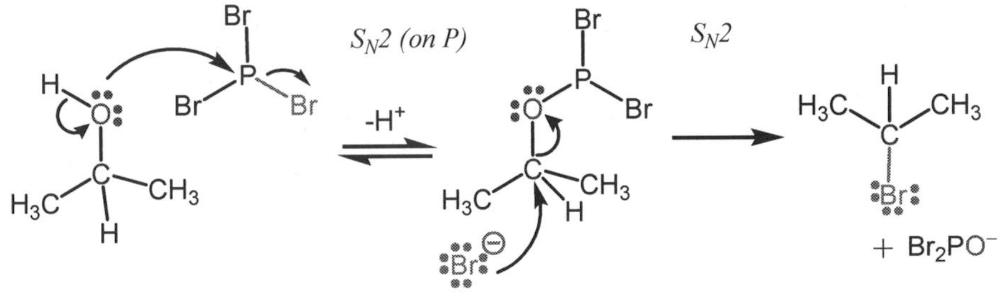

The reaction of an alcohol with SOCl₂ proceeds as follows:

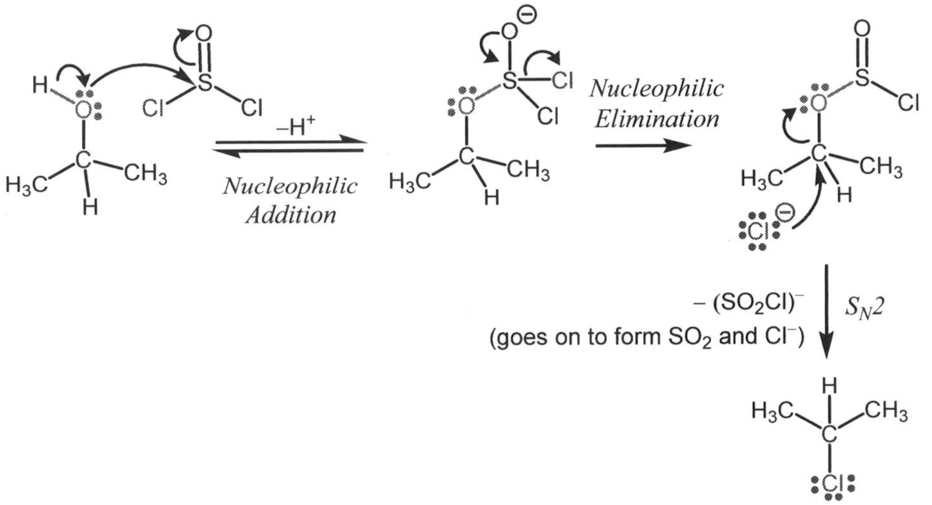

After the first activation step, the displacement of the OPBr₂ or OS(O)Cl group is an S$_N$2 reaction. Everything we learned about the S$_N$2 reaction in Lessons II.3 and II.5 still apply here, so a 3° alcohol still will not undergo an S$_N$2 reaction, even if we activate it with PBr₃ or SOCl₂, for example.

Lesson II.11.3: Changing an Alcohol into a Sulfonate Ester

The substitution reactions of alcohols we have examined all result in net substitution of an OH group for a halide. If we want to substitute an OH group with something else, a different activation pathway will be needed. One convenient approach is to convert the OH into a **sulfonate ester**, which proceeds via the following mechanism:

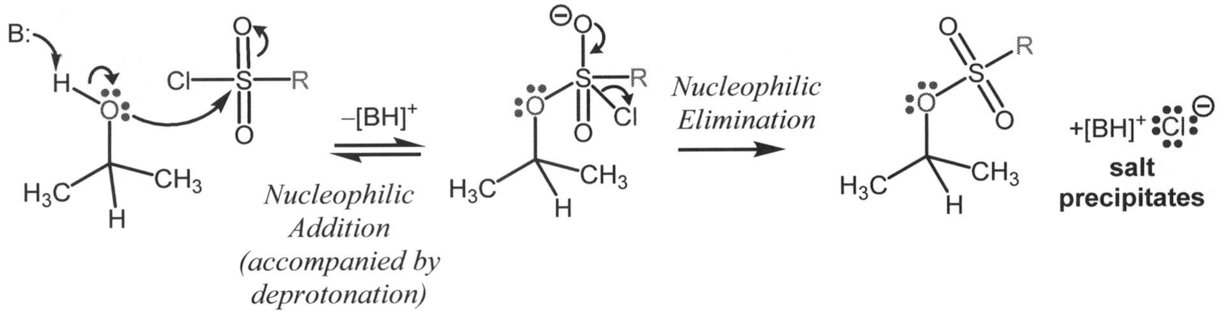

114

After the sulfonate ester unit has been formed, the compound is isolated. The sulfonate anion is an excellent leaving group due to its high resonance stabilization. Sulfonate anions are the best leaving groups that we will learn in this book, and they are so important that a few of them have been given common names and abbreviations (which you, the student, must memorize):

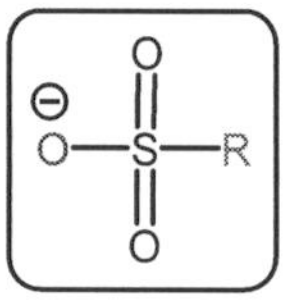

	When R =	Anion Name	Abbreviation
		Tosylate	TsO^-
	$-CH_3$	Mesylate	MsO^-
	$-CF_3$	Triflate	TfO^-

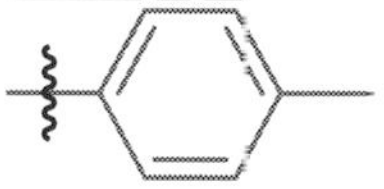

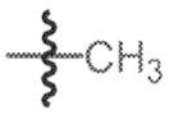

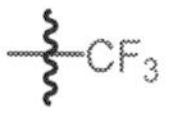

Example II.11.3

Provide a reasonable mechanistic pathway leading to the major product of the reaction shown:

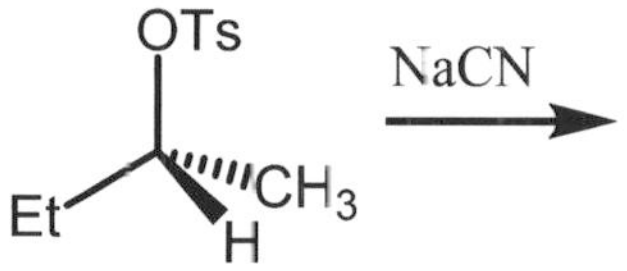

Solution II.11.3

The tosyl group (OTs) is a very good leaving group and will be readily displaced by the good nucleophile NC^- via an S_N2 pathway with inversion of configuration:

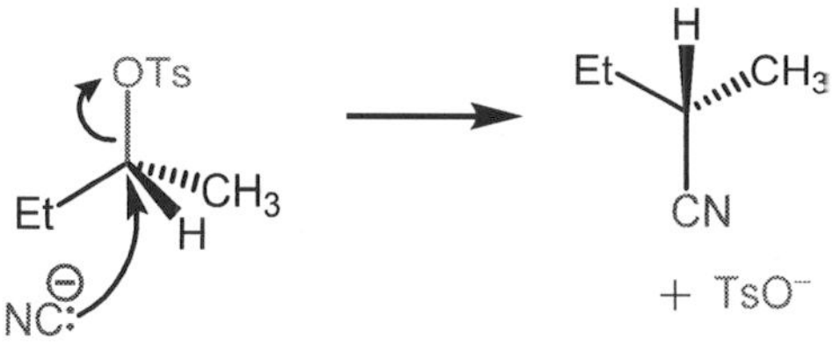

Additional help from "Organic Chemistry 1 Reactions and Practice Problems 2018" (Smith):

- After finishing Lesson II.11, you may want to review Reactions C.1, C.2 and C.4 in the companion book. These reaction summaries provide a quick review of key points, mechanism and stereochemistry related to alcohol substitution and elimination reactions.

Lesson II.12: Oxidation and Reduction: Definitions

In organic chemistry, we use a simplified definition of oxidation and reduction, with a focus on the carbon atoms in a structure. In the simplest definition, oxidation is defined as a reaction leading to more C–O bonds and/or fewer C–H bonds, whereas reduction is defined as a reaction leading to fewer C–O bonds and/or more C–H bonds. For a broader definition, we would substitute "C–O bonds" with "C–EN" bonds, where "EN" is any element more electronegative than C.

Example II.12.1

Label each of the following reactions as being an oxidation, a reduction or neither:

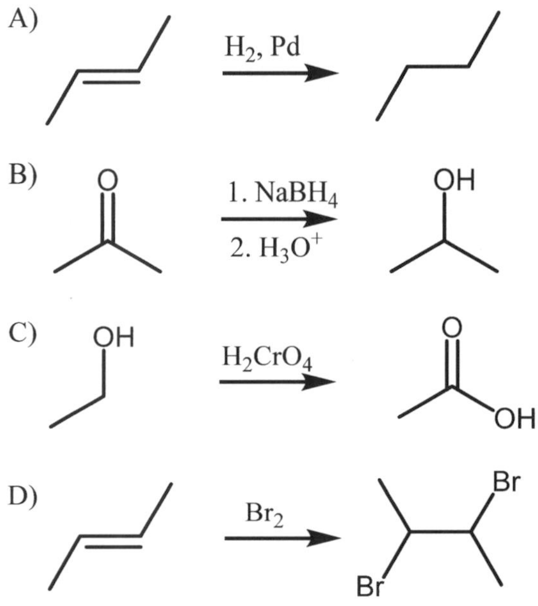

A)

H$_2$, Pd

B)

1. NaBH$_4$
2. H$_3$O$^+$

C)

H$_2$CrO$_4$

D)

Br$_2$

Solution II.12.1

Reaction A: has more C–H bonds in the product than in the reactant, so this is a reduction.
Reaction B has fewer C–O bonds in the product than in the reactant, so this is a reduction.
Reaction C has more C–O bonds in the product than in the reactant, so this is an oxidation.
Reaction D has more C–EN bonds in the product than in the reactant, so this is an oxidation.

Lesson II.13.1: Oxidation of Alcohols Using Chromium Reagents

The carbon in an alcohol to which the OH group is attached (called the "carbinol" carbon) can be oxidized by several chromium reagents, typically with added acid. Those that we will cover in this book are: H^+/CrO_4^{2-}, $H^+/Cr_2O_7^{2-}$, CrO_3/H_2SO_4 (reagents for what is called the "Jones Oxidation"), pyridinium chlorochromate (abbreviated PCC), and pyridinium dichromate (abbreviated PDC). For PCC and PDC, the proper solvent to assure the reactivity described here is CH_2Cl_2, so you will often see this written in the reaction conditions around the arrow as well.

PCC is a reagent that can replace one C–H bond on the carbinol with another bond to the O of the OH group (which must be accompanied by loss of H from the OH group). This leads to the formation of an aldehyde (from 1° alcohol) or ketone (from 2° alcohol):

All of the chromium reagents listed above, other than PCC, are more powerful oxidants. They are sufficiently strong oxidants to replace *all* of the C–H bonds on the carbinol with bonds to O. This will lead to the formation of ketones (from 2° alcohol) or carboxylic acids (from 1° alcohol):

Note that, in the case of 2° alcohols, reaction with PCC or the more powerful oxidizing agents both afford ketones because there is only one H on the carbinol that can be changed to a C–O bond. However, when the reactant is a 1° alcohol, PCC will yield different products than Jones Oxidation.

Example II.13.1

Provide the major product for each of the following reactions:

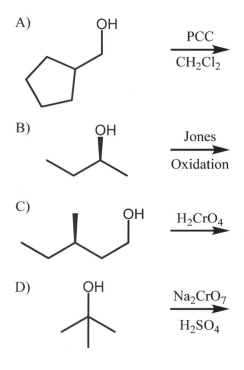

A) [cyclopentyl-CH₂OH] $\xrightarrow[CH_2Cl_2]{PCC}$

B) [2-butanol] $\xrightarrow[\text{Oxidation}]{\text{Jones}}$

C) [3-methylpentan-1-ol] $\xrightarrow{H_2CrO_4}$

D) [tert-butanol] $\xrightarrow[H_2SO_4]{Na_2CrO_7}$

Solution II.13.1

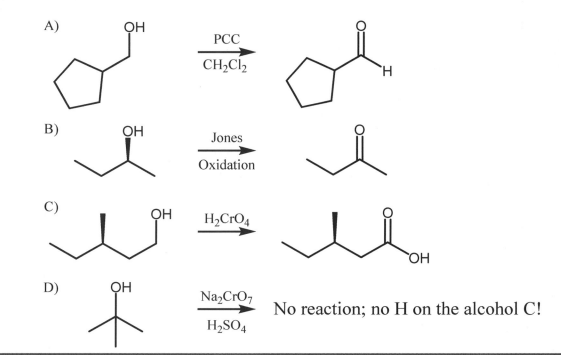

A) [cyclopentyl-CH₂OH] $\xrightarrow[CH_2Cl_2]{PCC}$ [cyclopentanecarbaldehyde]

B) [2-butanol] $\xrightarrow[\text{Oxidation}]{\text{Jones}}$ [butan-2-one]

C) [3-methylpentan-1-ol] $\xrightarrow{H_2CrO_4}$ [3-methylpentanoic acid]

D) [tert-butanol] $\xrightarrow[H_2SO_4]{Na_2CrO_7}$ No reaction; no H on the alcohol C!

118

Lesson II.13.2: Oxidation of Alcohols Using Swern Oxidation

Treating a 1° or 2° alcohol with trifluoroacetic anhydride (abbreviated TFAA, with formula $(CF_3C(O))_2O$) in DMSO at temperatures below –50 °C will afford an aldehyde or ketone, respectively. These reaction conditions are known as the **Swern Oxidation**. Note that these conditions **do not** oxidize an aldehyde to the carboxylic acid.

Example II.13.2

Draw the major product for each of the following reactions:

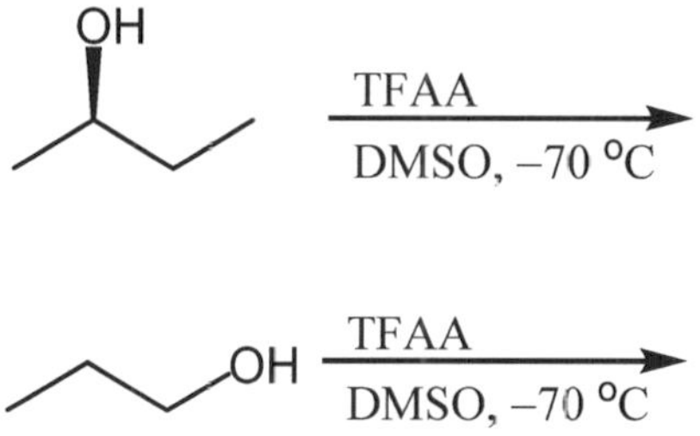

Solution II.13.2

Both reactions employ TFAA in DMSO at –70 °C, which are Swern Oxidation conditions, so the top reaction will convert (*R*)-2-butanol to 2-butanone and the bottom reaction will convert 1-butanol to butanal:

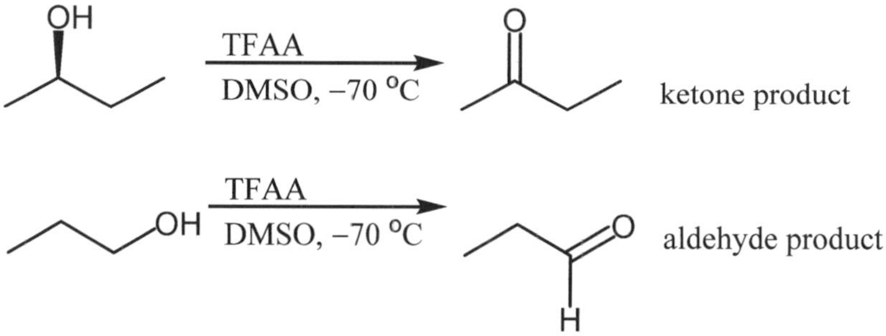

Additional help from "Organic Chemistry 1 Reactions and Practice Problems 2018" (Smith):

- After finishing Lesson II.13, you may want to review Reaction C.7 in the companion book. These reaction summaries provide a quick review of key points, mechanism and stereochemistry related to alcohol oxidation.

Lesson II.14: Acid Cleavage of Ethers

In Lesson II.11, we saw that HX (X = Cl, Br or I) simultaneously provides H^+, which activates an alcohol OH group, and X^-, the nucleophile which displaces water from the activated substrate. These same HX acids can undergo similar reactions with ethers. Acid cleavage of ethers is an important reaction because ethers are relatively inert under most of the reaction conditions we have studied. One important difference between ethers and alcohols is that, if S_N1 is possible, it will occur faster than S_N2. This means that the major product will come from an S_N1 pathway for nucleophilic attack on 2° or 3° ether carbons, and only by S_N2 on methyl or 1° ether carbons. Recall that the S_N1 reaction rate depends on the heterolysis step to create the carbocation intermediate (Lesson II.3). Heterolysis of the protonated ether oxonium intermediate is faster than in the analogous alcohol oxonium intermediate because there is greater steric hindrance in the ether-derived oxonium species:

Steric strain leads to more rapid heterolysis to form the carbocation (for S_N1)

Less steric strain allows this species to remain in solution longer, and S_N2 occurs

For this reason, the S_N1 pathway is so fast that it outpaces the S_N2 pathway for substitution at 2° ether carbons. The faster rate of heterolysis versus S_N2 has important ramifications, especially if the ether is not symmetrically substituted. Consider the reaction of ethyl isopropylether with HI:

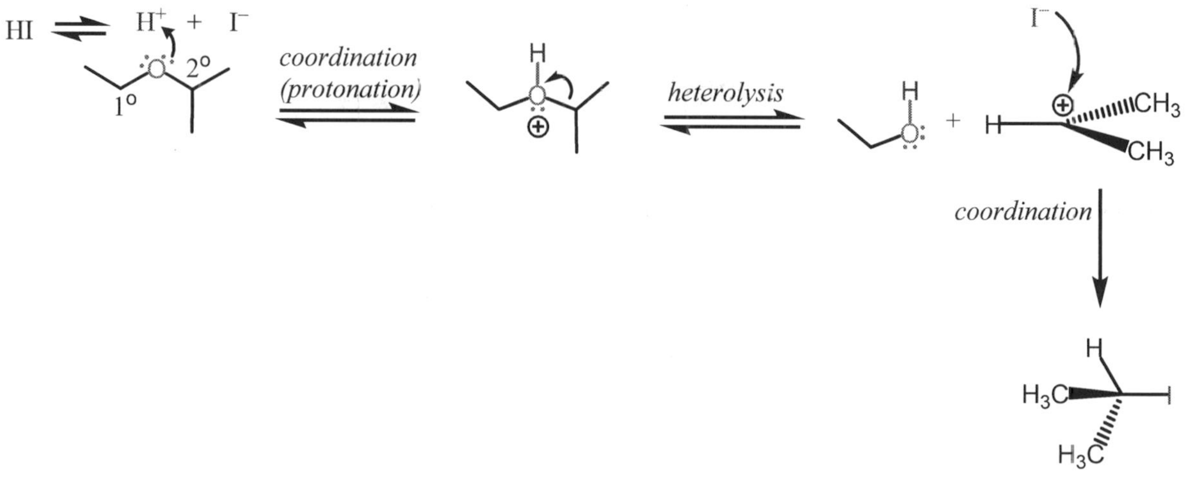

The net result is production of one equivalent of ethanol and one equivalent of 2-iodopropane as the major products. Once we have identified whether an S_N1 or S_N2 pathway is going to take place, we can use what we learned in Lessons II.3–II.5 to determine the major products of the reaction.

Example II.14.1

Provide the major product for each of the following reactions:

A)

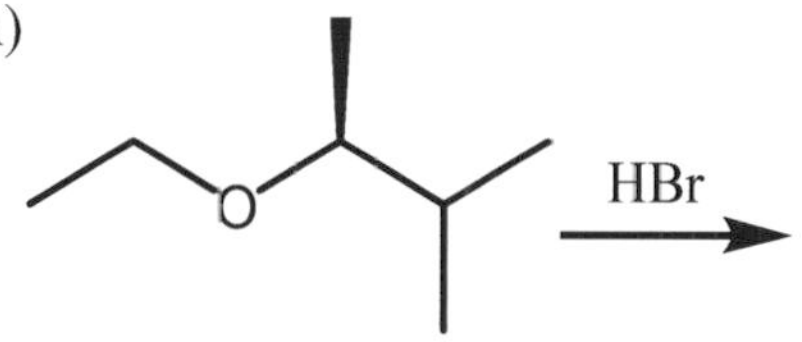

B)

Solution II.14.1

In reaction A, the left-hand ether carbon is primary and the right-hand ether carbon is secondary. The secondary site can undergo S_N1 reaction, so this will be the major pathway. The secondary carbocation will form (after protonation and heterolysis):

A)

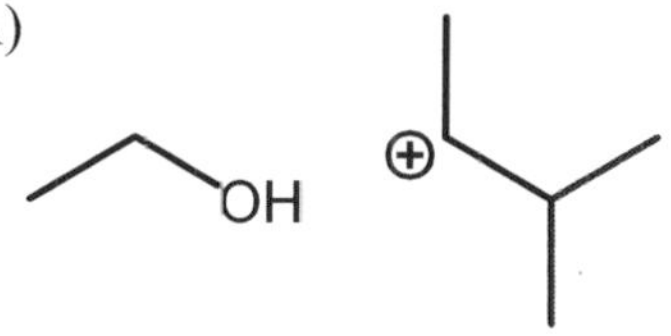

The secondary carbocation will rearrange to form the tertiary carbocation:

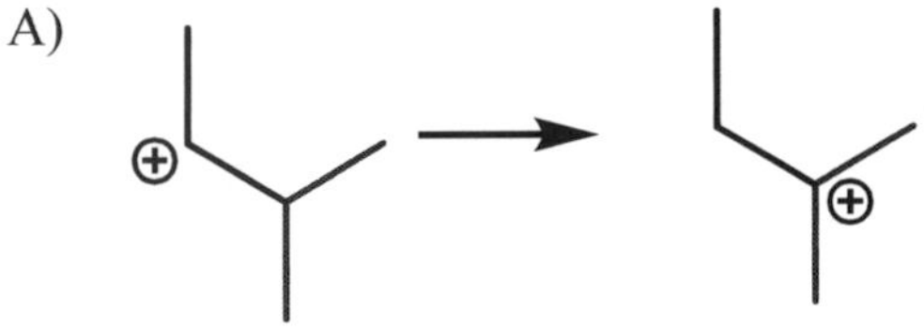

A)

The tertiary carbocation will then undergo coordination by the bromide. The final net reaction for reaction A is thus:

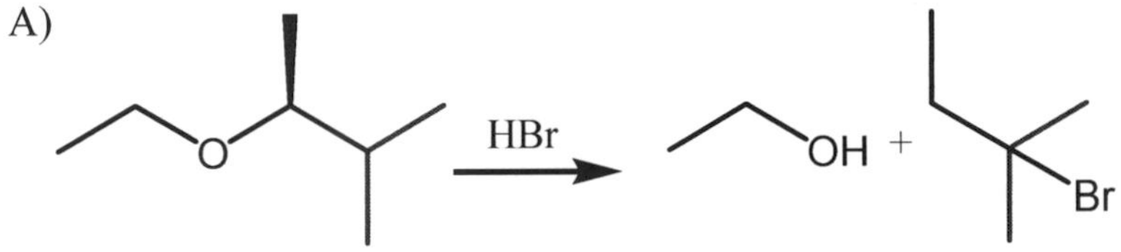

A)

In reaction B, the left-hand ether carbon is primary and the right-hand ether carbon is methyl. Neither site can undergo S_N1 reaction, so S_N2 will be the major pathway. For S_N2, we know nucleophilic attack will occur more rapidly at the less sterically hindered site, so the major product comes from nucleophilic attack on the methyl site:

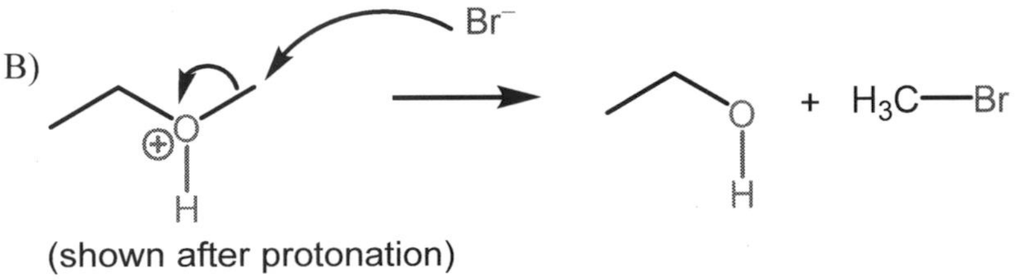

B)

(shown after protonation)

One additional note about this reaction is that we can use more than one equivalent of the acid and drive the reaction further. We learned in Lesson II.11 that ROH reacts with HX to form RX and water. If we perform the reaction in Example II.14.1A with 2 or more equivalents of HBr, the first equivalent of HBr will react as shown in Solution II.14.1A, but the second equivalent of HBr will convert EtOH to ethyl bromide:

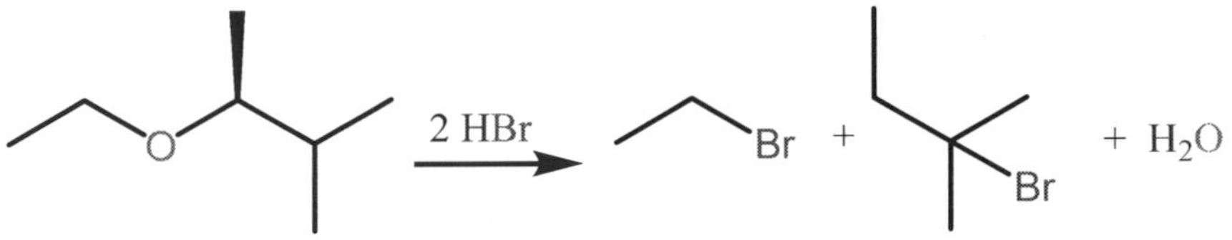

Additional help from "Organic Chemistry 1 Reactions and Practice Problems 2018" (Smith):

- After finishing Lesson II.14, you may want to review Reaction C.5 in the companion book. These reaction summaries provide a quick review of key points, mechanism and stereochemistry related to ether cleavage.

Lesson II.15.1: Epoxides are More Reactive than Other Ethers

Epoxides are ethers in which the O belongs to a three-membered ring:

In Lesson I.16, we learned that a three-membered ring has the most ring strain of any ring size. The significant ring strain in the epoxide makes it much less stable (more reactive) than acyclic ethers. The enhanced reactivity of epoxides means that the epoxide can react with good nucleophiles to open the epoxide ring, even if the epoxide O is not protonated:

Note that, although ring strain is alleviated by ring opening, the anion produced is still a strong base and is thus relatively unstable. Because the anion produced by ring opening is a strong base, not every nucleophile will react with the neutral epoxide. **The nucleophile must be a relatively unstable anion (a strong base)**, such that the reactant anion has similar stability to the product anion. The net reaction is spontaneous due to relief of ring strain (which is highly exothermic). It is also important to remember that, after nucleophilic attack under basic conditions, the resulting anion must be protonated to obtain the neutral alcohol product.

If the epoxide is reacted with a nucleophile under acidic conditions, however, even a poor nucleophile will react with the epoxide-derived oxonium intermediate, because the leaving group is a neutral OH group and quite stable:

Lesson II.15.2: Regioselectivity in Ring-Opening of Epoxides

We must determine which side of an asymmetrically-substituted epoxide will be attacked by the nucleophile in a ring-opening reaction. Regardless of conditions, if one side of the epoxide is primary and one is secondary, the less-substituted side is attacked because it is less hindered; the sterics win out in this case, as seen for this example under acidic conditions:

123

… and for this example under basic conditions (followed by protonation):

The only time that the more substituted side is attacked is if one side is tertiary and the reaction is under acidic conditions. The observed attack by the nucleophile on the tertiary site may seem to contradict the general trend that S_N2 reactions are faster at less sterically-hindered sites. In the case of a cation (in this case an oxonium), however, there is so much more partial positive charge on the more substituted carbon that the attraction of the nucleophile's electrons to this site is much stronger. All epoxide ring opening reactions undergo an S_N2-like ring opening, with inversion of configuration:

<u>Additional help from "Organic Chemistry 1 Reactions and Practice Problems 2018" (Smith):</u>

- After finishing Lesson II.15, you may want to review Reaction C.6 in the companion book.

- You will also be ready for Problem Set 6 in the companion book. This problem set is an arrow-pushing mechanism heavy test on Primer Lessons II.11-15.

- You will also be ready for Progress Check 2 in the companion book. Progress Check 2 is a cumulative practice exam covering materials from all of the Primer Lessons so far (Lessons I.1-16 and II.1-15).

Part III. Reactions Involving Alkenes, Alkynes and Radicals

Lesson III.1: Nomenclature II: Alkenes and the E-/Z- Convention

Lesson III.1.1: The "-ene" Suffix

In Lesson I.14, we learned how to name alkanes. We will use the core set of nomenclature rules from that lesson as the basis to name alkenes as well. When a hydrocarbon contains a C=C bond, we replace the "-ane" suffix with "-ene". So, if we have a 6-carbon chain with one C=C bond, it is a "hexene"; an 8-carbon chain with one C=C bond is an "octene". If two or three C=C bonds are present, we use the suffix "-diene" or "-triene", and we add an "a" to the end of the root. A 6-carbon chain with two C=C bonds is a "hexadiene", and an 8-carbon chain with three C=C bonds is an "octatriene".

Lesson III.1.2: Alkene Priority in Hydrocarbons

We first pick as parent the longest chain that contains the C=C bond. If multiple C=C bonds are present, we select as parent the chain that contains the greatest number of C=C bonds (these parent chain rules supersede the ones for alkanes). We then number the parent chain to give the C=C bond(s) the lowest possible substituent numbers.

Example III.1.1

Provide the unambiguous systematic name for the molecule shown below:

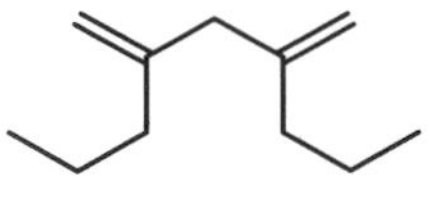

Solution III.1.1

Even though the longest chain present in this molecule has 9 carbons, we have to select as parent the chain that has the greatest number of C=C bonds. For this molecule, it is a 5-carbon chain with 2 C=C bonds. It does not matter if we start numbering left to right or right to left in this example, because the molecule is symmetric. The C=C bonds begin at carbons 1 and 4, so the parent is a 1,4-pentadiene. Two substituents are present at carbons 2 and 4. We would need to use the complex substituent rules to assign them names, and they are both propyl substituents. The complete systematic name is thus 2,4-dipropyl-1,4-pentadiene.

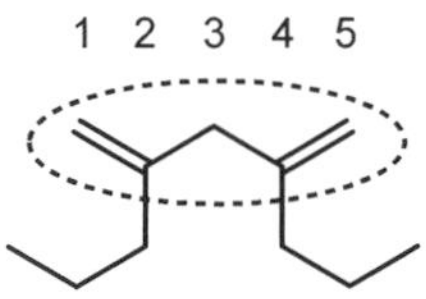

Lesson III.1.3: Alkene Priority in Heteroatom-Containing Compounds

If an alkene also contains an OH group, then that OH group takes priority over the C=C bond. Thus, we must select as parent the chain that contains an OH group, even if that results in fewer C=C bonds being included. Similarly, we must number the parent chain to give the OH group the lowest possible substituent number, regardless of what substituent numbers that assigns to the C=C bonds. To assign a name to the molecule, the "ene" suffix becomes "en" and is listed before the "ol" suffix which ends the name. A 6-carbon chain with one C=C bond and one OH group would thus be a "hexenol". For a complex molecule such as this, the substituent numbers can be placed immediately before the suffixes to enhance clarity.

Example III.1.2

Provide the unambiguous systematic name for the molecule shown below:

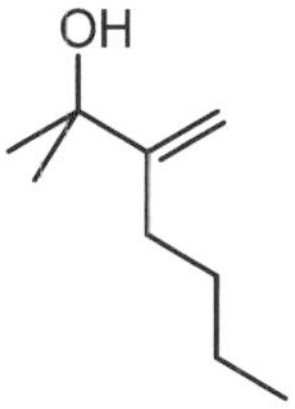

Solution III.1.2

The longest chain in this molecule has 7 carbons, but we must pick the longest one that has both the OH group and the C=C bond. The longest chain that meets these criteria has only 4 carbons, so the root is "butenol". We have to number from left to right because that gives the OH group a substituent number of 2 (going from right to left it would have a 3). As a result, the C=C bond begins at carbon 3, so the parent molecule is "3-buten-2-ol". We next need to identify the substituents and their positions in this molecule, which are methyl at carbon 2 and an *n*-butyl at carbon 3. The complete systematic name is thus "3-*n*-butyl-2-methyl-3-buten-2-ol".

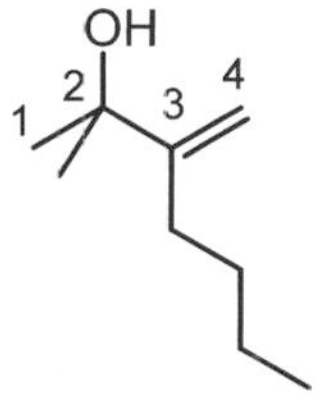

Lesson III.1.4: Hindered Rotation about C=C Bonds

As we learned in Lessons I.14 and I.15, rotation about carbon–carbon single bonds in alkanes and cycloalkanes can give rise to multiple conformational isomers, which readily interconvert at room temperature. In contrast, carbon–carbon double bonds do not undergo bond rotation. Rotating around a π-bond would require that bond to break. This means that alkenes can have configurational isomers (defined in Lesson I.17).

<u>Example III.1.3</u>

Indicate whether the following pair of molecules is identical or non-identical:

and

<u>Solution III.1.3</u>

The easiest way to approach this problem is to draw the Newman projection along the C(2)–C(3) bonds. For the molecule on the left, the ethyl substituents on carbons 2 and 3 are separated by 180° in the Newman projection, whereas the ethyl substituents in the molecule on the left are separated by 0°. When we were working with alkanes, we could freely rotate the substituents on the front and rear carbons in the Newman projection, because C–C σ-bonds can freely rotate at room temperature (and much lower!). With alkenes, there is a σ- and a π-bond present, which prevents free rotation about the C(2)–C(3) bond (we would need to break the π-bond before the σ-bond would be able to rotate freely). Because the C=C bond cannot freely rotate, these two molecules are non-identical (configurational isomers, to be precise).

Lesson III.1.5: The cis-/trans- Prefix Convention

The two isomers of 3-hexene shown in Example III.1.4 differ only by whether the two ethyl substituents are on the same side or opposite sides of the C=C bond. Rephrasing this in more general terms, the two isomers differ only by the spatial orientation of their substituents, and the two isomers cannot be interconverted without breaking any bonds. Thus, based on the definition in Lesson I.20, we would classify the two isomers of 3-hexene as stereoisomers. Because the presence of a C=C bond may give rise to multiple stereoisomers, we would classify that C=C bond as stereogenic. Note, however, that it is only when each carbon in a C=C bond has two non-identical substituents does that C=C bond become stereogenic; if two of the substituents on one C atom are identical, then switching them will not yield a different stereoisomer.

The simplest type of stereogenic C=C bond is one in which each carbon in the C=C bond has one hydrogen and one non-hydrogen substituent, and the term for this type of molecule is a disubstituted, internal alkene. In contrast, a disubstituted, external alkene is a molecule in which one carbon in the C=C bond has two hydrogen substituents and the other carbon and has two non-hydrogen substituents.

If we consider 2-methyl-1-pentene (see below), we can see that switching the methyl and *n*-propyl substituents does not produce a new molecule, so 2-methyl-1-pentene does not have multiple stereoisomers. For similar reasons, a monosubstituted alkene like 1-hexene (another constitutional isomer of 3-hexene) does not have multiple stereoisomers.

2-methyl-1-pentene

swapping these two substituents...   *...gives something that looks like this...*   180° *...but if we rotate 180° about this axis...*   *...we see it is the same as what we started with!*

180°

1-hexene

For an internal disubstituted alkene, if both substituents are on the same side of the line passing through the C=C bond, we apply the prefix "*cis*-". If the substituents are on opposite sides of the line passing through the C=C bond, we apply the prefix "*trans*-". Consider again the two configurational isomers of 3-hexene as an example:

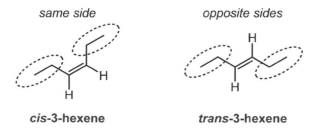

same side   *opposite sides*

cis-3-hexene   **trans-3-hexene**

Note that the "*cis*-" and "*trans*-" prefixes belong to a convention developed specifically for disubstituted, internal alkenes and they can only be used for disubstituted, internal alkenes and cycloalkanes (as described in Lesson II.17)!

Example III.1.4

Provide the appropriate name for the molecule shown below:

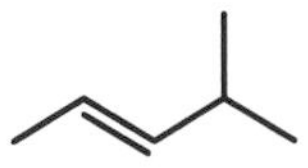

Solution III.1.4

The alkene carbon on the left has one non-hydrogen substituent, a methyl group. The carbon on the right also has one non-hydrogen substituent, an isopropyl group. Because these two non-hydrogen substituents are on opposite sides of the C=C bond with respect to each other, the proper stereochemical prefix for this molecule would be "*trans-*".

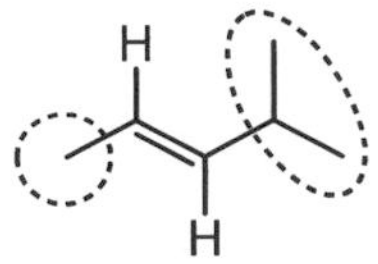

The complete name of the molecule is thus *trans*-4-methyl-2-pentene.

If a C=C bond is either (a) disubstituted and external or (b) monosubstituted, then it is not stereogenic and therefore no stereochemical prefix is necessary for an unambiguous name. Because the "*cis-*" and "*trans-*" convention was developed specifically for disubstituted, internal alkenes, stereogenic tri- and stereogenic tetrasubstituted C=C bonds require a different set of stereochemical prefixes, as described in Lesson III.1.6.

Lesson III.1.6: Tri- and Tetrasubstituted Alkenes and the E-/Z- Prefix Convention

When an alkene is tri- or tetrasubstituted, the *cis-/trans-* convention is inapplicable, but its C=C bond may still be stereogenic, so we need to have a way to describe the necessary stereochemical information in that molecule's name. For example, if we add a methyl substituent to the 3-position of 3-hexene, the C=C bond is still stereogenic: in one stereoisomer, the two ethyl substituents are on the same side of the C=C bond, and in the other stereoisomer, the two ethyl substituents are on opposite sides.

The terms "*zusammen*" (German: "together") and "*entgegen*" (German: "opposed") are used to describe stereoisomers of tri- and tetrasubstituted alkenes. The way that "*zusammen*" (abbreviated as the prefix "*Z-*") and "*entgegen*" (abbreviated as the prefix "*E-*") are used is to assign the Cahn-Ingold-Prelog (CIP) priority (see Lesson I.18) to the two substituents on each carbon in a C=C bond (i.e., each carbon has a "higher" and a "lower" priority substituent), and then we compare the relative spatial orientation of the two "higher" priority substituents. If the two "higher" priority substituents are on the same side of the C=C bond, then we say they are "together", or "*zusammen*", and we use the prefix "*Z-*

". If the two "higher" priority substituents are on opposite sides of the C=C bond, then we say they are "opposed", or "*entgegen*", and we use the prefix "*E-*".

Example III.1.5

Provide the appropriate stereochemical prefix for the molecule shown below:

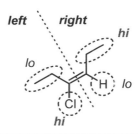

Solution III.1.5

The left carbon in the C=C bond has an ethyl substituent and a chlorine atom, and the Cl has higher priority. The right carbon in the C=C bond has an ethyl substituent and a hydrogen atom, and the Et has higher priority. Because the two "hi" substituents are on opposite sides of the C=C bond, this molecule would require a stereochemical prefix of "(*E*)-".

left   *right*

hi

lo

lo

H

Cl

hi

Lesson III.1.7: Alkene Priority in Molecular Nomenclature

If we look at the structure of 2,3-dimethyl-3-penten-2-ol (below left), we can see that the C=C bond is stereogenic, so the name must include a stereochemical prefix to be unambiguous, which in this case would be "(*E*)-". We would thus use the rules from Lesson I.14 to assemble the core name and place the label of configuration in front of the name in parentheses, in the same manner as we did with the *R*- and *S*- labels in Lesson I.18:

high on opposite sides

lo

hi

hi

lo H   OH

(*E*)-2,3-dimethyl-3-penten-2-ol

high on opposite sides   *lo* H   *lo*

hi

hi

lo   H *lo*

high on opposite sides

(3*E*,5*E*)-3,5-dimethyl-3,5-octadiene

What happens if a molecule has more than one stereogenic C=C bond? In this case, we would include a number with the stereochemical prefix to indicate which C=C bond has which stereochemistry. So,

131

for the stereoisomer of 3,5-dimethyl-3,5-octadiene shown above, the complete prefix would be "(3*E*,5*E*)-".

Example III.1.6

Provide the unambiguous name for the molecule shown below:

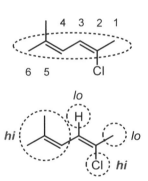

Solution III.1.6

The parent of the molecule is the 6-carbon chain containing the two C=C bonds, and we number from right to left to give a lower position number to the substituent that comes earlier in the alphabet ("chloro" vs. "methyl"). Although carbons 4 and 5 are connected by a C=C bond, this C=C bond is not stereogenic because carbon 5 has two identical substituents. The double bond between carbons 2 and 3 is stereogenic: on the left carbon, the hydrogen is lower priority than the carbon chain, and on the right carbon, the methyl is lower priority than the chlorine. Because the two "hi" substituents are on the same side of the C=C bond, the prefix should be "(*Z*)-". The proper name for the molecule would thus be "(*Z*)-2-chloro-5-methyl-2,4-hexadiene".

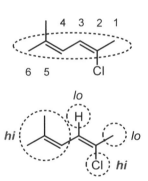

132

Lesson III.2.1: Intermolecular Packing and Melting/Boiling Points

Hydrocarbons that have π bonds are called **unsaturated**, because they are not "saturated" with as many H atoms as could be bound to the C atoms if all of the bonds were single bonds. You may be familiar with the terms "saturated fat" (generally solid fats like shortening and lard) and "unsaturated fat" (things like vegetable oil).

Unsaturated hydrocarbons, like their saturated counterparts, lack heteroatoms and thus do not contain bonds with significant polarity. As a result, the intermolecular forces (IMFs) in alkenes are dominated by London dispersion forces (LDFs). Look back at Lesson I.3 if you would like to review IMFs and an explanation of why stronger IMFs leads to higher melting/boiling points.

In Lesson I.3, we saw that increasing the size or linearity of an alkane led to increased IMFs/higher boiling points, and this trend is also observed with alkenes. For example, 1-hexene has a higher boiling point than 1-pentene (30 °C vs. 63 °C, respectively). Similarly, the more closely that alkene molecules can pack together, the stronger the IMFs will be. For alkenes, more rigid alkenes can pack more effectively than can flexible alkenes, just a box of rigid pencils can pack well, whereas a box of flexible pieces of rope forms a less well-packed assembly. The added conformational flexibility about sp^3 hybridized C3 in 1,4-pentadiene is thus the reason that its boiling point (26 °C) is lower than that of *trans*-1,3-pentadiene (42 °C). The stereochemistry of the C=C bond also influences the IMFs and properties of alkenes. For example, molecules of more linear *trans*-2-butene can pack together more closely than molecules of U-shaped *cis*-2-butene, which can be observed by the higher melting point of the former (−105 °C vs. −139 °C, respectively).

	1-pentene	bp = 30 °C
	1-hexene	bp = 63 °C
	1,4-pentadiene	bp = 26 °C
	trans-1,3-pentadiene	bp = 42 °C
	trans-2-butene	mp = −105 °C
	cis-2-butene	mp = −139 °C

Example III.2.1

Which of the following alkenes would have the higher melting point?

vs

<u>Solution III.2.1</u>

Both of these molecules are heptenes, so it cannot be molecular weight that causes them to have different melting points. However, we can see that the molecule on the left (2-methyl-1-hexene) has one branch, whereas the molecule on the right (1-heptene) has no branches. As a result, 1-heptene is able to pack together more densely than 2-methyl-1-hexene. Because the molecules of 1-heptene are able to pack more densely, the IMFs between the molecules are stronger. Because the IMFs between the 1-hexene molecules are stronger, it will require more energy to pull the molecules apart, which will be manifest in the form of a higher melting point.

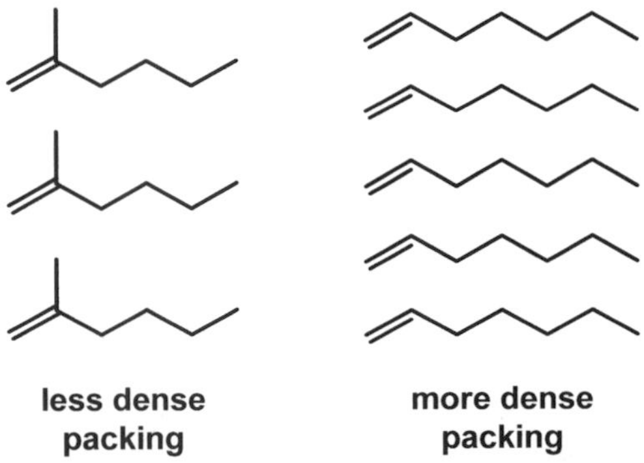

less dense packing   **more dense packing**

Lesson III.2.2: Hydrogenation of Alkenes to Alkanes

In Lesson I.11.1, we saw how the thermodynamics of alkene hydrogenation reactions can be used to infer stability, but we have not yet discussed the mechanism of the hydrogenation reaction. The typical conditions used to perform alkene hydrogenation reactions are H_2 (or D_2) in the presence of a group 10 transition metal (Ni, Pd, or Pt) as a catalyst. Under these conditions, a molecule of H_2 first reacts with the metal surface, then the alkene reacts via a series of steps shown below to form an alkane:

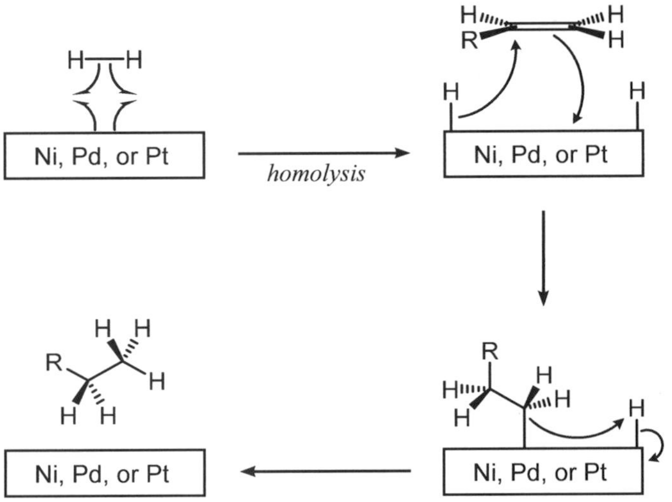

134

Because both H atoms added to the alkene come from the metal surface, both H atoms will add to the same face of the C=C bond (i.e., they will always add *syn*). This reaction does not proceed through any achiral intermediates or intermediates that can rearrange, so stereochemistry will be preserved. Note that each alkene has two faces, and, if there is no difference in energy between one face binding and the other face binding, both binding modes will occur in equal abundance and a 1:1 mixture of stereoisomers will be formed.

Example III.2.2

Draw the major product of the reaction shown below:

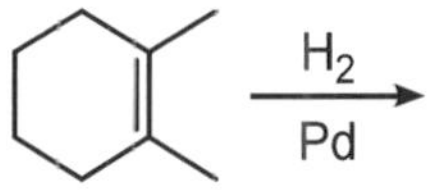

Solution III.2.2

In the presence of Pd metal, each molecule of H_2 undergoes homolysis to form 2 Pd–H bonds. When the reactant, 1,2-dimethyl-1-cyclohexene, then binds to the metal surface, both H atoms are transferred to the same face of the π-bond. The hydrogens add *syn* with respect to each other, which restricts the 2 methyl groups to be *syn* with respect to each other. An alkene can bind to the metal surface with either face of the π-bond, but *cis*-1,2-dimethylcyclohexane, the product of this reaction, is a meso compound, so only one stereoisomer is possible.

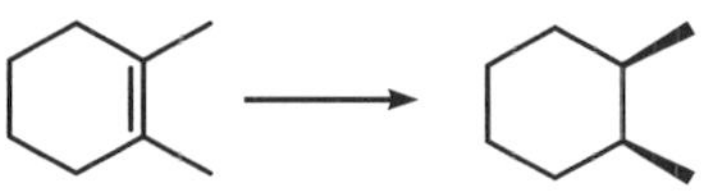

Additional help from "Organic Chemistry 1 Reactions and Practice Problems 2018" (Smith):

- After finishing Lesson III.2, you may want to review Reaction D.11 in the companion book. This is a quick review with key points and has a short self test with answers covering the reactions in this Primer Lesson.

- You will also be ready for Problem Set 7 in the companion book. This problem set covers material from Primer Lessons III.1-2.

- You will also be ready for Progress Check 2 in the companion book. Progress Check 2 is a cumulative practice exam covering materials from all of the Primer Lessons so far (Lessons I.1-16 and II.1-15).

Lesson III.3.1: The C=C Bond is a Nucleophile

By this point in the course, we have already covered a number of nucleophilic substitution reactions, many of which involve a lone pair on a heteroatom as the nucleophile. Lone pair electrons are generally held less tightly than are bonding electrons, so lone pairs are more easily removed by an electrophile. A C=C bond can also be a nucleophile, because π-bonding electrons are less tightly bound than are σ-bonding electrons. Consequently, electrophiles will react with the π-bonds in alkenes. The simplest electrophile to consider is H^+ and the simplest alkene to consider is ethylene:

Here, the two π-electrons in the C=C bond coordinate to the H^+ and produce a C–H σ-bond on the right-hand carbon, leaving a formal charge of +1 (i.e., is a carbocation) on the carbon that now has only three bonds.

In general, the reaction of an electrophile (E^+) with an alkene will afford a C–E σ-bond at one carbon and a carbocation at the other. The two carbons in the C=C bond of ethylene are identical, however, so the stability of the carbocation is the same regardless of which carbon is made into the carbocation. If the two carbons in a C=C bond are inequivalent, then formation of the more stable carbocation will be thermodynamically favored. Considering the reaction of propylene with H^+:

2° carbocation   1° carbocation

We see that attachment of the hydrogen to either carbon 1 or carbon 2 will afford non-identical products. Because a 2° carbocation is more stable than a 1° carbocation, the reaction of H^+ with propylene would proceed exclusively through the 2° carbocation (i.e., C–H σ-bond formation would only occur at carbon 1).

Example III.3.1

What would be the most stable carbocation intermediate formed in the reaction shown below?

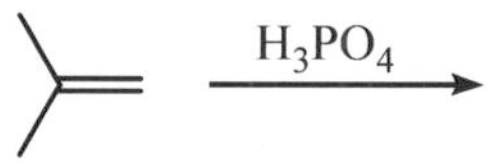

Solution III.3.1

As a strong mineral acid, H_3PO_4 will readily supply the H^+ electrophile for electrophilic addition to the alkene, forming a C–H bond at the less substituted carbon and a carbocation at the more substituted carbon (3°).

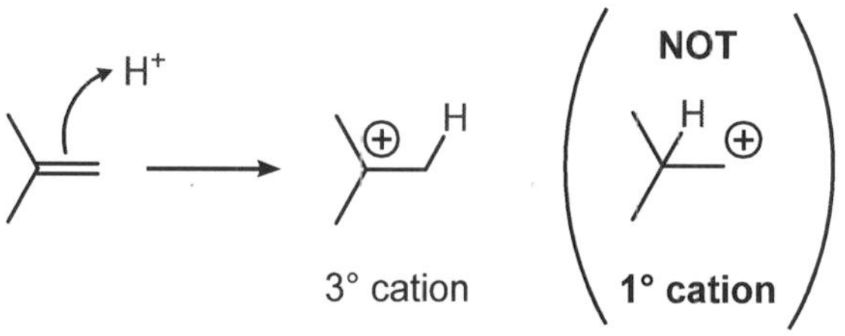

3° cation   1° cation

The reason that H^+ attaches to the less substituted carbon is because it forms a more stable carbocation. If the H^+ had attached to the more substituted carbon, the carbocation would form at the less substituted carbon (1°), a much less thermodynamically favorable reaction.

Lesson III.3.2: Carbocation Intermediate Rearrangement

As we saw in Lesson II.3, carbocations intermediates will always rearrange to the most stable carbocation achievable. When 3-methyl-1-butene reacts with H^+, the C–H σ-bond forms at the less substituted carbon to generate a 2° carbocation. However, this carbocation is adjacent to a tertiary carbon, and 1,2-hydride shift would afford a more stable 3° carbocation. Thus, the 2° carbocation would very rapidly rearrange to give the 3° carbocation. As we saw for S_N1 and E1 reactions in Lesson II.3, the rearrangement of cations happens prior to any further reactivity of the carbocation.

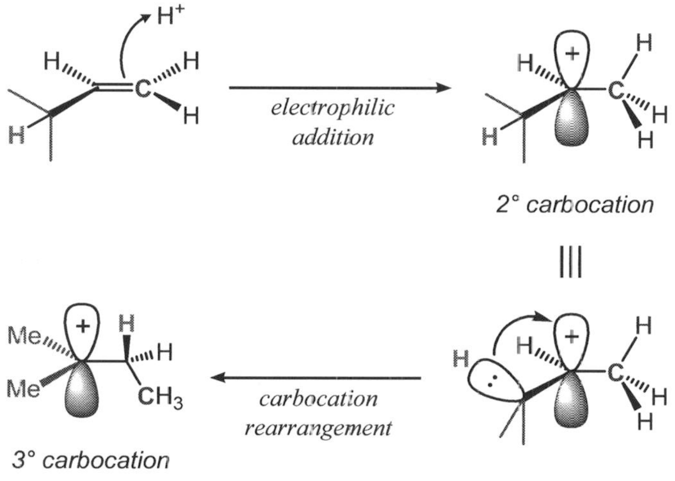

electrophilic addition

2° carbocation

carbocation rearrangement

3° carbocation

137

Example III.3.2

Draw the most stable carbocation that will form in the reaction shown below:

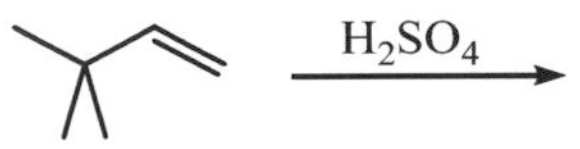

Solution III.3.2

The H$^+$ released from H$_2$SO$_4$ does electrophilic addition to the alkene π-bond (step *i*) to form a C–H σ-bond at the less substituted alkene carbon and a 2° carbocation at the more substituted alkene carbon. This carbocation is adjacent to a quaternary carbon, from which a methyl group does a 1,2-alkyl shift from the quaternary carbon to the 2° carbocation (step *ii*). This rearrangement allows the carbocation to achieve greater stability by moving to a 3° position.

Lesson III.4: Markovnikov's Rule, *Syn*- and *Anti*- Addition

Lesson III.4.1: Nucleophile Coordination to the Carbocation Intermediate

A nucleophile will readily coordinate to a carbocation due to its positive charge and empty *p*-orbital. In Lesson II.3, we learned that the carbocation generated during an SN1 reaction can be coordinated by either anionic or neutral nucleophiles (Nu^- or Nu–H, respectively). Because reaction of an alkene with an electrophile (E^+) also produces a carbocation, both anionic and neutral nucleophiles can coordinate to the carbocation generated by electrophilic addition:

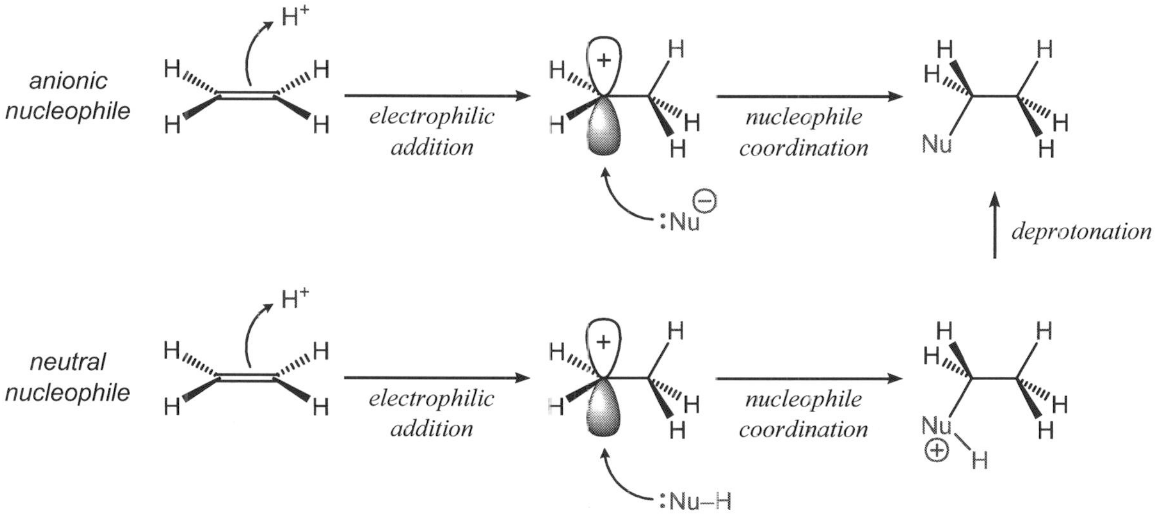

Example III.4.1

Draw the major product for the reaction shown below:

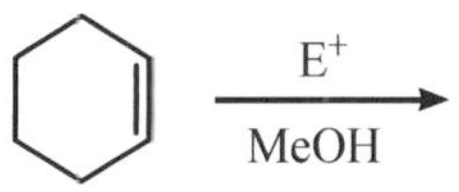

Solution III.4.1

In the first step, E^+ does electrophilic addition to the π-bond in cyclohexene (step *i*). Remember that the C=C bond is planar, and the electrophile can add to either the top or bottom face, so there will be two carbocation stereoisomers formed. Next, one of the lone pairs on the oxygen atom in methanol will do nucleophilic coordination to the carbocation carbon (step *ii*). Because the carbocation carbon is planar, the MeOH can coordinate from either above or below this plane, therefore each carbocation stereoisomer will yield two MeOH coordination stereoisomers (i.e., one in which the E and MeOH are *syn*, and one in which they are *anti*), for a total of four possible stereoisomers. Coordination of MeOH to the carbocation results in a positive charge on oxygen, which will significantly increase the acidity of the O–H proton. Subsequent deprotonation of these cationic O–H groups (step *iii*) will afford the major reaction products, in which E has added to one carbon and OMe has added to the other. Because we started with a symmetric alkene, there is no regioisomerism to consider (i.e., electrophilic addition will afford a 2° carbocation regardless of which carbon it binds to). A total of four stereoisomers will be produced in this reaction, with two enantiomeric pairs (top left and bottom right form one pair, top right and bottom left form the other pair).

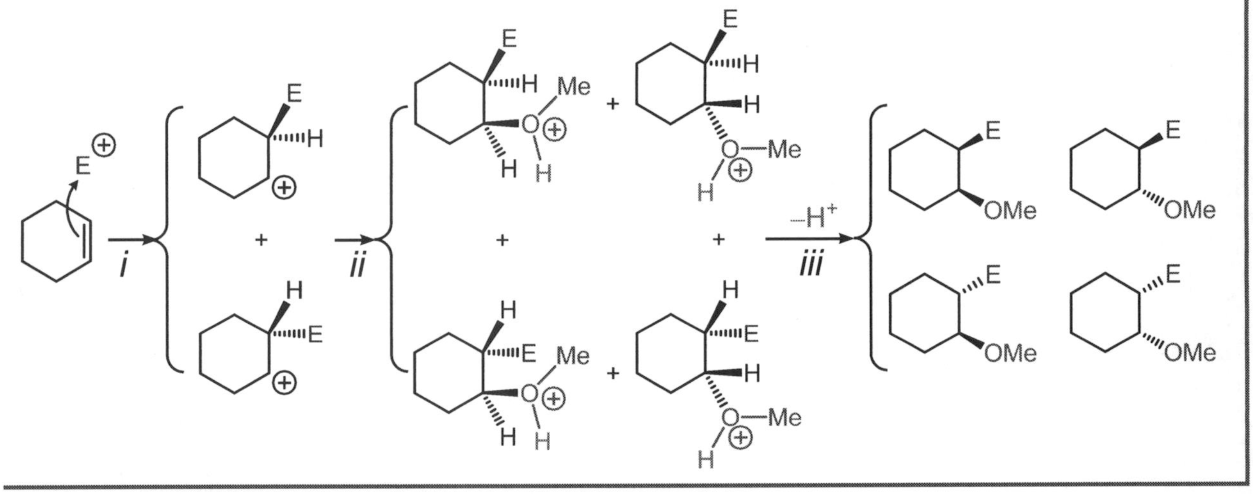

Lesson III.4.2: Concerted Addition of Electrophile and Nucleophile

It is also possible for an electrophile and a nucleophile both to add to the C=C bond in an alkene in a single concerted step, but this can only occur when the electrophile and nucleophile are connected by a bond (i.e., E–Nu). This bond will be polarized such that the electrophile carries a δ+ charge and the nucleophile carries a δ– charge. In this manner, E and Nu each add to a different carbon from the same face of the C=C bond. Because everything happens in a single concerted step and no carbocation forms, no rearrangement can occur.

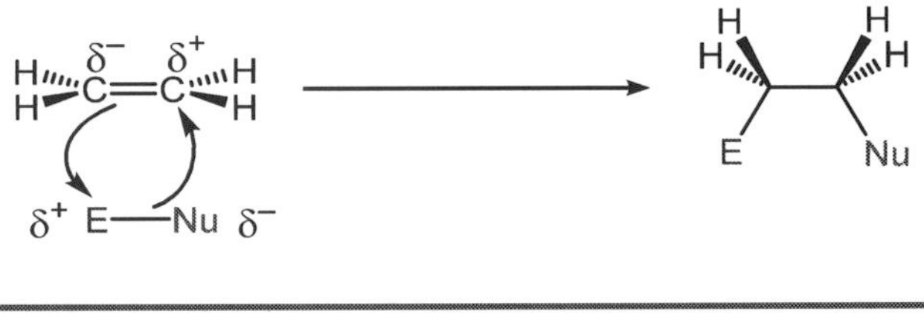

Example III.4.2

In Example III.4.1, we saw that the stepwise addition of an electrophile followed by coordination of a nucleophile afforded a mixture of four stereoisomers. How many unique stereoisomers will be formed if the same substrate, cyclohexene, undergoes concerted addition of E–Nu? (shown above)

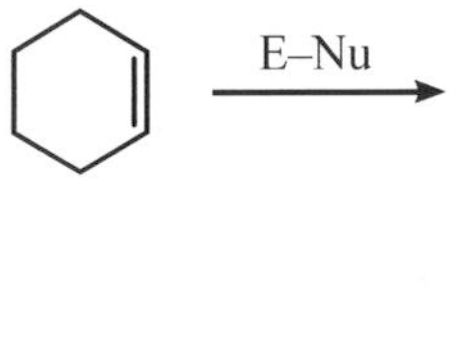

140

When the addition of an electrophile and nucleophile to the π-bond in cyclohexene is concerted, then both E and Nu will add simultaneously to the same face of the π-bond (i.e., *syn* addition). Remember that when molecules add to π-bonds in alkenes, the addition can occur on either side of the C=C plane will occur with equal probability because there is no energy difference between the addition of E–Nu above vs. below the plane. Two stereoisomers will thus be formed. For the concerted addition of E–Nu to cyclohexene, an enantiomeric pair will be produced:

Lesson III.4.3: Regioisomerism and Markovnikov's Rule

Because there are two carbons in a C=C bond, electrophilic addition to an alkene followed by nucleophile coordination could theoretically afford two products that differ in relative arrangement of electrophile and nucleophile (i.e., E on carbon A and Nu on carbon B, or vice versa), and these are termed "regioisomers". However, as we showed in Lesson III.3.1, the addition of E^+ to an alkene affords a carbocation intermediate, so E^+ will add to the less substituted carbon, leaving the more stable cation on the more substituted carbon, as illustrated in the electrophilic addition of E^+ to 1-butene:

Subsequent coordination of Nu^- to this carbocation affords the major product, wherein the electrophile has attached to the less substituted carbon and the nucleophile to the more substituted carbon. Because the reaction inherently favors one regioisomer, the reaction is said to be "regioselective".

If we consider a reaction in which the initially-generated carbocation rearranges, this rearrangement will take place prior to coordination of the nucleophile:

141

Markovnikov's rule is an empirical rule based on a collection of experimental observations obtained from a significant number of reactions. Markovnikov's rule states that, for the addition of a given molecule X–Y to an alkene, the more electronegative element ends up on the more substituted carbon.

Example III.4.3

Draw the possible Markovnikov product(s) of the reaction shown below:

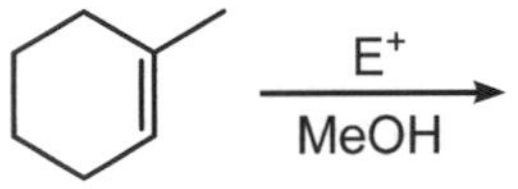

Solution III.4.3

The reactant 1-methyl-1-cyclohexene will first undergo electrophilic addition by E^+ (step *i*), which can occur from either above or below the alkene plane with equal probability, to yield an enantiomeric pair of carbocation intermediates. Next, a lone pair on the oxygen of MeOH will do nucleophilic coordination to the empty *p*-orbital (step *ii*). Because the nucleophile can coordinate from either above or below the sp^2-plane, each carbocation intermediate from step *i* will give rise to two nucleophile coordination products, for a total of four stereoisomers. In the last step, the protonated OMe group will be deprotonated (step *iii*). In this reaction, a single reactant stereoisomer gives rise to four Markovnikov product stereoisomers.

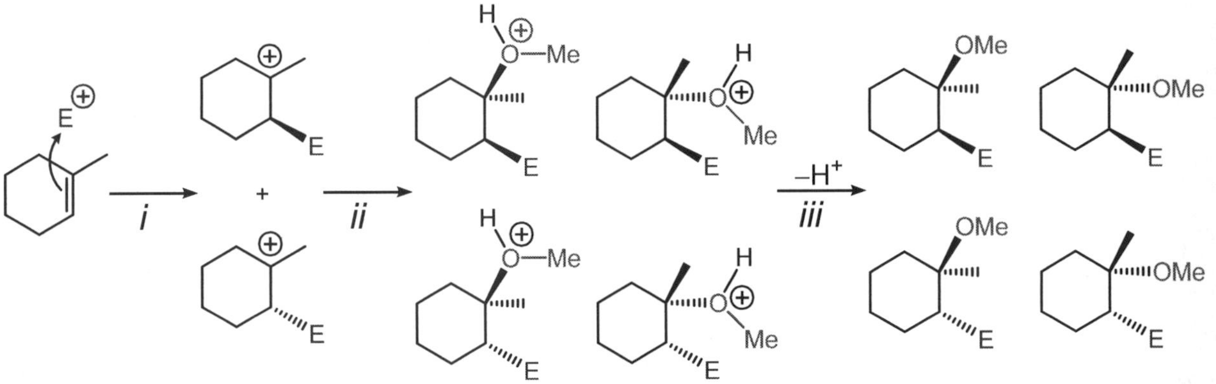

Lesson III.4.4: Stereoisomerism and Syn- vs. Anti- Addition

We showed in Lesson III.4.3 that the addition of E^+ to 1-butene, followed by Nu^- coordination to the resulting carbocation, afforded a single regioisomer with E on carbon 1 and Nu on carbon 2. From Lesson I.17, however, we can easily recognize carbon 2 as a chiral center, so stereochemistry must be considered when predicting reaction products. A carbocation is sp^2-hybridized, which means the σ-bonds to the carbon are coplanar and the empty *p*-orbital is perpendicular to that plane. The Nu^- can attack the *p*-orbital from either above or below the sp^2-orbital plane to yield a non-planar sp^3-hybridized carbon, in which the Nu substituent is pointing out of or into the plane of the page, respectively. For the

142

reaction with 1-butene shown below, there is no difference in energy between Nu⁻ approaching the carbocation from above or below the plane, so the reaction would yield a 50:50 mix of the two stereoisomers (i.e., a racemate).

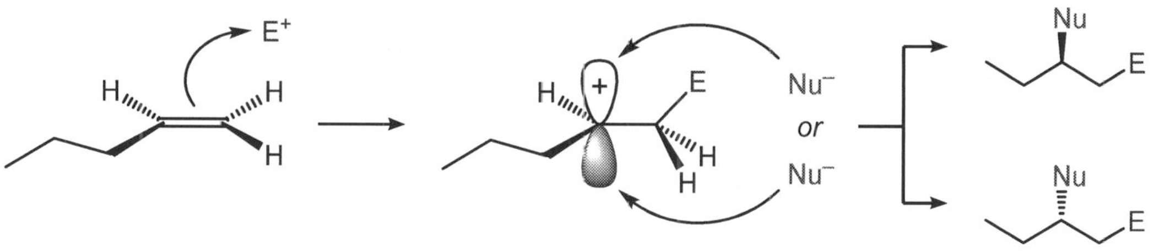

In the reaction above, the possible product stereochemistry was simplified by the fact that E ended up on an achiral carbon. If both E and Nu end up on chiral carbons, then the reaction can yield up to four different stereoisomers, such as in the electrophilic addition to cyclohexene followed by coordination of a nucleophile:

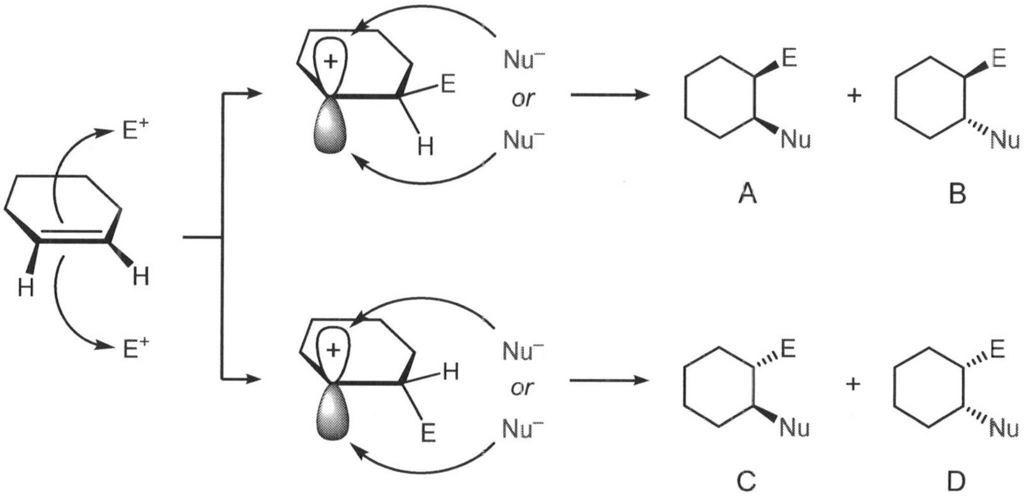

We clearly see that, when a carbocation is formed, the addition of an electrophile followed by coordination of a nucleophile is not stereoselective for *syn* or *anti*. In subsequent Lessons, however, we will learn some addition reactions to alkenes that do not form carbocation intermediates. Some reactions even involve simultaneous addition of both electrophile and nucleophile.

Example III.4.4

Draw the major product of the reaction shown below, assuming concerted addition of a nucleophilic part (Nu) and electrophilic part (E) of a molecule to an alkene π-bond:

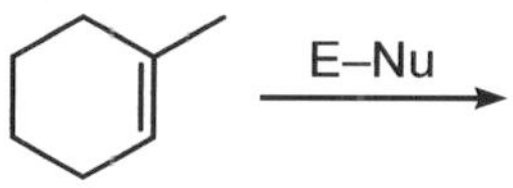

143

<u>Solution III.4.4</u>

The E–Nu bond is polarized as $E^{\delta+}$ and $Nu^{\delta-}$, so simultaneous nucleophilic and electrophilic addition of E–Nu to 1-methyl-1-cyclohexene will place Nu on the more substituted carbon and E on the less substituted carbon. Because this is a concerted addition reaction, both E and Nu will add to the same face of the π-bond (i.e., *syn* addition). There is no difference in energy between this addition occurring from above vs. below the alkene plane, which means that a 1:1 mixture of stereoisomers will be formed.

Lesson III.5.1: Hydrohalogenation – Electrophilic Addition by H⁺, then Coordination by X⁻

Hydrohalogenation refers to the addition of H–X (X = Cl, Br, I) across a C=C bond. H–X is a strong acid, so it will dissociate to H^+ and X^- in solution. Thus, H^+ is the electrophile that reacts with the C=C bond at the less substituted carbon to afford a carbocation at the more substituted carbon. If rearrangement (1,2-hydride shift, 1,2-alkyl shift, ring expansion) will afford a more stable structure, then the carbocation intermediate will rearrange. Once the most stable carbocation has been formed, X^- will attack the empty *p*-orbital on the sp^2-hybridized carbon. When there is no difference in energy between X^- approaching the carbocation from above vs. below the plane, which is generally the case, then the reaction products will be derived equally from both approaches.

Example III.5.1

Draw the major product of the reaction shown in the box:

Solution III.5.1

In the first step of the reaction, the electrophile H^+ adds to the π-bond and forms a C–H bond at the less substituted alkene carbon, which allows the carbocation to form at the more substituted carbon. There is no ring and no way to form a 3° carbocation, so no rearrangement occurs. After the carbocation has formed, X^- will then coordinate to the empty *p*-orbital from either above or below the sp^2-hybridized carbon's plane. Because there is no difference in energy between these two approaches, a 1:1 mixture of the two enantiomers will be formed.

145

Lesson III.5.2: Hydration – Electrophilic Addition by H⁺, then Coordination by H₂O

Hydration refers to the addition of H–OH (i.e., water) across a C=C bond. However, H_2O is a weak acid and is not electrophilic enough to react with the C=C bond. Thus, hydration reactions require the addition of a catalytic amount of a strong acid. HX (X = Cl, Br, I) is not used because then the highly nucleophilic X⁻ would be the nucleophile and the result would be hydrohalogenation, not hydration. The most commonly-used acid for alkene hydration reactions is a catalytic amount of H_2SO_4. As before, H^+ is the electrophile that reacts with the C=C bond to form a carbocation. Remember that the carbocation might rearrange, and that would occur prior to the next step. Coordination of water to the carbocation, followed by deprotonation of the oxonium intermediate, leads to the formation of the Markovnikov alcohol product. When the proton leaves the oxonium intermediate, it can re-enter the reaction cycle (which is why a catalytic amount of acid is sufficient and a stoichiometric amount of acid is unnecessary).

If an alcohol (ROH) is used as the solvent instead of water, the net reaction will be the addition of H–OR across the C=C bond. The mechanism for this reaction is identical to the hydration but with RO in place of HO on the product.

<u>Example III.5.2</u>

Draw the major product of the reaction shown below:

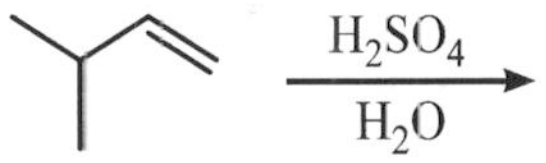

<u>Solution III.5.2</u>

This reaction begins with electrophilic addition to the alkene π-bond (step *i*), forming a 2° carbocation. The carbocation rearranges because it can form a more stable 3° carbocation (step *ii*). Water then coordinates to the carbocation (step *iii*) to form an oxonium intermediate. Deprotonation of the oxonium oxygen (step *iv*) leads to the final product alcohol:

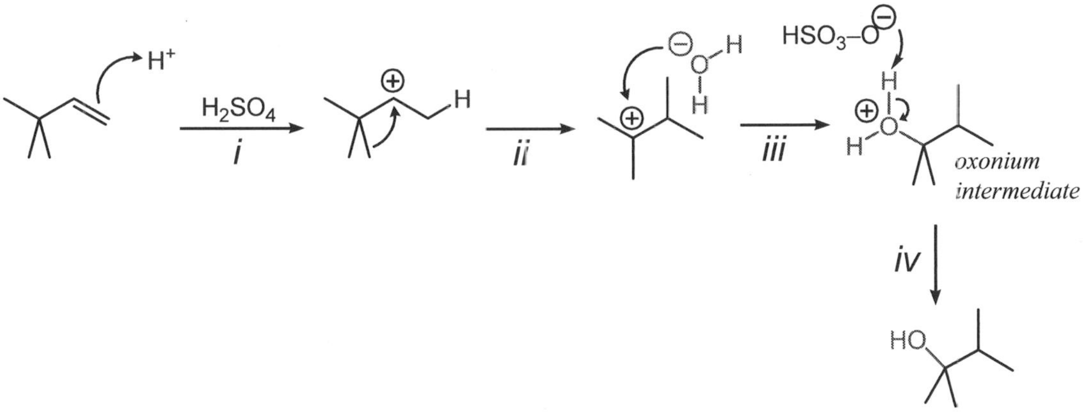

oxonium intermediate

<u>Additional help from "Organic Chemistry 1 Reactions and Practice Problems 2018" (Smith):</u>

- After finishing Lesson III.5, you may want to review Reactions D.1 (hydrohalogenation) and D.2 (hydration) in the companion book. Each is a quick review with key points and has a short self test with answers covering the reactions in this Primer Lesson.

Lesson III.6.1: The Halonium Intermediate

In the previous Lesson, we considered the reaction of an alkene with H^+ as the electrophile, which forms a carbocation intermediate. The carbocation carbon has only 6 e^-, so it cannot achieve an octet if there are no lone pair e^- or π-bonds adjacent to it. If an electrophile E^+ has one or more lone pairs, those e^- would make it possible for all atoms to have an octet and no carbocation would form.

The simplest electrophile that has lone pairs would be a cationic halogen X^+ (e.g., Cl^+ or Br^+). If X^+ reacted with a C=C bond via the same mechanism as H^+, the C–X bond would form at the less substituted carbon and the carbocation would form on the more substituted carbon. Unlike hydrogen, the halogen substituent has 3 lone pairs, one of which could coordinate to the adjacent carbocation to give it an octet, forming a halonium intermediate:

The proper mechanism for halonium formation does not involve the reaction of a C=C bond with free X^+, but rather with polar or polarizable X–Y (X and Y are halogens and may be identical or different). Upon encountering the halogen, π-electrons from the C=C bond attack $X^{\delta+}$ while *simultaneously*, a lone pair on X coordinates to the more substituted carbon in the C=C bond, with release of a halide anion. Note that the halonium can form on either face of the C=C unit and, if there is no energy difference between X–Y approaching the C=C bond from above or below, then a 50:50 mixture of both stereoisomers will be formed:

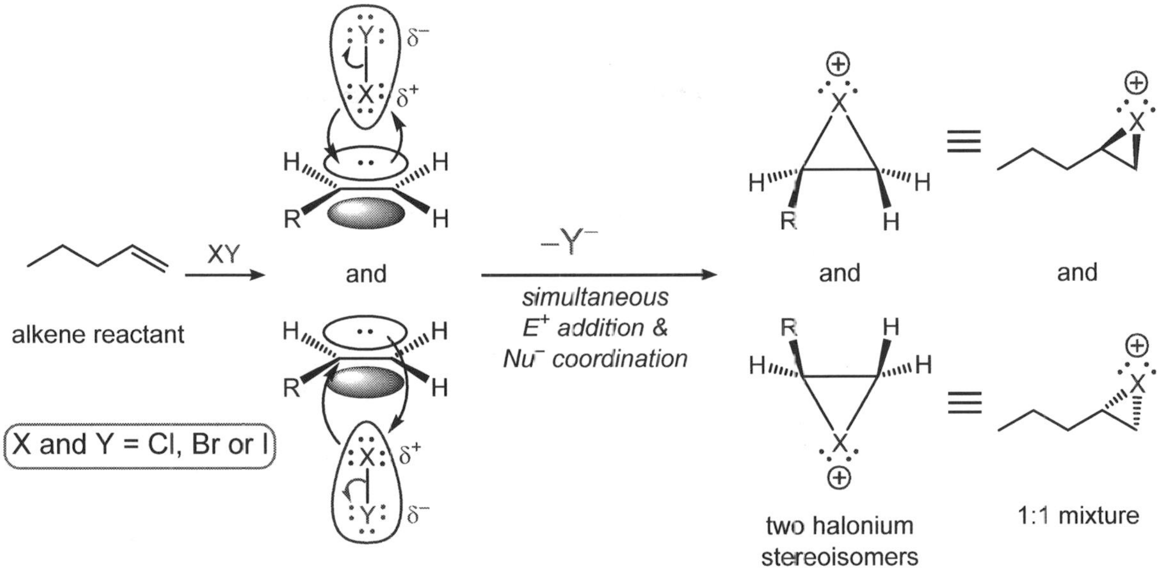

X and Y = Cl, Br or I

alkene reactant

two halonium stereoisomers

1:1 mixture

Example III.6.1

How many stereochemically unique halonium isomers will form in the reaction shown below?

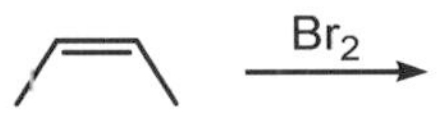

Solution III.6.1

The bromonium intermediate is formed when one of the Br atoms in Br_2 adds to one face of the alkene π-bond:

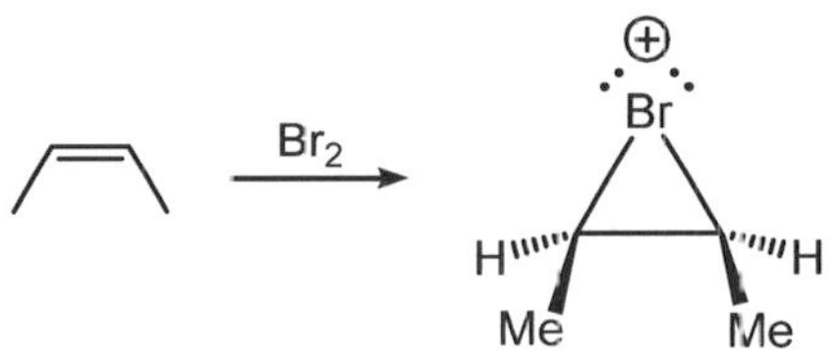

When we check to see if another stereoisomer can be formed, we see that the product is a *meso* compound (which is achiral), so it does not have an enantiomer. Thus, there is only one possible stereochemically unique isomer that will form in this reaction.

Once formed, the halonium intermediate undergoes ring-opening by reaction with a nucleophile. This step is similar to the ring opening of the epoxide that we saw in Lesson II.15. **For the halonium, the more substituted C is selectively attached by the nucleophile** because it has a greater δ+. The nucleophilic substitution occurs via an S$_N$2-like mechanism with inversion of configuration. When this transformation is complete, the net resultant is *anti*-addition of X and Y to the C=C bond:

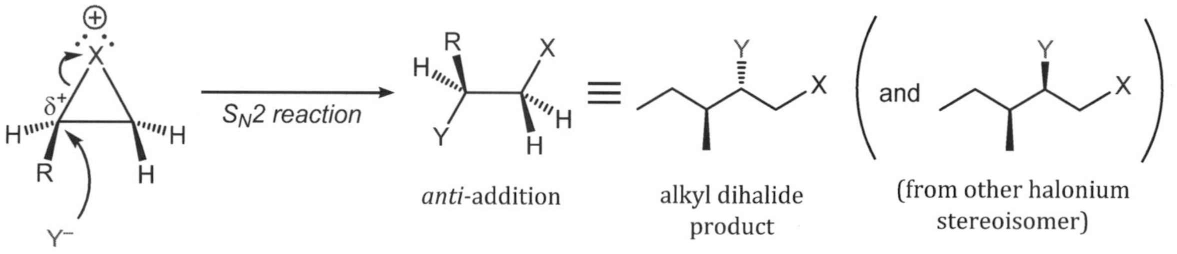

anti-addition	alkyl dihalide product	(from other halonium stereoisomer)

Example III.6.2

Draw the major product(s) of the reaction shown below:

Solution III.6.2

Because iodine is less electronegative than chlorine, I–Cl will be polarized such that iodine is δ+ and Cl is δ–, so the iodonium intermediate forms:

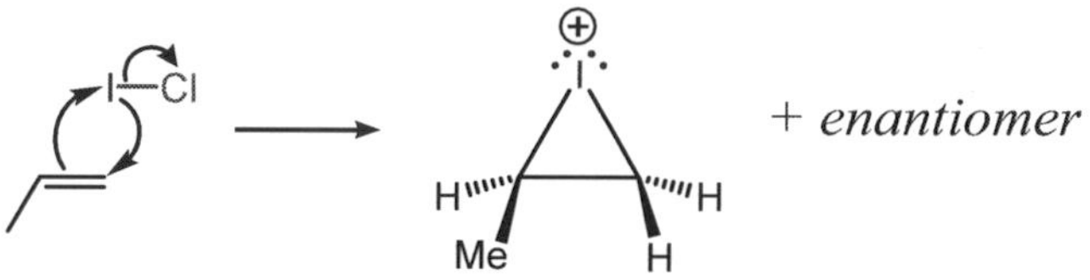

+ *enantiomer*

Note that the iodonium formed is chiral, so it will be produced as a racemic mixture from the achiral starting materials. The subsequent addition of chloride to the *more substituted* C of the iodonium ring leads to 2-chloro-1-iodopropane. For this final step, both enantiomers of the iodonium intermediate are shown to illustrate how both enantiomers of the racemic product are formed:

Lesson III.6.3: Halohydrin Formation – Nucleophilic Addition of H_2O to the Halonium Intermediate

So far, we have only considered halogenation reactions where no other nucleophiles are around. If a halogenation reaction is performed in H_2O as the solvent, there will be far more water than there is Y^- in solution. We also know that even a relatively poor nucleophile like water is reactive enough to undergo electrophilic addition to a cationic species such as a protonated epoxide – or a halonium ion. The much higher concentration of H_2O than Y^- means that all of the halonium intermediate will react with H_2O before Y^- even has a chance. Fortunately, the mechanism of this reaction is again identical to ring-opening of a protonated epoxide that we saw in Lesson II.15, and again, the oxygen and X end up *anti* with respect to each other, with OH on the more substituted site (Markovnikov addition). The product is a molecule with an alcohol adjacent to an alkyl halide, and the term for this is "halohydrin". Because no carbocation intermediate is generated, no rearrangement of the carbon skeleton will occur.

If a halogenation reaction is performed in an alcohol solvent (i.e., HO–R') instead of H_2O, then the nucleophile that will react with the halonium will be HO–R'. This S_N2 reaction will produce a protonated ether substituent, which also gets deprotonated by Y^-. The net product of this reaction will contain an ether adjacent to an alkyl halide which are *anti* with respect to each other.

151

Example III.6.3

Draw the major product of the reaction shown below:

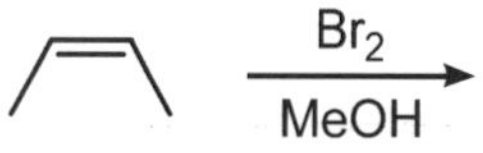

Solution III.6.3

Bromine will undergo simultaneous electrophilic and nucleophilic addition to the π-bond in *cis*-2-butene (step *i*) to afford a bromonium intermediate. This bromonium intermediate is a meso compound, so only one stereoisomer is possible from step *i*. Because the reaction is performed in a nucleophilic solvent, MeOH, it will do an S$_N$2 reaction at a bromonium carbon (step *ii*). Each carbon in the bromonium has identical δ+, so the S$_N$2 reaction will occur at each carbon with equal probability, to give a 1:1 mixture of stereoisomers. Finally, the protonated OMe group will be deprotonated (step *iii*) without inducing any changes in stereochemistry. This reaction exhibits Markovnikov regiochemistry and *anti* stereochemistry.

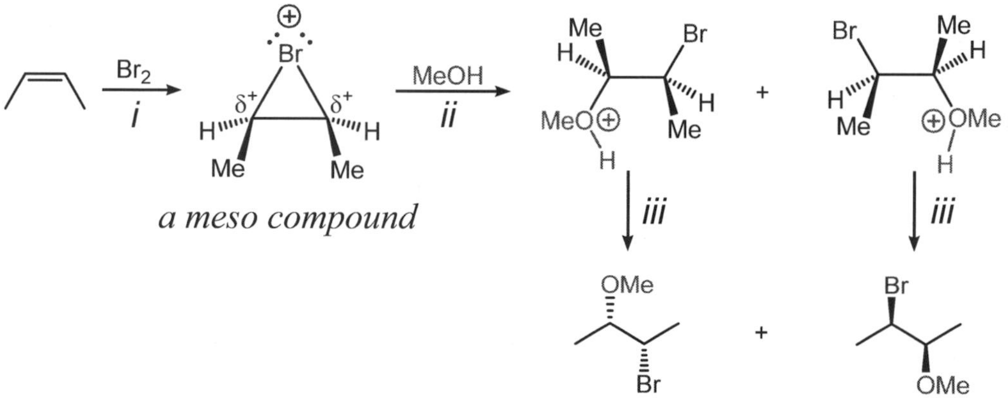

a meso compound

Additional help from "Organic Chemistry 1 Reactions and Practice Problems 2018" (Smith):

- After finishing Lesson III.6, you may want to review Reactions D.3 and D.4 in the companion book. Each is a quick review with key points and has a short self test with answers covering the reactions in this Primer Lesson.

Lesson III.7: Reactions of Alkenes III: Oxymercuration/Reduction

Lesson III.7.1: The Mercurinium Intermediate

A major limitation to alkene hydration with H_2SO_4 is that it proceeds through a carbocation intermediate which can rearrange. In some cases, we may want to convert an alkene to an alcohol and not have rearrangement occur.

The solution is to use mercuric acetate ($Hg(OAc)_2$) as the electrophile and water as the nucleophile. Oxygen is significantly more electronegative than mercury, so there is substantial positive charge on Hg. Mercury is a late transition metal and has multiple lone pairs, so the reaction of $Hg(OAc)_2$ with π-electrons in the C=C bond is analogous to the reaction of a π-bond with X–Y. The result is a 3-membered ring, which is termed a "mercurinium" intermediate. Because all of these bond-forming and bond-breaking reactions occur simultaneously, no carbocation intermediate is formed, thus no rearrangement will occur. Note that the mercurinium intermediate can form on either side of the C=C bond and a 50:50 mixture of both stereoisomers will be formed if there is no energy difference between $Hg(OAc)_2$ approaching the C=C bond from above or below.

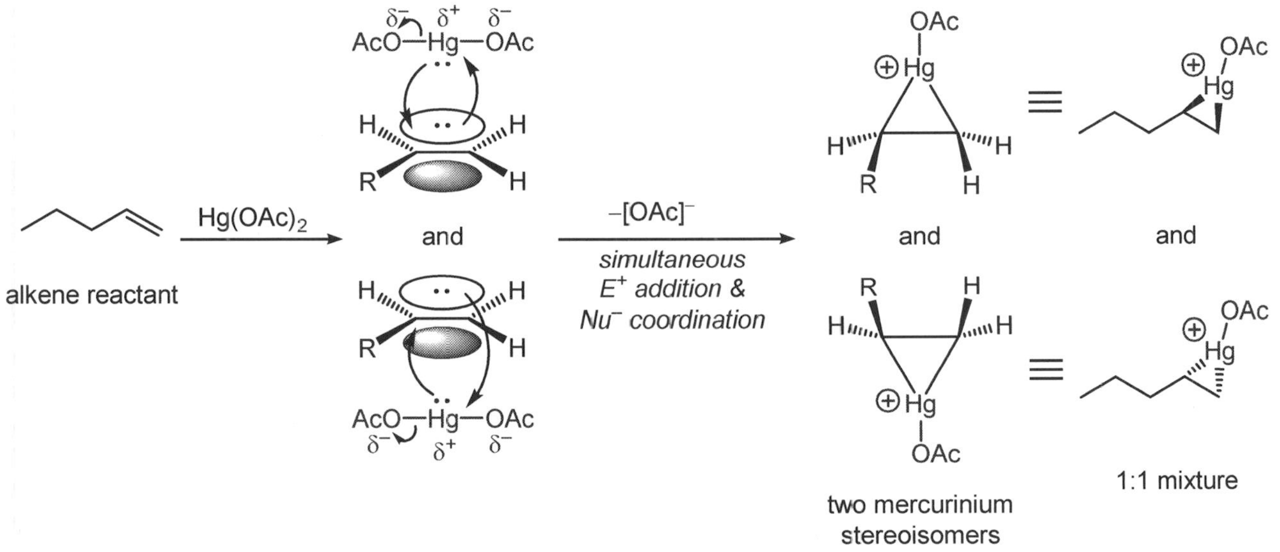

Example III.7.1

How many unique mercurinium stereoisomers will form in the reaction shown below?

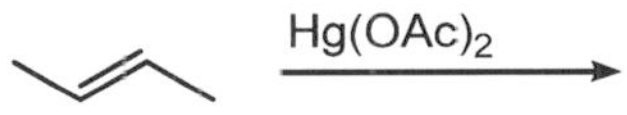

Solution III.7.1

The mercury center in Hg(OAc)$_2$ will do simultaneous electrophilic and nucleophilic addition to the π-bond in *trans*-2-butene, and release AcO$^-$ in the process, to afford a mercurinium intermediate. Unlike the halonium intermediates in Examples III.6.1–III.6.3, this mercurinium intermediate is not a meso compound. As a result, this mercurinium intermediate does have an enantiomer, and thus the addition of Hg to *trans*-2-butene, which can occur from above or below the alkene plane, will afford a 1:1 mixture of the two mercurinium enantiomers.

Lesson III.7.2: Nucleophilic Addition of H$_2$O to the Mercurinium Intermediate

As with the halonium intermediate and a protonated epoxide, the more substituted C of the mercurinium intermediate has more positive charge on it and this C is thus selectively attacked by the nucleophile. When this transformation is complete, the protonated OH group is deprotonated by AcO$^-$. This series of steps is called the "oxymercuration" reaction, the product of which has an OH group on the more substituted carbon and an Hg(OAc) group on the less substituted carbon, on opposite sides of what used to be the C=C bond. Thus, the oxymercuration reaction exhibits both regioselectivity (Markovnikov product) and stereoselectivity (*anti* product).

(from other mercurinium stereoisomer)

oxymercuration product

154

Example III.7.2

Draw the major product of the oxymercuration reaction of the alkene shown below:

Solution III.7.2

First, we notice that the reactant is the same as in Example III.5.2, so this will be a useful example to contrast oxymercuration with acid-catalyzed hydration. When 3-methyl-1-butene is reacted with $Hg(OAc)_2$, the Hg will add to either the top or bottom face of the π-bond, which affords a 1:1 mixture of mercurinium stereoisomers (step i). Unlike Example III.5.2, this does not form any carbocation, so no rearrangement can occur. One mercurinium carbon is 2° and the other is 1°, therefore the 2° carbon will have a greater $\delta+$. The other reactant in this reaction, H_2O, functions as a nucleophile via a lone pair on its oxygen and does an S_N2 reaction at the more substituted mercurinium carbon (step ii). Formation of the O–C bond at this carbon is accompanied by breakage of the Hg–C bond at the same position, whereupon the Hg(OAc) unit swings over to the other carbon. Recall that when H_2O functions as a nucleophile, the resulting molecule contains a protonated OH group that is rapidly deprotonated by another molecule of H_2O. Thus, the reaction of H_2O with a mercurinium intermediate affords a product with an OH group on the more substituted carbon, and an Hg(OAc) group on the less substituted carbon. In this Example, there are two mercurinium stereoisomers that form in equal abundance, so the products of the S_N2 reactions of each with H_2O will also be formed in equal abundance. Note that, because the Hg(OAc) group ends up on a carbon that is not chiral, there will only be two oxymercuration stereoisomers produced in this Example.

155

Lesson III.7.3: Reduction – Replacing Hg(OAc) with H

Our stated goal at the beginning of the lesson was to make an alcohol without the possibility for carbocation rearrangement that is observed in hydration. To accomplish this goal, we still have to devise a second reaction to replace the Hg(OAc) group with a hydrogen atom. A commonly-employed reagent to accomplish this transformation is $NaBH_4$. This reagent facilitates the exchange via a series of steps involving a radical intermediate:

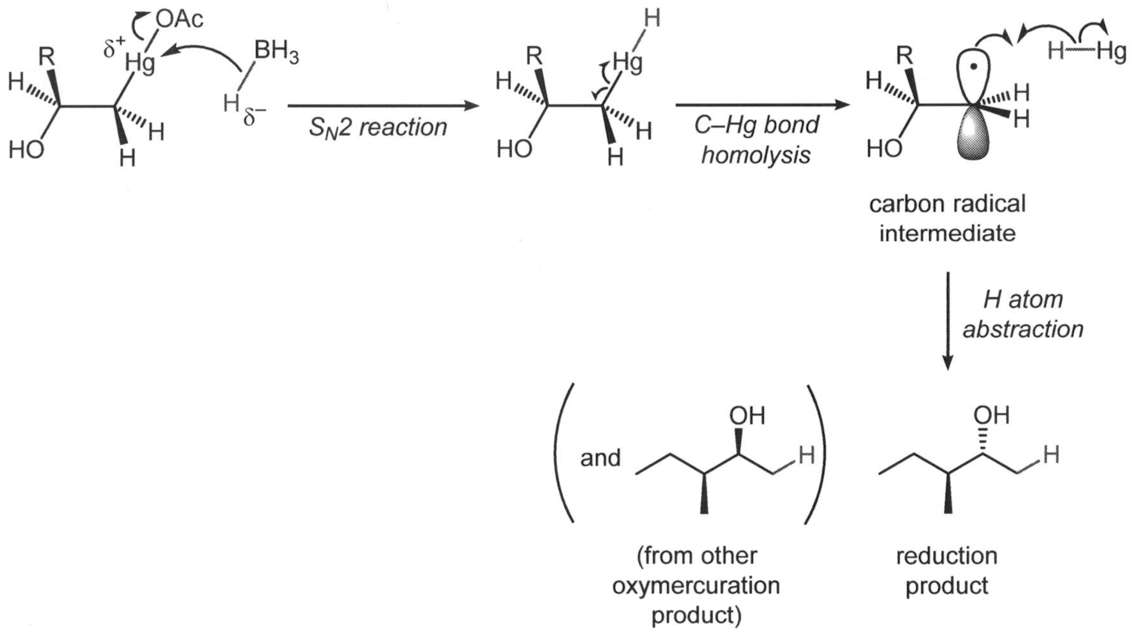

carbon radical
intermediate

*H atom
abstraction*

(and (from other oxymercuration product))

reduction product

Recall that a carbon radical is sp^2-hybridized and therefore planar, which means that H• abstraction can occur from either above or below this plane, so this reduction reaction is not stereoselective. Consequently, the *sequence of two reactions*, which is written as **"oxymercuration/reduction"**, converts an alkene to an alcohol with regioselectivity (forms Markovnikov product) but not stereoselectivity (forms a mixture of *anti* and *syn* products).

Example III.7.3

Provide the major product(s) of the reaction shown below.

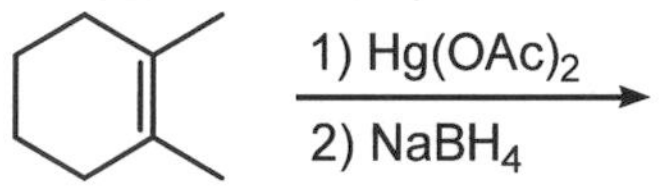

1) Hg(OAc)$_2$
2) NaBH$_4$

Solution III.7.3

When 1,2-dimethyl-1-cyclohexene is treated with Hg(OAc)$_2$, a mercurinium intermediate is initially formed (step *i*). Because the alkene is symmetric, this mercurinium intermediate is a meso compound, so there is only one possible stereoisomer. Subsequent S$_N$2 reaction of this intermediate with H$_2$O, followed by deprotonation of the protonated OH group (step *ii*), will afford the oxymercuration product. Each carbon in the mercurinium intermediate has identical δ+, thus an S$_N$2 reaction by H$_2$O will occur at each carbon with equal probability, resulting in a 1:1 mixture of oxymercuration stereoisomers. Note that, as a result of S$_N$2 occurring at the carbon on the opposite side from the Hg, the Hg(OAc) and OH groups will always end up *anti* with respect to each other. In the second reaction, the reactant NaBH$_4$ causes the Hg(OAc) group to come off as HgH and leave behind a carbon radical at that position. Remember that a carbon radical is *sp*^{2}-hybridized, so it is planar (and thus achiral) at that position. This radical then abstracts a hydrogen atom from HgH to afford the alcohol product. Remember that the H atom can be attached above or below the *sp*^{2}-hybrid plane, which will push the Me group at that position down or up, respectively. Each oxymercuration product makes one achiral carbon radical intermediate, which can afford a 1:1 mixture of stereoisomers. Because there are two possible oxymercuration products, the "oxymercuration/reduction" sequence of reactions will afford a 1:1:1:1 mixture of four alcohol stereoisomers.

Additional help from "Organic Chemistry 1 Reactions and Practice Problems 2018" (Smith):

- After finishing Lesson III.2, you may want to review Reaction D.5 in the companion book. This is a quick review with key points and has a short self test with answers covering the reactions in this Primer Lesson.

Lesson III.8.1: Cyclopropanation – Simultaneous Nucleophilic and Electrophilic Addition of "CH$_2$"

In Lessons III.6 and III.7, we learned that sometimes a single atom in a reagent molecule will react as both an electrophile and nucleophile toward a C=C bond, affording an intermediate that contains a 3-membered ring (i.e., halonium and mercurinium, respectively). By carefully selecting an appropriate reagent, we can convert an alkene to a 3-membered ring-containing molecule that is a stable, neutral product.

The simplest atom to consider that can react as both electrophile and nucleophile is an atom that has one empty orbital (electrophilic) and one lone pair (nucleophilic). Although this sounds like a very exotic species, one can easily be generated by treating CHCl$_3$ with KO'Bu. As a strong base but a poor nucleophile, 'BuO$^-$ can only deprotonate CHCl$_3$. As the H is being removed as H$^+$, one of the Cl atoms begins to leave the carbon as Cl$^-$, which produces ":CCl$_2$". This carbon has only 6 valence electrons but is neutral, a species known as a **carbene**. The carbene carbon in :CCl$_2$ is sp^2-hybridized, with an empty p-orbital and a lone pair in an sp^2-orbital. Normally, a carbon without an octet would be very unstable, but the lone pairs on the Cl atoms donate into the empty p-orbital and stabilize the carbene via hyperconjugation (Lesson I.11).

Once the dichlorocarbene (:CCl$_2$) has been generated, the π-electrons in a C=C bond will attack the empty p-orbital to form a bond between the less substituted alkene carbon and the carbene carbon. At the same time as this, the lone pair on the carbene carbon will attack the more substituted alkene carbon to form another C–C bond. The product is a cyclopropane ring, and this reaction is referred to as **cyclopropanation**. Because everything happens in a single, concerted step, the relative spatial orientation of the alkene substituents is retained. If the C=C bond in the reactant has *trans*-stereochemistry, then its substituents will end up *trans*- to each other on the cyclopropane ring. If the C=C bond has *cis*-stereochemistry, the substituents on cyclopropane ring will be *cis*. Remember that :CCl$_2$ can approach the C=C bond from either above or below, and if the two approaches are identical in energy, then a 1:1 mixture of stereoisomers will be formed.

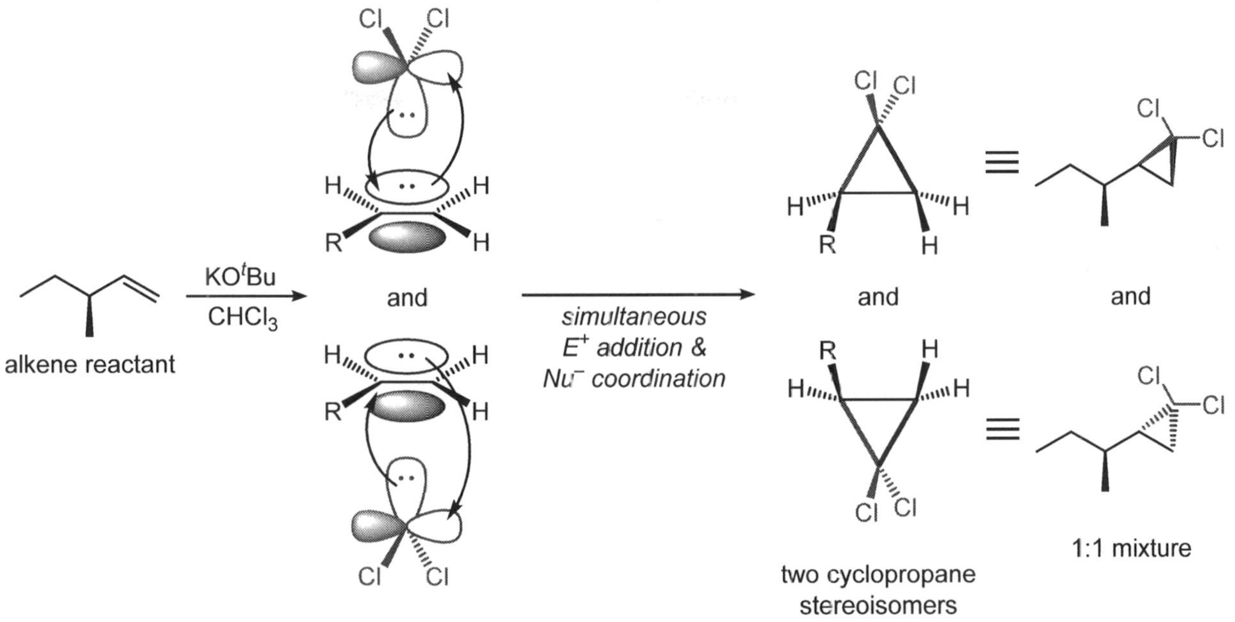

alkene reactant

KO^{t}Bu / CHCl$_3$

and

simultaneous E$^+$ addition & Nu$^-$ coordination

and

and

two cyclopropane stereoisomers

1:1 mixture

What do we do if we want a cyclopropane ring without the two Cl atoms? This would require a carbene with the structure ":CH$_2$", but this carbene is too unstable to form, so we must use a species of the form X–CH$_2$–Y that is not a carbene but does react like one. This type of species is called a "carbenoid".

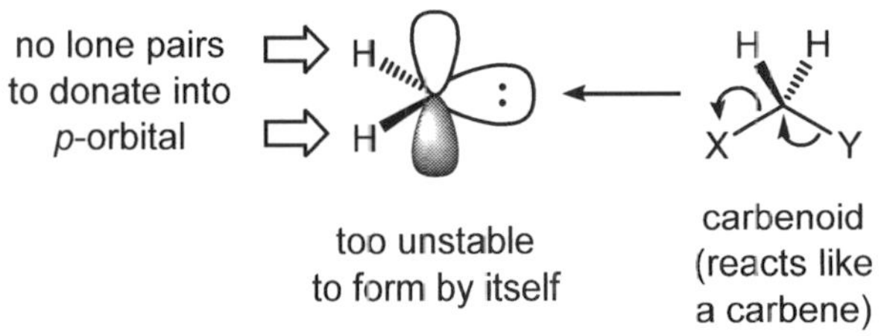

no lone pairs to donate into p-orbital

too unstable to form by itself

carbenoid (reacts like a carbene)

The reaction of CH$_2$I$_2$ with zinc in the presence of copper (written as "Zn(Cu)") can generate a carbenoid. When the I–CH$_2$–ZnI carbenoid is generated, it will react like ":CH$_2$" with the C=C bond. The reaction of this carbenoid to form a cyclopropane derivative is called the **Simmons-Smith** reaction. Again, everything happens in a single concerted step, so if we begin the reaction with a *trans*-alkene, those substituents in the cyclopropane ring will also be *trans* to each other. Keep in mind that the carbenoid can react either above or below the plane of the alkene, and if there is no difference in energy between the two approaches, a 1:1 mixture of stereoisomers will be produced.

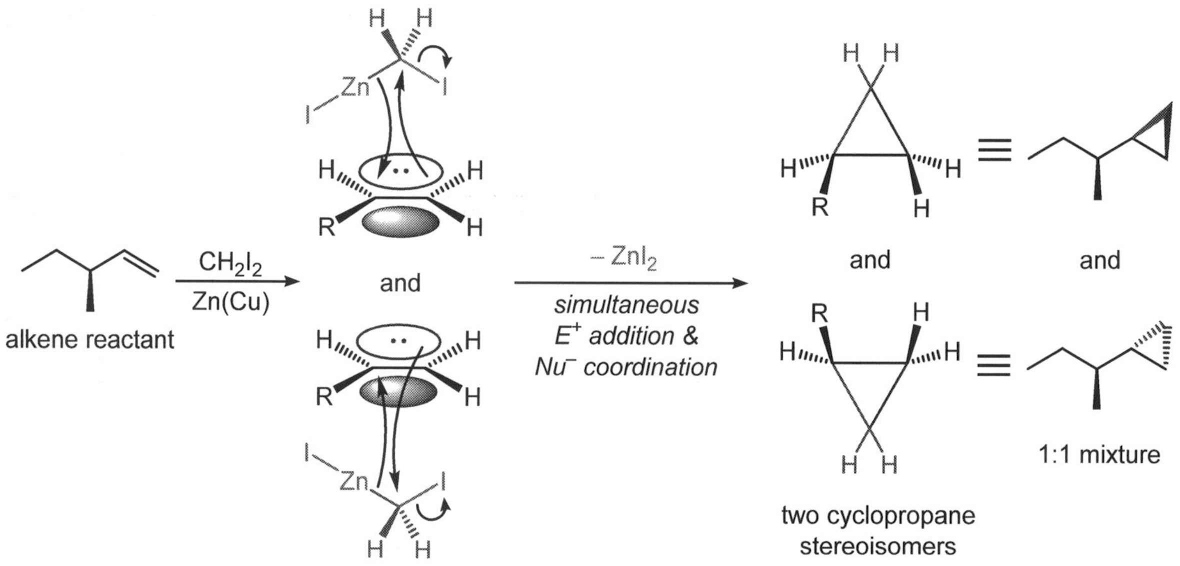

Example III.8.1

What is the major product of the reaction shown below?

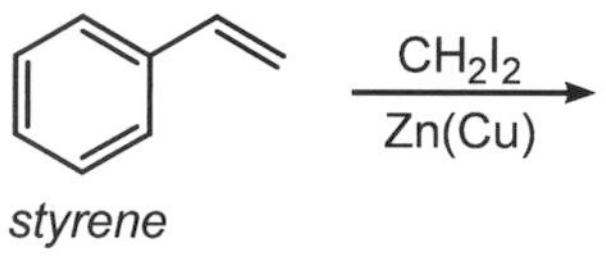

styrene

Solution III.8.1

The reactant CH_2I_2, in the presence of Zn(Cu), is converted to the carbenoid $I–CH_2–ZnI$, which acts as a source of ":CH₂" (but does not actually generate free ":CH₂"). In the presence of styrene, this reacts to add ":CH₂" to the π-bond, leading to achiral phenylcyclopropane. Phenyl is the name given to a $–C_6H_6$ (benzene) substituent.

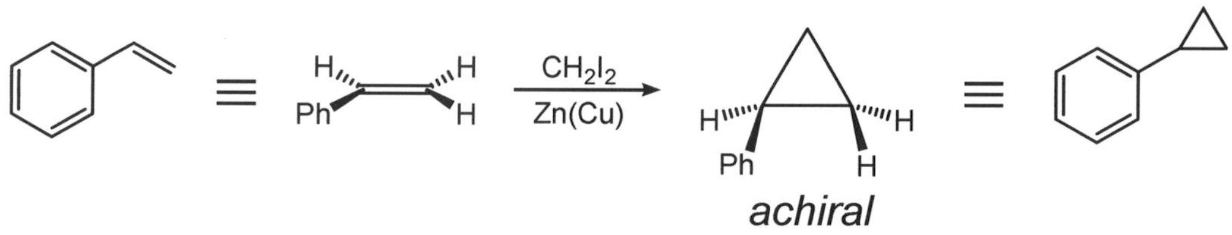

achiral

We learned in Lesson II.15 about the reactions that epoxides undergo, but we did not discuss how epoxides were formed. A simple synthetic route would be to treat an alkene with a free oxygen atom "O" (which has only 6 valence electrons), which would react similar to :CCl$_2$, but such a species is too unstable to be generated. Analogous to the carbenoid reaction in Lesson III.8.1, here we need an X–O–Y fragment that will react with the alkene as if it were a free oxygen atom. A widely-used reagent is *m*-chloroperoxybenzoic acid (mCPBA), which contains a peroxycarboxylic acid group R–C(=O)–O–O–H. The prefix "peroxy-" indicates that there is an O–O single bond present, which is very weak and can be easily broken.

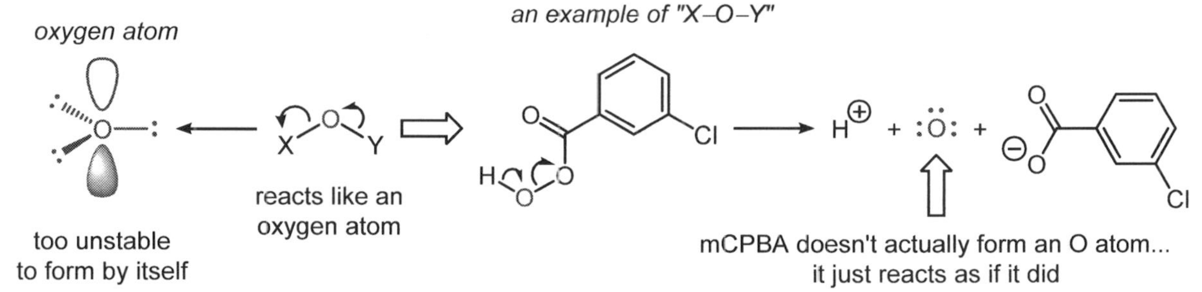

oxygen atom

an example of "X–O–Y"

too unstable to form by itself

reacts like an oxygen atom

mCPBA doesn't actually form an O atom... it just reacts as if it did

The mechanism by which a peroxyacid mediates the epoxidation is shown here:

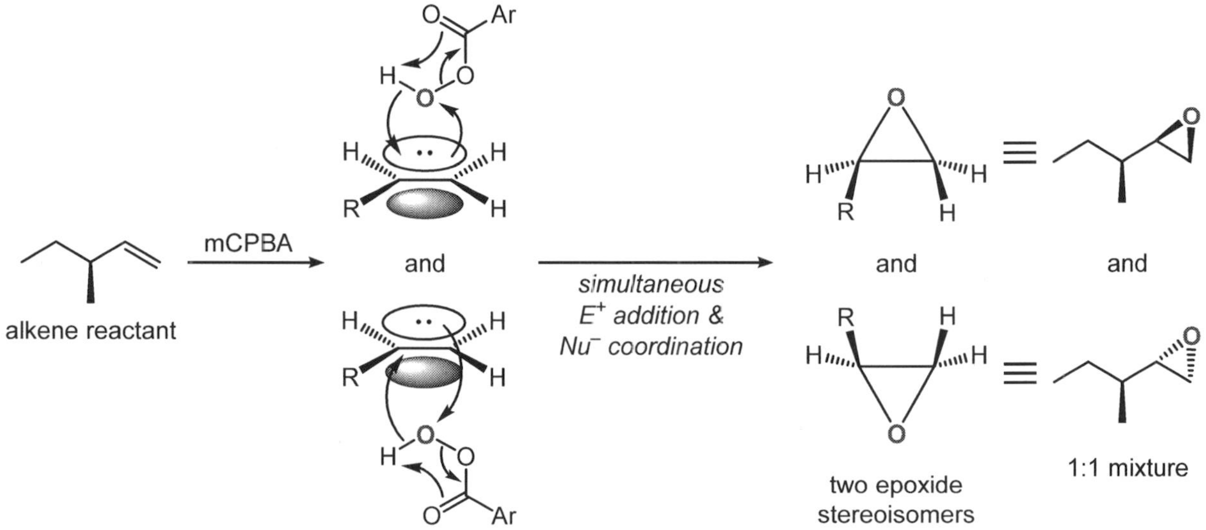

alkene reactant

mCPBA

and

simultaneous E$^+$ addition & Nu$^-$ coordination

and

and

two epoxide stereoisomers

1:1 mixture

Because all of these transformations occur in a single, concerted step, if we begin the reaction with a *trans*-alkene, those substituents in the epoxide ring will also be *trans* to each other. The reactant mCPBA can react either above or below the plane of the alkene, so a 1:1 mixture of stereoisomers will be produced if there is no difference in energy between these two approaches.

Example III.8.2

What is the major product of the reaction shown below?

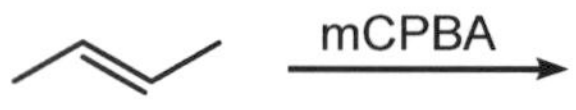

Solution III.8.2

The reactant mCPBA functions as a source of "O" atom, which will react with the π-bond in an alkene to make an epoxide. This addition can occur from either above or below the C=C plane, which in the case of *trans*-2-butene will afford a 1:1 mixture of enantiomers.

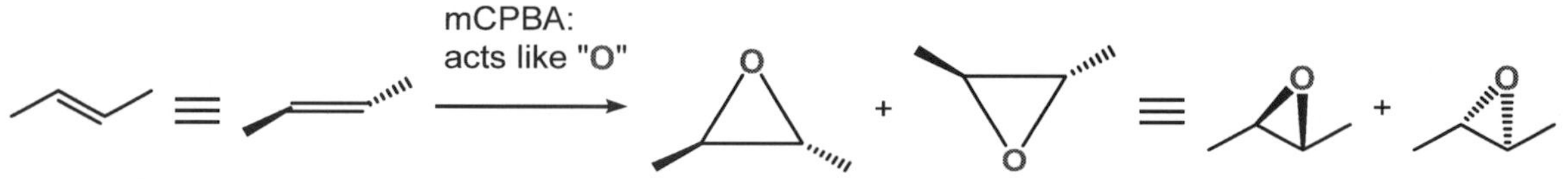

Additional help from "Organic Chemistry 1 Reactions and Practice Problems 2018" (Smith):

- After finishing Lesson III.8, you may want to review Reactions D.6 and D.7 in the companion book. Each is a quick review with key points and has a short self test with answers covering the reactions in this Primer Lesson.

Lesson III.9.1: Hydroboration – Concerted Addition of $B^{\delta+}-H^{\delta-}$ to a C=C Bond

The alkene reactions we have studied so far have given us Markovnikov products, but there are instances in which it might be synthetically useful to be able to access an anti-Markovnikov product. Say, for example, we wish to make an anti-Markovnikov alcohol. The reagent to use in such a scenario is BH_3 (which is occasionally written as B_2H_6) because its bonds are polarized as $B^{\delta+}-H^{\delta-}$ (H is more electronegative than B). As a result, the B–H bond will align over the C=C bond such that the $H^{\delta-}$ is above the $\delta+$ of the more substituted carbon and the $B^{\delta+}$ is above the less substituted carbon. The π-electrons of the C=C bond then attack the $B^{\delta+}$ (which has a strong pull for electrons because it only has 6 valence electrons) to make a C–B bond, while simultaneously, the $H^{\delta-}$ attacks the more substituted carbon with the electrons from the B–H bond to make a C–H bond. This **hydroboration** step is concerted – there are no intermediates of any kind, so no rearrangement can occur, which makes this reaction regioselective. In addition, the H and BH_2 groups end up on the same side of what used to be the C=C bond (the product is *syn*), so this reaction also exhibits stereoselectivity. Keep in mind, though, that the B–H bond can add either above or below the C=C bond, so unless there is a difference in energy between the two approaches, a mixture of stereoisomers will be formed.

Lesson III.9.2: Oxidation – Replacing BH_2 with OH

If our goal is to make an anti-Markovnikov alcohol, we need to replace the BH_2 group with an OH group, which can be achieved under oxidizing conditions: H_2O_2, NaOH, H_2O. This oxidation occurs via a series of steps that retain stereochemistry at the C:

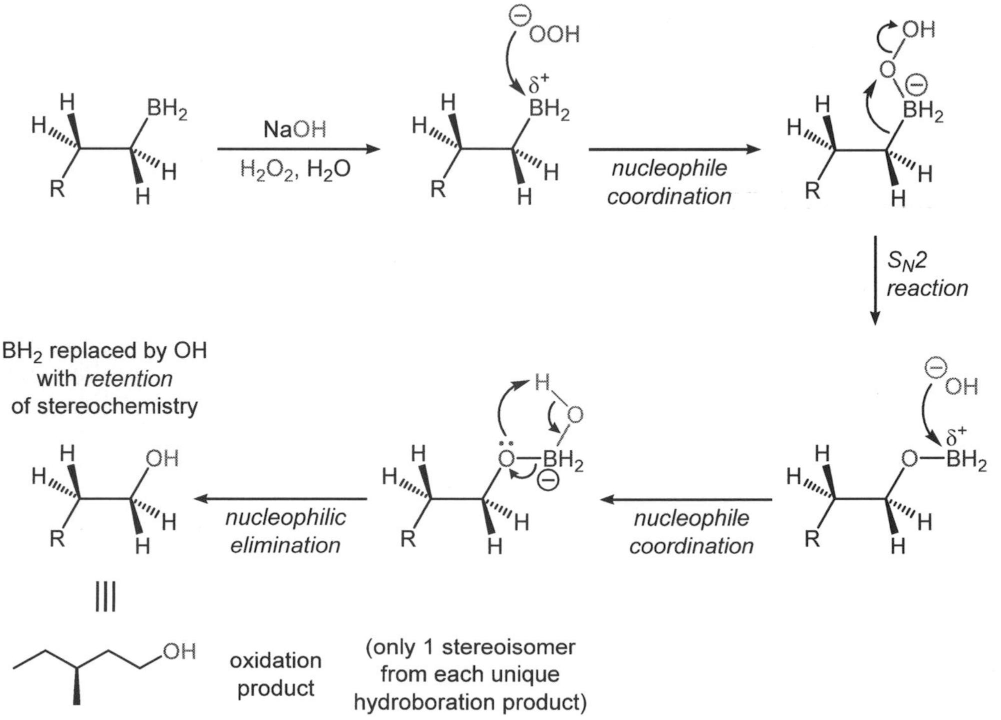

OOH
BH₂

NaOH
H₂O₂, H₂O

nucleophile
coordination

S_N2
reaction

BH₂ replaced by OH
with *retention*
of stereochemistry

*nucleophilic
elimination*

*nucleophile
coordination*

OH

oxidation
product

(only 1 stereoisomer
from each unique
hydroboration product)

This series of steps results in the net conversion of BH₂ to OH without rearrangement and with retention of stereochemistry (i.e., regioselective and stereoselective). The combination of these two reactions, written as **"hydroboration/oxidation", results in anti-Markovnikov addition of H–OH across a C=C bond with *syn*- stereochemistry.**

Example III.9.1

What is the major product of the reaction shown below?

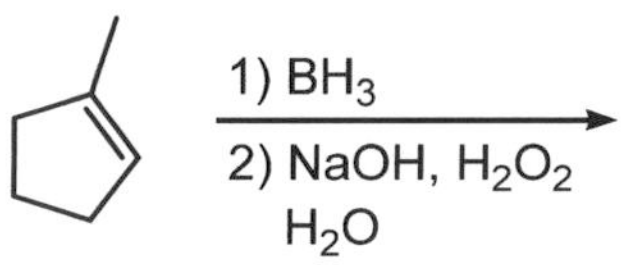

1) BH₃
2) NaOH, H₂O₂
   H₂O

Solution III.9.1

The reagent BH₃ will react with an alkene π-bond to add H to the more substituted alkene carbon and BH₂ to the less substituted carbon with *syn* stereochemistry. With 1-methyl-1-cyclopentene as the reactant, BH₃ can add from either above the C=C plane, pushing the Me substituent down, or below the C=C plane, pushing the Me substituent up (step *i*). As a result, the first reaction, hydroboration, forms a 1:1 mixture of enantiomers, in which the BH₂ and Me groups end up *anti* with respect to each other (because the H, which is usually not drawn, is *syn* with respect to the BH₂). The second reaction, oxidation with H₂O₂ under basic conditions, replaces the BH₂ group with an OH group with retention of stereochemistry at the carbon, so each hydroboration product

164

stereoisomer will produce only one alcohol product stereoisomer. Thus, the net hydroboration/oxidation of 1-methyl-1-cyclohexene will afford a 1:1 mixture of an enantiomeric pair of alcohols, in which the OH has been added to the less substituted alkene carbon.

Additional help from "Organic Chemistry 1 Reactions and Practice Problems 2018" (Smith):

- After finishing Lesson III.9, you may want to review Reaction D.8 in the companion book. This is a quick review with key points and has a short self test with answers covering the reactions in this Primer Lesson.

Lesson III.10.1: The Ozonide Intermediate

In the Lewis dot structure of ozone (O_3), the very polar O–O bonds (there is a formal +1 charge on the central O) allows the flow of electrons between ozone and an alkene to occur as follows to form an unusual 5-membered ring termed a "molozonide":

A molozonide rearranges (over complex steps) to give a more stable ozonide:

Lesson III.10.2: Ozonolysis – Replacing C=C with C=O Bonds

Ozonolysis is an alkene oxidation reaction that breaks one C=C bond and replaces it with two C=O bonds. In the first step of ozonolysis, an alkene reacts with O_3 to form an ozonide as described in the previous section. In the second step, the ozonide is subjected to either reducing conditions (common reductants are R_2S or Zn/H_2O) or oxidizing conditions (a common oxidant is H_2O_2). Under reducing conditions, any H atoms attached to the alkene carbons will be retained in the C=O bond-containing products (i.e., as aldehydes). Under oxidizing conditions, any H atoms attached to the alkene carbons will be replaced with OH groups in the C=O bond-containing products (i.e., as carboxylic acids). With a tetrasubstituted starting alkene, both reducing and oxidizing conditions afford the same products (i.e., only ketones will be formed).

166

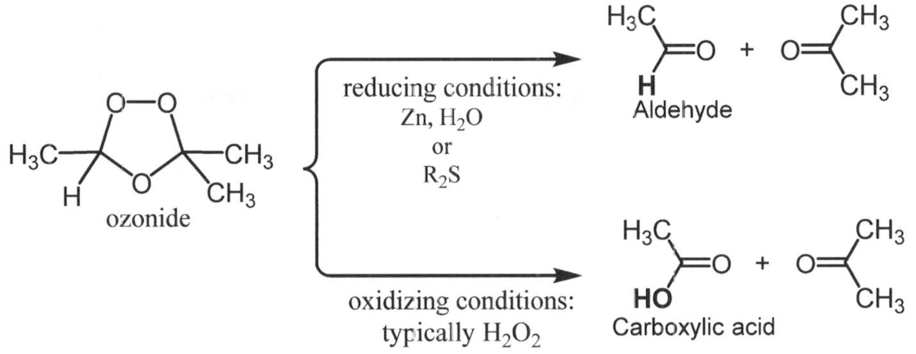

Example III.10.1

What is the major product of the reaction shown below?

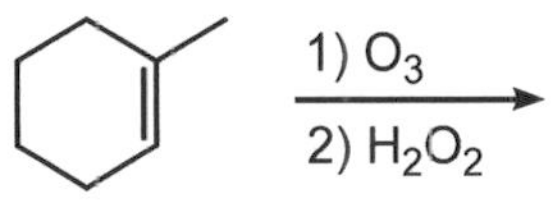

Solution III.10.1

The two reactions in this Example have the net effect of cleaving a C=C bond and replacing it with two C=O bonds. When 1-methyl-1-cyclohexene reacts with O_3, a molozonide intermediate is formed initially (step *i*), which then rearranges to a more stable ozonide intermediate (step *ii*). Note that O_3 can add either from either above or below the C=C plane, so for an asymmetric alkene like 1-methyl-1-cyclohexene, we would actually get a 1:1 mixture of enantiomers. We typically omit drawing all the possible molozonide/ozonide stereoisomers because the net reaction is replacing an achiral functional group (i.e., a C=C bond) with other achiral functional groups (i.e., C=O bonds). In the second reaction, the ozonide intermediate is being oxidized with H_2O_2 (step *iii*). An easy way to determine the product of this 2nd reaction is to look at the substituents on the alkene carbons in the original reactant. Any alkene carbon with two alkyl substituents will be converted to a ketone, regardless of whether oxidizing or reducing conditions are used. Hydrogen substituents, however, will only be retained under reducing conditions, and will be replaced with OH groups under oxidizing conditions. Thus, the oxidation of the ozonide intermediate in this Example will afford a ketone and a carboxylic acid functional group. If we had instead used reducing conditions, the product would have had a ketone and an aldehyde functional group.

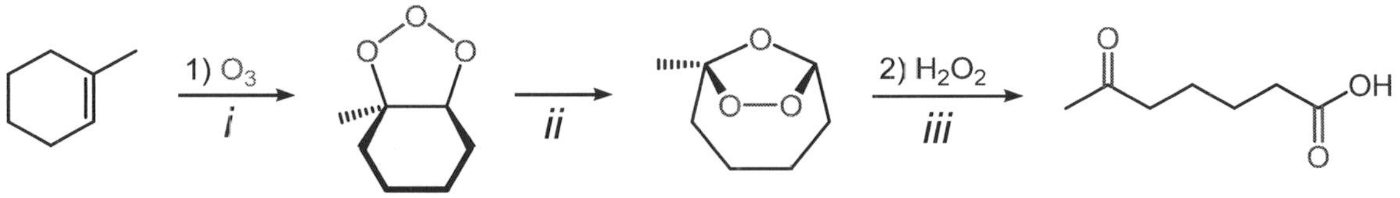

Lesson III.10.3: Preparation of Vicinal Diols – Adding "OH" to Each Carbon in a C=C Bond

We have seen that ozonolysis is a way to cleave the C=C bond and add two doubly-bound O atoms. Other reactions have been developed to add two singly-bound O atoms across the π bond of an alkene. Reaction of an alkene with OsO_4 (osmium tetroxide) is one example. The osmium in OsO_4 is electron deficient due to the presence of four oxygen atoms around it, so it will want to react in such a way to decrease this electron deficiency. This facilitates the flow of electrons between an alkene and OsO_4 in a way that pushes an electron pair onto the osmium atom:

alkene reactant

and

simultaneous E^+ addition & Nu^- coordination

and

two osmate ester stereoisomers

and

$NaHSO_3/H_2O$ or Na_2SO_3/H_2O

and

and

Os–O replaced by O–H bonds with *retention* of stereochemistry

vicinal diol product (1:1 mixture of stereoisomers)

The formation of the osmate ester is concerted. Note that both oxygen atoms have added to the same face of the alkene (i.e., *syn* addition). Remember that OsO_4 can add from either above or below the C=C plane, and because OsO_4 is achiral, if the alkene lacks chiral centers, a 1:1 mixture of stereoisomers will be produced. After the cyclic osmate ester has formed, $NaHSO_3/H_2O$ or Na_2SO_3/H_2O is then added, which causes the O–Os bonds to be replaced with O–H bonds (the mechanism for this second step is a topic for an inorganic chemistry course and is not covered here). The net reaction is the conversion of a C=C group into a vicinal diol group (i.e., two C–OH groups adjacent to each other).

Example III.10.2

What is the major product of the reaction shown below?

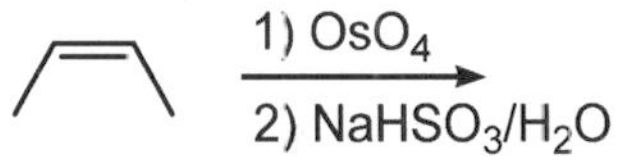

Solution III.10.2

The reagent OsO_4 adds to one side of the π-bond in *cis*-2-butene to afford an osmate ester (step *i*). Because the alkene reactant is symmetric, the osmate ester is a meso compound, and thus there is only one stereoisomer product possible from this reaction. In the second reaction, $NaHSO_3/H_2O$ causes the O–Os bonds to be replaced with O–H bonds with retention of stereochemistry at the carbon. The net result of these two reactions is the *syn* addition of two OH groups to the same side of a C=C bond. As we noted in Example III.6.2, *syn* specifically refers to the stereochemistry of the addition across the π-bond, and not the stereochemistry of the OH groups in the product. When we allow the σ-bonds to rotate in the vicinal diol product to afford the lowest energy conformation, we can see that one OH substituent has a bold wedge and the other has a hashed wedge. With *cis*-2-butene as our reactant, there is only one vicinal diol product stereoisomer formed. If *trans*-2-butene had been our reactant instead, then two osmate ester stereoisomers would have formed, and subsequent oxidation would have afforded a 1:1 mixture of enantiomeric vicinal diols.

note that even though addition is syn-, one can draw the product like this by rotating around the C–C bond!

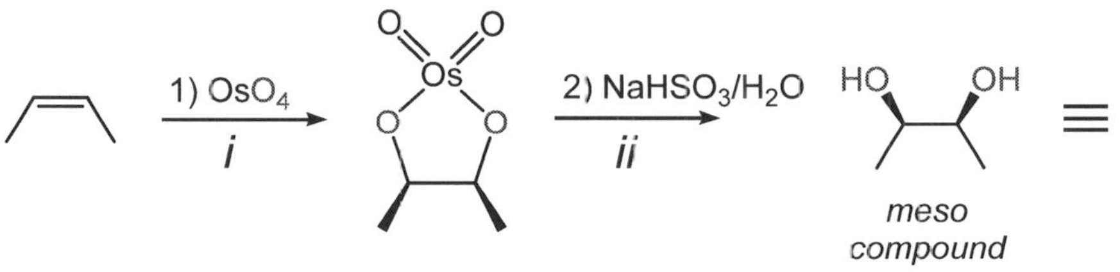

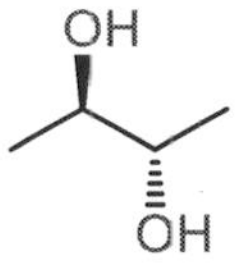

Additional help from "Organic Chemistry 1 Reactions and Practice Problems 2018" (Smith):

- After finishing Lesson III.10, you may want to review Reactions D.9 and D.10 in the companion book. This is a quick review with key points and has a short self test with answers covering the reactions in this Primer Lesson.
- You will also be ready for Problem Set 8 in the companion book. This problem set covers material from Primer Lessons III.2-10.

Lesson III.11.1: The "-yne" Suffix

When naming alkynes, we make use of the core nomenclature rules found in Lesson I.14. For an alkyne, we replace the "-ane" suffix with "-yne". So, if we have a 5-carbon chain with one C≡C bond, it is a "pentyne"; a 9-carbon chain with one C≡C bond is a "nonyne". If two or three C≡C bonds are present, we use "-diyne" or "-triyne", and we add an "a" to the end of the root. A 5-carbon chain with two C≡C bonds is a "pentadiyne", and a 9-carbon chain with three C≡C bonds is a "nonatriyne".

Lesson III.11.2: Alkyne Priority in Hydrocarbons

To determine the name for an alkyne, we first pick as parent the longest chain that contains the C≡C bond. If multiple C≡C bonds are present, we select as parent the chain that contains the greatest number of C≡C bonds. We then number the parent chain to give the C≡C bonds the lowest possible substituent numbers. If both C=C and C≡C bonds are present, we number the parent chain to give the multiple bond substituents the lowest possible numbers, regardless of whether they are C=C or C≡C bonds. If, and only if, a C=C bond and a C≡C bond would have the exact same number, do we employ the alphabetization rule, and assign priority to the C=C bond over the C≡C bond ("ene" comes before "yne" alphabetically). When both a C=C bond and a C≡C bond are present in a molecule's structure, the suffix for the C=C bond becomes "en" and it is listed before the C≡C suffix "yne". So, a 5-carbon chain with one C=C bond and one C≡C bond would be a "pentenyne". For complex molecule names such as these, it is most convenient to list the substituent numbers immediately before the suffixes.

Example III.11.2

Provide an unambiguous systematic name for the molecule shown below:

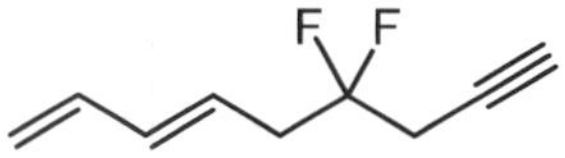

Solution III.11.2

In this molecule, we can see that the parent chain contains 9 carbons, 2 C=C bonds, and 1 C≡C bond, so the base name will be "nonadienyne". We have to number from left to right to give the multiple bonds the lowest possible substituent numbers, which are 1, 3, and 8. Numbering from right to left would have given 1, 6, and 8. There are 2 fluorine substituents at carbon 6, and the C=C bond beginning at carbon 3 is stereogenic (the two non-hydrogen substituents are *trans*). The systematic name for this molecule is "*trans*-6,6-difluoronona-1,3-dien-8-yne".

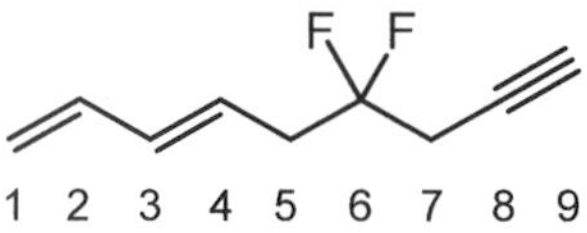

1 2 3 4 5 6 7 8 9

Lesson III.11.3: Alkyne Priority in Heteroatom-Containing Compounds

If an alkyne also contains an OH group, then that OH group takes priority over the C≡C bond. Thus, we must select as parent the chain that contains an OH group, even if that results in fewer C≡C bonds being included. Similarly, we must number the parent chain to give the OH group the lowest possible substituent number, regardless of what substituent numbers that assigns to the C≡C bonds. To assign a name to the molecule, the "yne" suffix becomes "yn" and is listed before the "ol" suffix which ends the name. A 5-carbon chain with one C≡C bond and one OH group would thus be a "pentynol". Again, for a complex molecule such as this, we would list the substituent numbers immediately before the suffixes.

Example III.11.3

Provide an unambiguous systematic name for the molecule shown below:

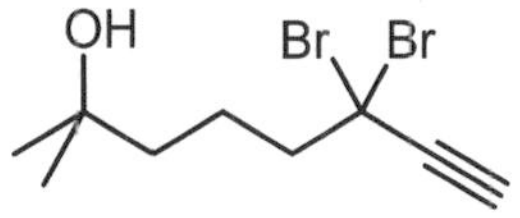

Solution III.11.3

The parent chain for this molecule contains 8 carbons, 1 C≡C bond, and 1 OH group, so the base name will be "octenol". We number this chain from left to right to place the OH group at carbon 2 (going right to left would place it at 7) and the C≡C begins at carbon 7. There is 1 Me group at carbon 2, 2 Br substituents at carbon 6, and no stereocenters or stereogenic bonds. The systematic name for this molecule is "6,6-dibromo-2-methyloct-7-yn-2-ol".

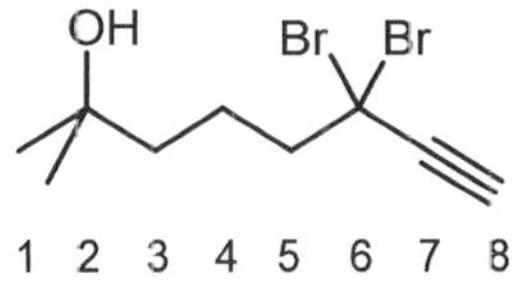

1 2 3 4 5 6 7 8

Lesson III.11.4: The C≡C Bond is Not Stereogenic

As we discussed in Lesson III.1, a C=C bond may need a label of configuration (i.e., *cis* vs. *trans* or *E* vs. *Z*). In contrast, each carbon in a C≡C bond can have only one substituent, so no stereoisomerism is possible and thus a stereochemical prefix is unnecessary.

Lesson III.12.1: The Nucleophilic C≡C Bond and the Vinyl Cation Intermediate

In Lesson III.3, we demonstrated that the π-bond in an alkene can function as a nucleophile. An alkyne has two π-bonds, thus the C≡C bond in an alkyne can also function as a nucleophile. However, the mechanisms of alkyne reactions exhibit important differences from those of alkenes. With an alkene, two π-electrons in R–CH=CH₂ will coordinate to an electrophile (E^+) and form a C–E σ-bond on the less substituted carbon and carbocation on the more substituted carbon. The carbocation is sp^2-hybridized with the +1 charge in an empty p-orbital. This empty p-orbital can be stabilized by electrons in adjacent C–H or C–C σ-bonds. If an alkyne reacted via this mechanism, the carbocation would be sp-hybridized. Because the carbon adjacent to the carbocation is sp^2-hybridized, its C–H and C–C bonds will be pointed further away from the empty p-orbital than those on an sp^3-hybridized carbon (i.e., 120° vs. 109.5°), so the positive charge is stabilized less via hyperconjugation. Moreover, an sp-hybridized carbon is more electronegative than an sp^2-hybridized carbon, so the addition of a positive charge to an sp-hybridized carbon will be significantly less favorable. For these reasons, carbocation intermediates do not form during alkyne addition reactions.

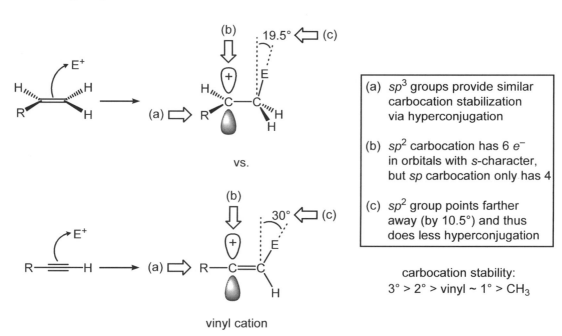

(a) sp^3 groups provide similar carbocation stabilization via hyperconjugation

(b) sp^2 carbocation has 6 e^- in orbitals with s-character, but sp carbocation only has 4

(c) sp^2 group points farther away (by 10.5°) and thus does less hyperconjugation

carbocation stability:
3° > 2° > vinyl ~ 1° > CH₃

vinyl cation

What happens instead is the formation of what is called a "π-complex". The π-electrons in a π-bond in R–C≡C–H are Coulombically attracted to the δ+ on E in the molecule E–Nu (or the induced δ+ in the case of Br₂, etc.). This interaction results in E–Nu being bound (albeit weakly) to the π-bond in the alkyne (hence the term "π-complex"). Because no carbocation forms, no rearrangement of the σ-bond framework will occur. Interaction of the π-bond with E–Nu draws electrons out of the π-bond, which induces a δ+ on the alkyne carbons, with the bigger δ+ residing on the more substituted carbon (in this

172

way, a π-complex is similar to the halonium and mercurinium intermediates). On the opposite side of the alkyne from the π-complexed E–Nu, another molecule of E–Nu aligns such that the $\delta-$ on Nu is oriented towards the alkyne carbon with the bigger $\delta+$. Then, the E–Nu bond heterolyzes to release E^+ and form a C–Nu bond at the more substituted alkyne carbon. At the same time, electrons in the C=C π-bond undergo nucleophilic attack by $E^{\delta+}$, and the E–Nu bond also heterolyzes to release Nu$^-$ and form a C–E bond at the less substituted alkyne carbon. In this way, E^+ and Nu$^-$ add *anti* to the less and more substituted alkyne carbon, respectively, making this reaction regioselective and stereoselective.

Lesson III.12.2: Hydrohalogenation – Electrophilic Addition by H^+, then Coordination by X^-

When an alkyne is reacted with H–X, a π-complex is formed with the $H^{\delta+}$ bound to an alkyne π-bond. On the other side of the C≡C bond, another molecule of HX aligns with $X^{\delta-}$ oriented towards the more substituted alkyne carbon, whereupon the two electrons from the H–X bond do nucleophilic attack at the more substituted carbon and, simultaneously, the two electrons from the alkyne π-bond attack $H^{\delta+}$ to form a C–H bond at the less substituted alkyne carbon. Thus, H–X undergoes *anti* addition to afford the Markovnikov product, a vinyl halide. If this vinyl halide product then is reacted with a second equivalent of H–X, then carbocation will form at the carbon with the X substituent, because the halogen lone pairs stabilize the empty *p*-orbital more effectively than electrons in a C–H σ-bond. As a result, the reaction of an alkyne with two equivalents of H–X will result in both X substituents being attached to the same carbon.

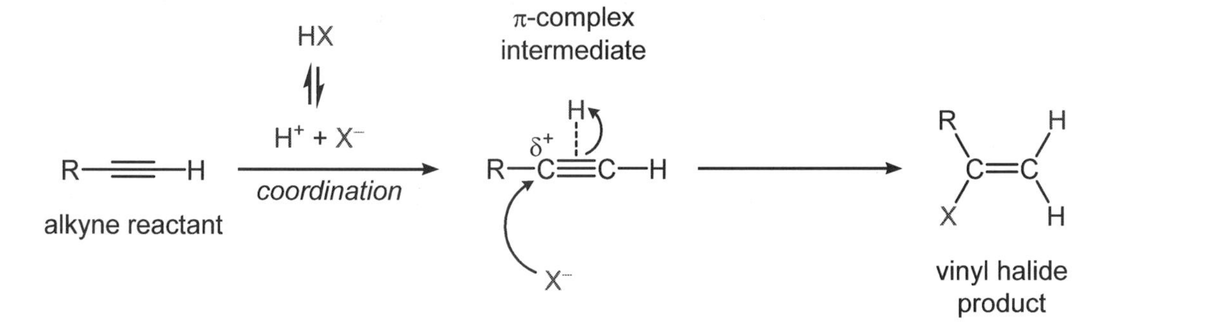

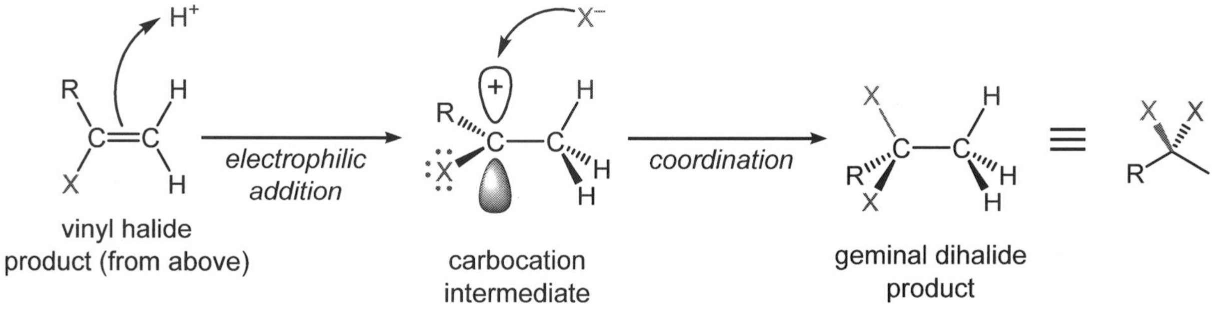

The top reaction scheme shows:

R≡H (alkyne reactant) → (with HX, H⁺ + X⁻, *coordination*) → π-complex intermediate → vinyl halide product

R—C≡C—H (δ⁺) with H and X⁻ arrows →

vinyl halide product (R, H, X, H arrangement)

Second reaction scheme:

vinyl halide product (from above) → (*electrophilic addition*, losing H⁺) → carbocation intermediate (with X⁻) → (*coordination*) → geminal dihalide product

---

Example III.12.1

Draw the major product of the two-step reaction sequence shown below:

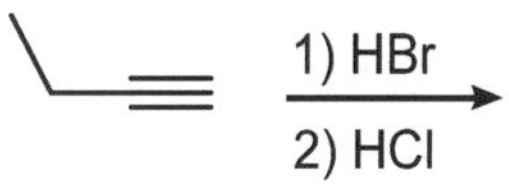

1) HBr
2) HCl

Solution III.12.1

We know that the first reaction, with HBr, will lead to Markovnikov addition of H and Br *anti-* to one another:

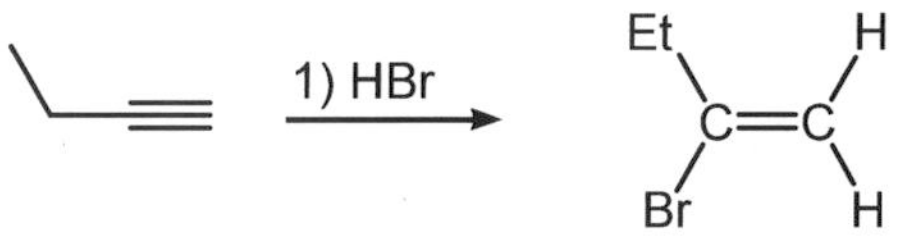

1) HBr →

(product with Et, H, Br, H on a C=C double bond)

The second step, reaction with HCl, will result in Markovnikov addition of H and Cl. This generates a chiral center, so a racemate results:

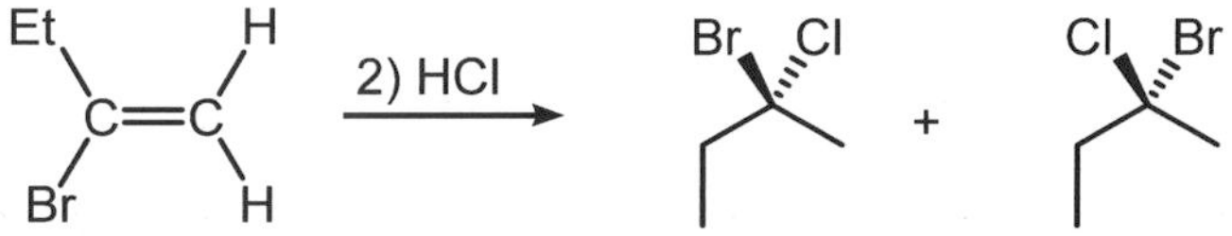

2) HCl →

(Br, Cl product) + (Cl, Br product)

174

Lesson III.12.3: Halogenation - Electrophilic Addition by X^+, then Coordination by X^-

Although molecules with the formula X_2 have no net dipole, in Lesson III.6.1 we discussed how the electrons in a π-bond can induce a dipole such that the bond is polarized as $X^{\delta+}$ and $X^{\delta-}$. When polarized like this, the molecule X_2 will form a π-complex with the alkyne π-bond. On the other side of the C≡C bond, another molecule of X_2 aligns with the $X^{\delta-}$ oriented towards the alkyne carbon with the greater δ+. The reaction then proceeds via exactly the same mechanism as the hydrohalogenation reaction we discussed in Lesson III.12.2. As with hydrohalogenation, the two X substituents added to the C≡C bond will end up *trans* with respect to each other in the alkene product.

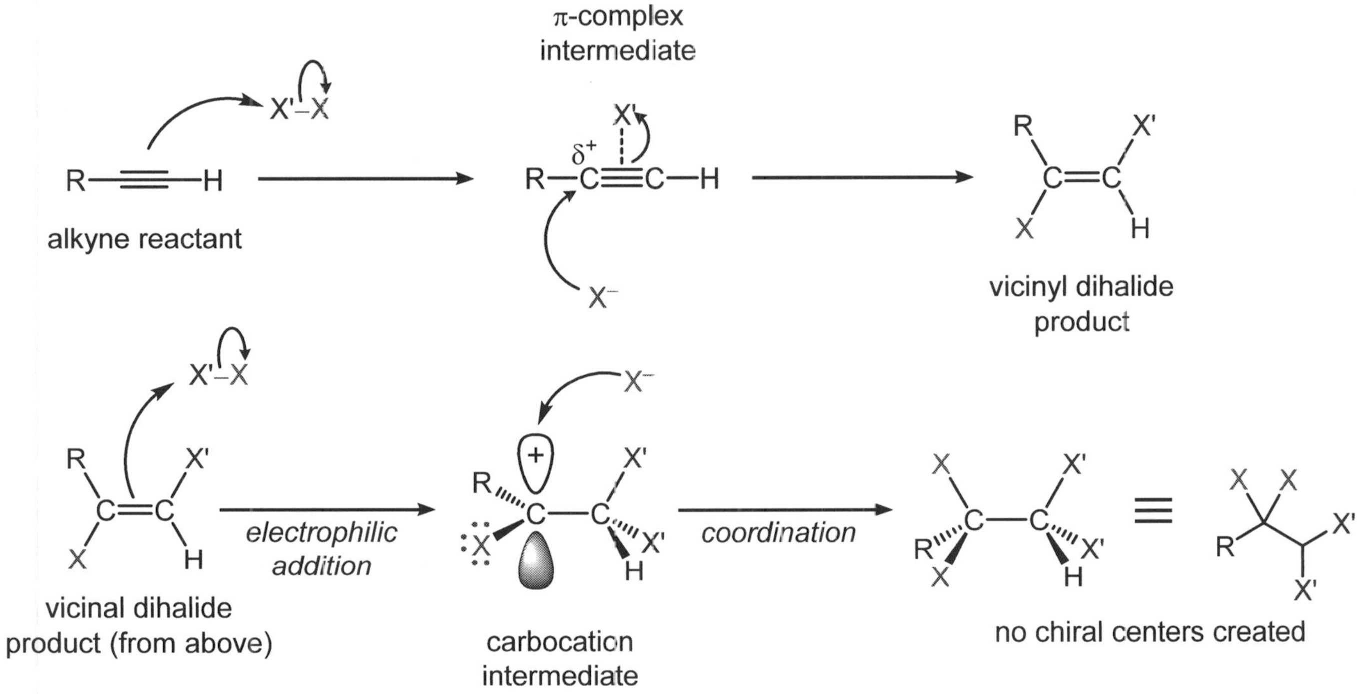

Example III.12.3

Draw the major product of the reaction shown below:

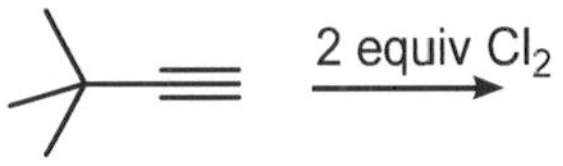

Solution III.12.3

We know that the first equivalent of Cl_2 will undergo *anti*-addition to one of the π-bonds of the alkyne, following the mechanistic progression shown in steps *i-iii*:

Next, the resulting alkene undergoes halogenation by the route we learned in Lesson III.6, first by forming the chloronium intermediate (step *iv*), then undergoing S_N2-like ring opening (step *v*):

Additional help from "Organic Chemistry 1 Reactions and Practice Problems 2018" (Smith):

- After finishing Lesson III.12, you may want to review Reactions E.1-2 in the companion book. Each is a quick review with key points and has a short self test with answers covering the reactions in this Primer Lesson.

Lesson III.13: Alkyne Reactions II: Three Ways to Reduce Alkynes

Lesson III.13.1: Alkyne to Alkane – Exhaustive Hydrogenation

In Lesson III.2, we discussed hydrogenation of an alkene to an alkane. If we perform hydrogenation on an alkyne, the first equivalent of H_2 would convert the C≡C bond to a C=C bond. Once formed, the alkene is even more reactive than the alkyne, so the alkene will be rapidly hydrogenated to the alkane. It is not feasible to stop the hydrogenation of the alkyne using H_2 with Ni, Pd, or Pt metal after only one hydrogenation reaction to isolate the alkene. This is termed "exhaustive hydrogenation". Alkyne hydrogenation operates via the same mechanism as alkene hydrogenation, so each equivalent of H_2 is added *syn* across the C≡C bond.

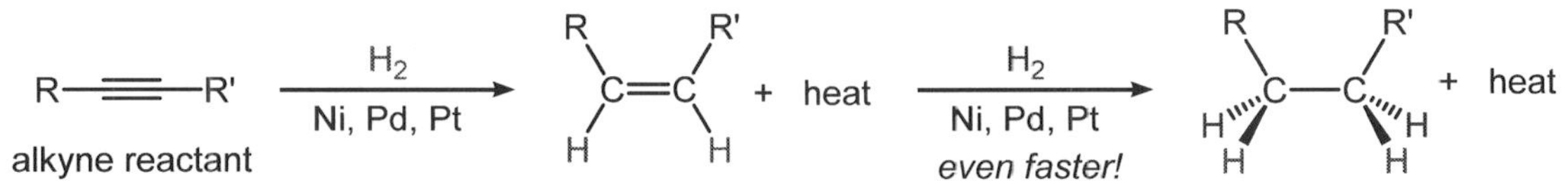

Example III.13.1

Draw the major product of the reaction shown below:

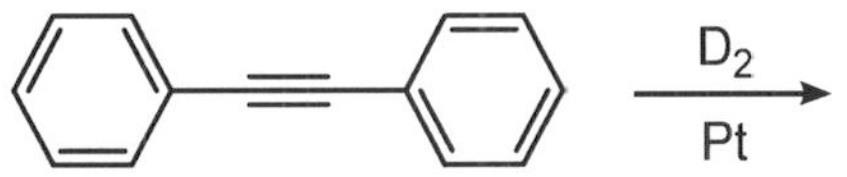

Solution III.13.1

Remember that D_2 will exhibit the same chemical reactivity as H_2 because D is just a heavier isotope of H. initially, two D atoms add *syn-* to the first π-bond (step *i*). Remember that the Pt catalyst is active enough to continue the reaction, adding two more D atoms in step *iii*:

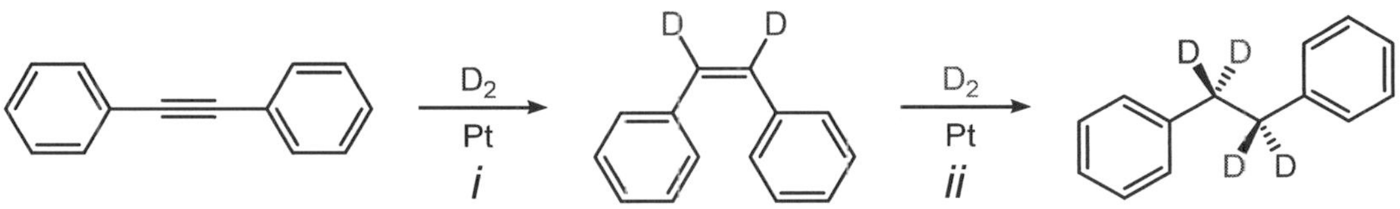

The final product is 1,2-diphenylethane. Phenyl is the name given to a –C_6H_6 (benzene) substituent.

Lesson III.13.2: Syn Addition of H_2 to Alkyne - Poisoned Hydrogenation

In some instances, it may be useful to have a means to convert an alkyne to an alkene without the hydrogenation proceeding all the way to the alkane. If we can add a compound that reduces the effectiveness of the catalyst (such a compound is called a "poison"), the hydrogenation reaction will proceed more slowly, which will make it possible to stop the reaction from hydrogenating the alkene to

177

alkane. Herbert Lindlar discovered that the addition of lead or sulfur compounds poisoned the Pd catalyst used for hydrogenation, hence the system named "Lindlar's catalyst" will only hydrogenate an alkyne to an alkene. Quinoline (shown below) is also used to poison Ni/Pd/Pt hydrogenation catalysts. Keep in mind, however, that the mechanism of the hydrogenation reaction is unchanged, so the H_2 is always added *syn* across the C≡C bond. Thus, both Lindlar's catalyst and Ni/Pd/Pt in the presence of quinoline will selectively convert an alkyne to a *cis* alkene (i.e., this reaction is stereoselective).

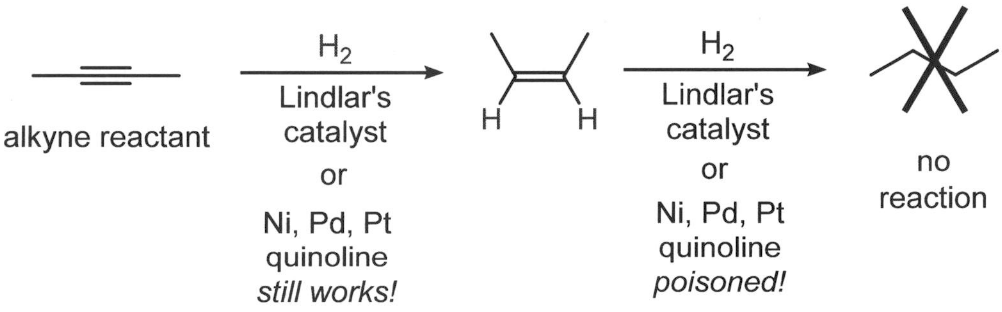

Example III.13.2

Draw the major product of the reaction shown below:

Solution III.13.2

Similar to Example III.13.1, H_2 in the presence of Pd will result in *syn* addition of H atoms to each carbon in the π-bond of diphenyl acetylene (Phenyl is the name given to a –C_6H_6 (benzene) substituent.) to afford a *cis*-alkene. However, the presence of quinoline impairs the activity of the Pd catalyst and, as a result, the catalyst is insufficiently active to be able to hydrogenate an alkene to an alkane. Thus, the reaction stops when *cis*-1,2-diphenylethylene has been formed.

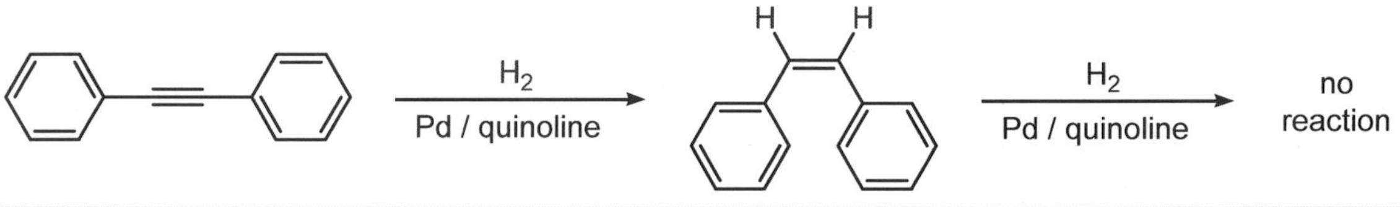

Lesson III.13.3: Anti Addition of H_2 to Alkyne - Electron Transfer, then Coordination by H^+

Our synthetic toolbox now contains reaction conditions that can convert an alkyne to an alkane and *syn* addition of hydrogen to give an alkene. How would we go about *anti* addition of hydrogen to an alkyne? We need an entirely different mechanism for adding H_2 than is operative in the H_2 and Ni/Pd/Pt reaction conditions.

Hydrogenation reactions are reduction reactions. One way to reduce a compound is to add electrons to it. Elemental sodium will react as a one-electron reductant, and dissolving Na metal in liquid ammonia provides a means to add this one-electron reductant to an alkyne in a controllable manner. Exposing an alkyne R–C≡C–R' to the conditions Na/NH$_3$(l) will result in electron transfer from Na to one of the alkyne carbons. Simultaneous with this electron transfer, one of the C≡C π-bonds breaks homolytically to place one electron on each alkyne carbon. The net result will be that one alkyne carbon gains two electrons (i.e., becomes an anion), the other alkyne carbon gains one electron (i.e., becomes a radical), and the C≡C bond is decreased to a C=C bond:

The resulting anionic sp^2-hybridized carbon is less stable than an anionic sp^3-hybridized nitrogen, so the carbanion will deprotonate a molecule of NH$_3$ and form a C–H bond:

net *anti*-addition of two H

Remember that the carbon radical is still short one electron from having a complete octet, so it will undergo one-electron reduction by a second equivalent of Na and become a carbanion. This carbanion will tend to form with the R groups *trans* to one another to avoid steric clashes. Lastly, the resulting carbanion deprotonates another equivalent of NH$_3$ to form another C–H bond. The C=C bond is unreactive under these conditions, and no further reduction by Na/NH$_3$(l) occurs. Because only the *trans*-alkene is formed, this reaction is stereoselective.

In the initial electron transfer from Na to R–C≡C–R', one of the alkyne carbons becomes anionic and the other becomes a radical. If R = R' (i.e., a symmetric alkyne), it does not matter which carbon we draw as the anion or the radical. However, if R ≠ R', then we would need to consider which substituent would better stabilize an anion or radical. If R is more electron donating than R', then the radical would form on the carbon to which R is attached (and vice versa). The rest of the mechanism would proceed as discussed above. Although you can get the correct product regardless of where you place the anion/radical, you may lose points if the question asks you to draw the mechanism and you fail to draw the more stable anion/radical intermediate.

Example III.13.3

Draw the major product for the reaction shown below:

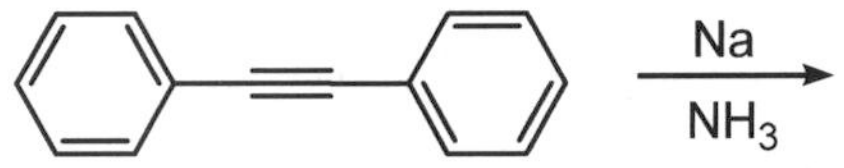

$$\xrightarrow[\text{NH}_3]{\text{Na}}$$

Solution III.13.3

The combination of Na and NH_3 leads to *anti*-addition of two H, in this case yielding *trans*-1,2-diphenylethylene. Phenyl is the name given to a $-C_6H_6$ (benzene) substituent. The mechanistic pathway is shown below:

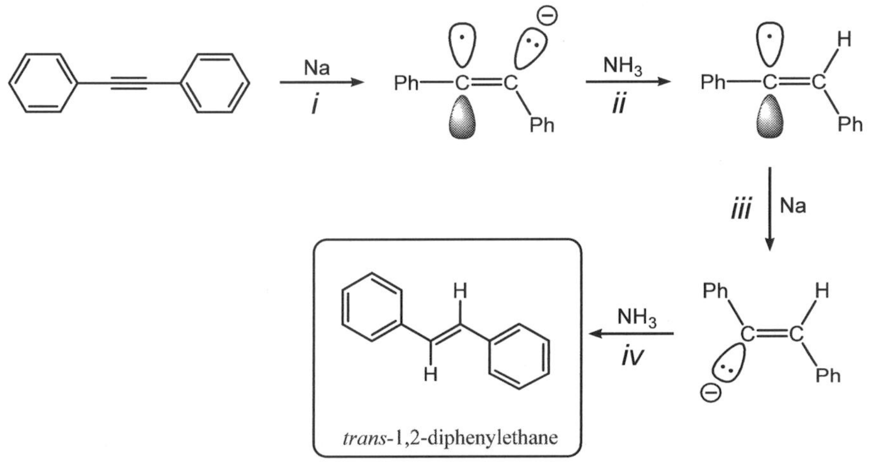

trans-1,2-diphenylethane

Additional help from "Organic Chemistry 1 Reactions and Practice Problems 2018" (Smith):

- After finishing Lesson III.13, you may want to review Reactions E.6 and E.7 in the companion book. Each is a quick review with key points and has a short self test with answers covering the reactions in this Primer Lesson.

Lesson III.14.1: Enol and Keto Tautomers – A Special Class of Constitutional Isomers

We learned about constitutional isomers in Lesson I.14. Remember that constitutional isomers are non-identical molecules with identical molecular formulae, but different bond connectivity, which cannot be interconverted without breaking one or more σ-bonds. In general, σ-bond breakage does not occur readily and requires a significant amount of energy to overcome the activation barrier. However, there are special classes of constitutional isomers that can readily interconvert because the activation barrier to this interconversion is low. Tautomers are one such class, and their constitutional isomerism derives from a C_2H_2O subunit. In the "enol" form, the C_2H_2O subunit comprises an OH group attached to a C=C bond. In the "keto" form, the C_2H_2O subunit comprises a CH_2 group adjacent to a C=O. As we will see in the next Lesson, these two species exist in chemical equilibrium with each other.

Lesson III.14.2: Keto–Enol Tautomerization and the Keto–Enol Equilibrium

Tautomerization refers to a chemical reaction that converts one tautomer to another. Keep in mind that this is NOT resonance: resonance only involves π-bonds and lone pairs. Any process that breaks a σ-bond (i.e., O–H) is a chemical reaction. Tautomerization can be catalyzed by both acids and bases, because tautomerization requires shuffling of protons:

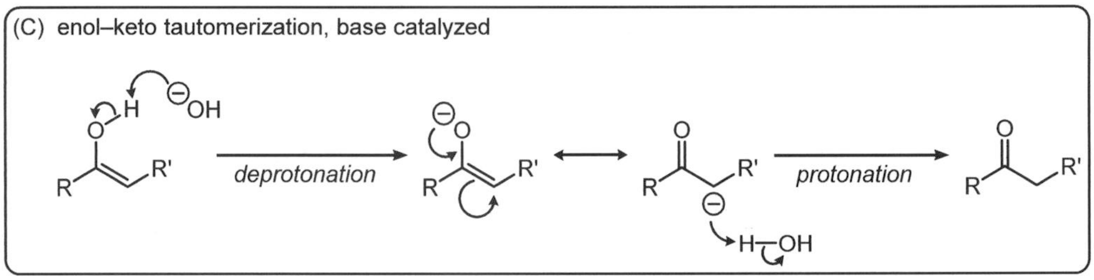

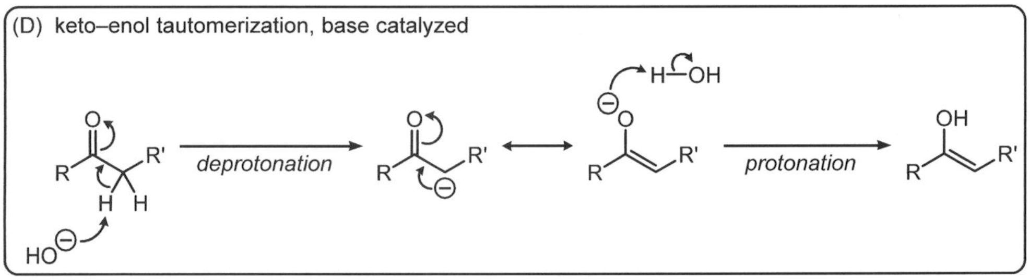

(C) enol–keto tautomerization, base catalyzed
deprotonation
protonation

(D) keto–enol tautomerization, base catalyzed
deprotonation
protonation

The way to represent the interconversion of two molecules via forward and reverse chemical reactions is with an equilibrium arrow. The specific chemical equilibrium that interrelates tautomers is termed the "keto–enol equilibrium". In general, the enol form is thermodynamically less favorable than the keto form because the bonds in the former (O–H and C=C) are weaker than the bonds in the latter (C–H and C=O). As a result, the keto form usually predominates over the enol form in solution. However, when deprotonated, the enol and keto forms are resonance structures, and the enol is more favorable than the keto, because a negative charge is more stable on oxygen than on carbon.

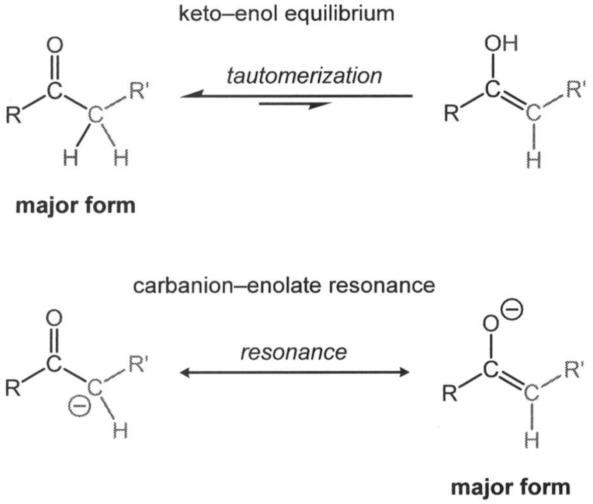

keto–enol equilibrium
tautomerization
major form
carbanion–enolate resonance
resonance
major form

Additional help from "Organic Chemistry 1 Reactions and Practice Problems 2018" (Smith):

After finishing Lesson III.14, you may want to review Reaction E.3 in the companion book. This is a quick review with key points and has a short self test with answers covering the reactions in this Primer Lesson.

Lesson III.15.1: Oxymercuration/Demercuration: Markovnikov Enol Formation

Let us examine what will happen if we subject an alkyne to oxymercuration/reduction conditions as we saw for alkenes in Lesson III.7. One difference in typical alkyne reactions is that $HgSO_4$ is generally used instead of $Hg(OAc)_2$. Both π-bonds in an alkyne are nucleophilic and they will be Coulombically attracted towards the electrophilic Hg center in $HgSO_4$. However, the reactivity of an alkyne proceeds via a different mechanism than an alkene, because the 3-membered ring containing Hg and a C=C bond that would result in the alkyne is far too unstable. Therefore, no such mercurinium intermediate can form in reaction of alkynes.

Instead, $HgSO_4$ makes a π-complex, similar to what we saw in Lesson III.12, with a greater $\delta+$ on the more substituted carbon. Water then does nucleophilic attack at the more substituted alkyne carbon on the opposite side of the π-bond from the π-complexed $HgSO_4$. As the O–C bond begins to form, an alkyne π-bond breaks heterolytically to form a C–Hg bond. The cationic oxygen is then deprotonated by H_2O to afford the product, in which the more electronegative OH is on the more substituted carbon and the Hg(OAc) is *anti* with respect to the OH group. Therefore, oxymercuration of an alkyne is both regioselective (Markovnikov) and stereoselective (*anti*).

anti addition
Markovnikov product

Whereas alkene hydration required oxymercuration followed by a second step (i.e., reduction with NaBH4), alkyne hydration will continue from the oxymercuration product with the acid generated in the first step. The two electrons in the C=C π-bond deprotonate a molecule of H_3O^+ to form a C–H bond at the same carbon to which the Hg is attached and to form a carbocation at the carbon to which the OH is attached. The carbocation is more stable at this position because the lone pair electrons on the oxygen atom can donate into the empty *p*-orbital to stabilize it. The resonance structure that results from this features a carbonyl group with a positive charge on the oxygen. Because of this, the Hg–C bond breaks heterolytically to form a C=C bond and, at the same time, the C=O bond heterolyzes to place its two electrons as a lone pair on the oxygen and remove its positive charge. The product, an enol, then tautomerizes to the more stable keto form.

The net result of oxymercuration/demercuration is the conversion of an alkyne to a ketone with Markovnikov regioselectivity. Due to tautomerization, one alkyne carbon becomes a C=O group and is sp^2-hybridized, and the other becomes sp^3-hybridized, but has two identical substituents (i.e., H atoms). Therefore, neither alkyne carbon becomes a stereocenter in the product, and thus there is no stereoisomerism possible at these positions.

The discussion above used a terminal alkyne (i.e., R–C≡C–H) as the reactant, but what about an internal alkyne (i.e., R–C≡C–R')? The π-complex with HgSO4 would induce roughly the same $\delta+$ on each alkyne carbon, so the net result of the oxymercuration/demercuration reaction of this alkyne would be a mixture of two different ketones: R–C(=O)–CH$_2$–R' and R–CH$_2$–C(=O)–R'.

Example III.15.1

Draw the major product of the reaction shown below:

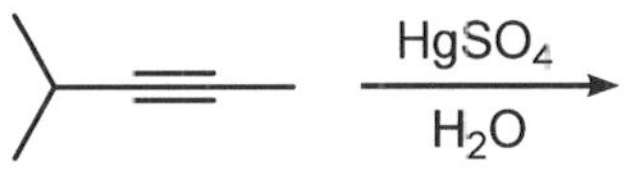

Solution III.15.1

We know that oxymercuration of an alkyne initially leads to Markovnikov addition of an H and an OH from water. In this reaction, both sides of the triple bond are equally substituted, so a mixture of both initial products will result:

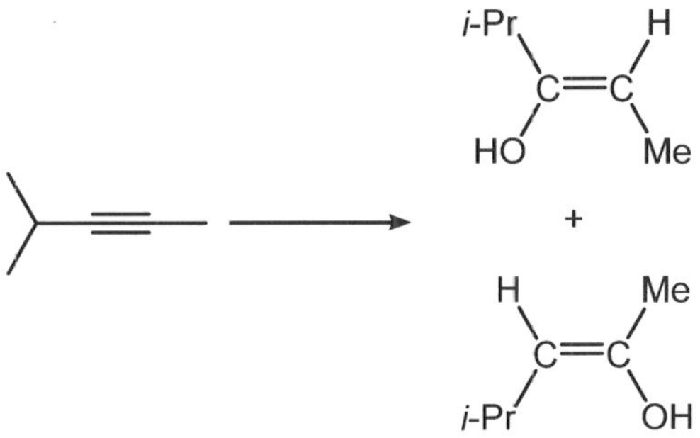

We recognize that these structures are **enols**, so they will favor the keto tautomers:

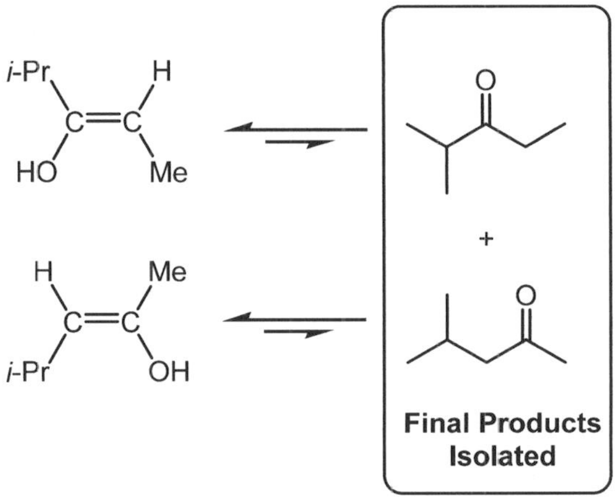

Final Products Isolated

Lesson III.15.2: Hydroboration/Oxidation: Anti-Markovnikov Enol Formation

Hydroboration/oxidation of alkynes proceeds via a mechanism very similar to that of alkenes. In the first reaction (hydroboration), the B$^{\delta+}$–H$^{\delta-}$ bond adds across the C≡C bond such that the H ends up on

185

the more substituted alkyne carbon and the BH_2 ends up on the less substituted carbon. Because this all happens in a single concerted step, the H and BH_2 end up *syn* with respect to each other. In the second reaction (oxidation), the BH_2 is replaced by OH via the same mechanism as that with alkenes. The product is an enol, which tautomerizes to the more stable form, which is an aldehyde. Thus, the net result of hydroboration/oxidation of an alkyne is the hydration of an alkyne to an aldehyde with anti-Markovnikov regioselectivity. As in the oxymercuration/demercuration reaction, neither alkyne carbon becomes a stereocenter in the product, thus no stereoisomerism is possible at these positions.

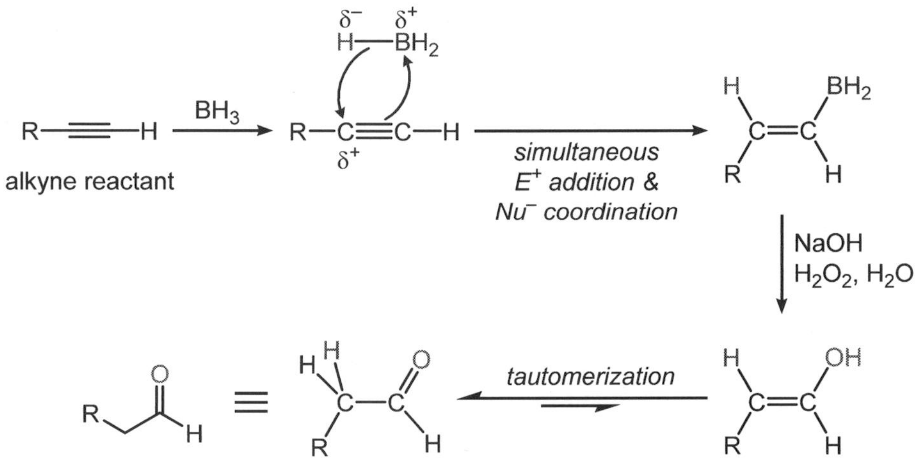

Similar to Lesson III.15.1, if an internal alkyne (i.e., R–C≡C–R') is used, there is no significant difference in the δ+ on each alkyne carbon, so hydroboration across the C≡C can occur with both orientations. Thus, the net result of the hydroboration/oxidation reaction of this alkyne would also be a mixture of two different ketones: R–C(=O)–CH₂–R' and R–CH₂–C(=O)–R'.

Example III.15.2

Draw the major product of the reaction shown below:

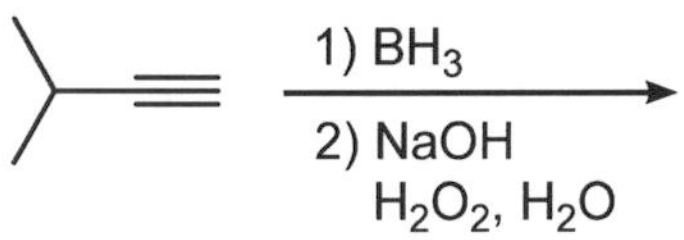

Solution III.15.2

Just as would be the case for the hydroboration/oxidation of an alkene, in hydroboration/oxidation of an alkyne, we expect non-Markovnikov addition of an H and an OH:

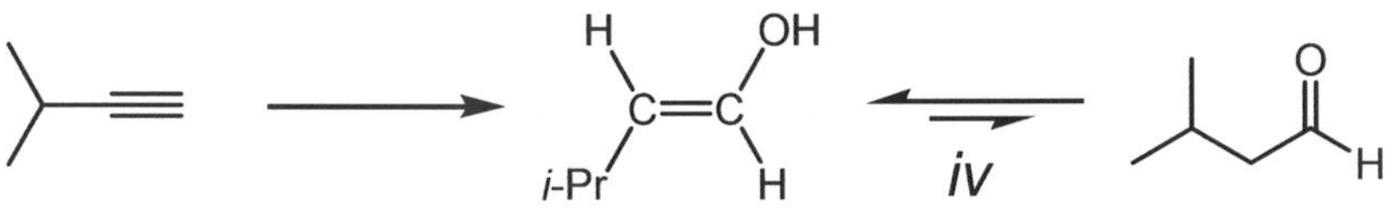

186

We then recognize that this initial product is an unstable enol. The enol will not be isolable, but instead will tautomerize to the keto form to give our final aldehyde product:

Additional help from "Organic Chemistry 1 Reactions and Practice Problems 2018" (Smith):

- After finishing Lesson III.15, you may want to review Reactions E.4 and E.5 in the companion book. Each is a quick review with key points and has a short self test with answers covering the reactions in this Primer Lesson.

Lesson III.16: Alkyne Reactions IV: Acetylide Anion Preparation and its use as a Nucleophile

Lesson III.16.1: Atomic Orbital Hybridization and Effective Electronegativity

In Lesson I.6, we discussed how greater percent *s*-character of a hybrid orbital was equivalent to higher electronegativity, from the perspective of stabilizing anions. The relative stability of a negative charge in a hybrid orbital will therefore be $sp > sp^2 > sp^3$. In fact, this effect is so dramatic that a negative charge is more stable on an *sp*-hybridized carbon than on an sp^3-hybridized nitrogen. Consequently, the equilibrium $R–C≡C–H + H_2N^- \rightleftharpoons R–C≡C^- + NH_3$ lies entirely to the right. It is therefore possible to easily generate this "acetylide anion" and use it in chemical reactions.

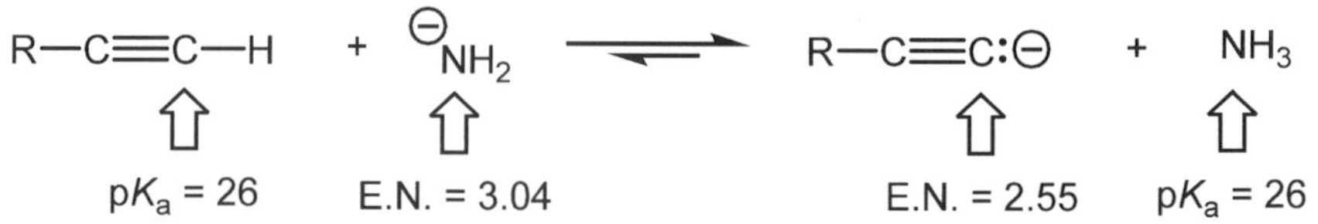

R—C≡C—H
+
⊖NH2
R—C≡C:⊖
+
NH3
pKa = 26
E.N. = 3.04
E.N. = 2.55
pKa = 26

Example III.16.1

Which of the two alkynes shown below would be easier to deprotonate with $NaNH_2$?

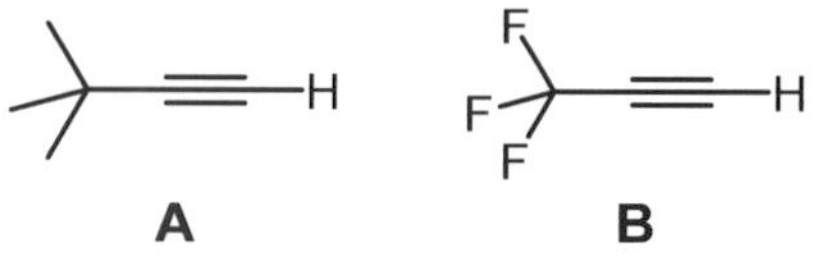

H
F
F
F
H
A
B

Solution III.16.1

In essence, this question is asking us which of the anions generated by deprotonation of **A** and **B** will be more stable. Both **A** and **B** will yield a negative charge residing on an *sp*-hybridized carbon, so any differences in stability will not be due to size, electronegativity, or delocalization. It is convenient to view both **A** and **B** as propynes trisubstituted at the 3-position: **A** has 3 methyl groups, whereas **B** has 3 fluoro substituents. We know from Lesson I.10 that methyl is electron donating and fluorine is electron withdrawing. As a result, the 3 fluorines in **B** will create a δ+ at the 3-position, whereas the 3 methyl groups in **A** will create a δ– at the 3-position. Thus, alkyne **B** will be more easily deprotonated by $NaNH_2$ than alkyne **A** due to the inductive effects of the substituents at the 3-position.

Lesson III.16.2: The Lone Pair of the Acetylide Anion is More Nucleophilic than the π-Bonds

All of the alkyne reactions we have covered so far involved a C≡C π-bond functioning as a nucleophile. In the acetylide anion, however, the lone pair on carbon is more nucleophilic than its two π-bonds. This may seem counterintuitive at first, but keep in mind what a nucleophile needs to do: a nucleophile must form a covalent bond with another atom, which requires it to extend an orbital to the other atom and to share two electrons to make that bond. Although a π-bond is made up of *p*-orbitals and will not be held as tightly to the nucleus as the *sp*-hybridized orbital carrying the carbon lone pair, the *p*-orbitals in the π-bond are already spatially diffused by spreading out to overlap with each other. Even though the *sp*-hybridized orbital carrying the carbon lone pair has 50% *s*-character, this orbital is spatially focused into a much smaller volume pointed along the C≡C bond vector. As a result, the lone pair of the acetylide anion is essentially preconfigured to overlap with another atom and form a new covalent bond. It is important to note that an *sp*-hybridized carbanion is the only carbanion which is less basic than it is nucleophilic. Both *sp*²- and *sp*³-hybridized carbanions are more basic than nucleophilic.

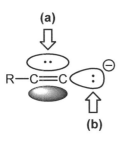

(a)

⇩

R—C≡C

(b)

bonding electrons (in either σ or π bonds) are always lower in energy than lone pair electrons, so **(b) is more energetically available than (a)** to form bonds with other atoms

electrons in π bonds are spread out over multiple atoms above and below the C=C plane, whereas lone pair electrons are localized on one atom and directed along a specific vector, so **(b) is more spatially available than (a)** to form bonds with other atoms

---

Example III.16.2

Why are the electrons in the *sp*-hybridized orbital of the acetylide anion unable to delocalize over multiple atoms via the π-bonds?

Solution III.16.2

The *sp*-hybridized orbital of the acetylide anion is orthogonal to the *p*-orbitals that make up the alkyne π-bonds. The amount of interaction between two orbitals contains a cosine θ term, where θ refers to the angle between the two orbitals, and the cosine of 90° is zero. Because of the 90° between these orbitals, the *sp*-orbital cannot interact with either of the π-bonds.

Lesson III.16.3: Forming Carbon–Carbon Bonds via S_N2 with the Acetylide Anion

Now that we have a way to access nucleophilic carbon, we can start developing strategies to increase the number of carbon atoms in a molecule. The most straightforward approach is to generate an acetylide anion and to react it with an S_N2 substrate. For example, if we start with propyne and our reaction arrow has "1) NaNH₂; 2) 1-bromobutane", the product of the first reaction will be the acetylide anion formed by deprotonating propyne, and this anion will then do S_N2 at the primary alkyl bromide carbon, displacing Br⁻ and forming a new C–C σ-bond. The product of these two steps will be 2-heptyne.

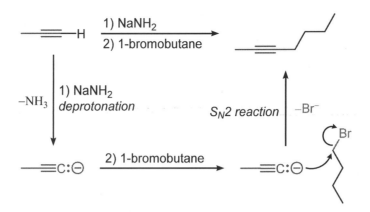

Example III.16.3

Propose a synthesis of the molecule shown below starting with acetylene and assume you have access to any acid, base, and alkyl halide you might need:

Solution III.16.3

We have seen in this Lesson that a primary way to make internal alkynes is by adding the required chains to the acetylide anion. So, we start with acetylene and deprotonate it to make the necessary acetylide (step i). Next, we can add either of the two chains. For this example, we will put the ethyl on before the propyl (step ii). We then need to regenerate an acetylide (step iii), which serves as the nucleophile for S_N2 reaction to add the propyl group (step iv).

Additional help from "Organic Chemistry 1 Reactions and Practice Problems 2018" (Smith):

- After finishing Lesson III.16, you may want to review Reaction E.8 in the companion book. This is a quick review with key points and has a short self test with answers covering the reactions in this Primer Lesson.

- You will also be ready for Problem Set 9 in the companion book. This problem set covers material from Primer Lessons III.11-16, with some review of prior chapters.

Lesson III.17.1: Radical Initiation: Homolysis of RO–OR and H–Br Bonds

The O–O single bond in a peroxide (RO–OR) is very weak and can easily be broken. Homolysis of the O–O bond can be induced by light or by heat. If this homolysis occurs in the presence of HBr, an alkoxy radical (RO$^{\bullet}$) will abstract a hydrogen atom (i.e., H$^{\bullet}$) and generate a bromine radical (Br$^{\bullet}$), which is the radical propagating species. The peroxide most commonly used for these types of reactions is benzoyl peroxide (BPO, shown below).

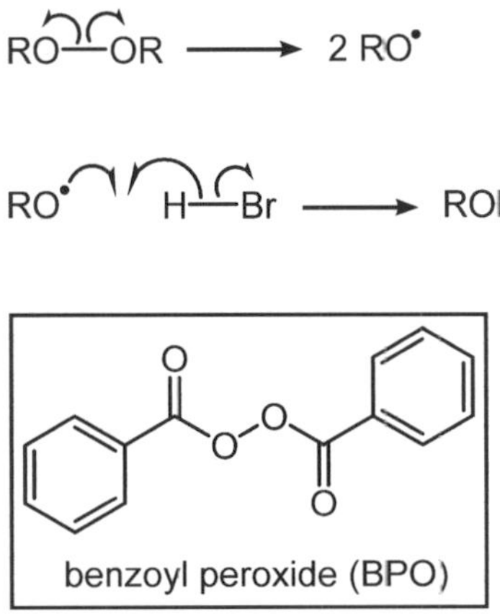

a common ROOR for this reaction

benzoyl peroxide (BPO)

Lesson III.17.2: Radical Propagation: Electrophilic Addition of Br$^{\bullet}$ to a C=C π-Bond

As is the case for any atom without a complete octet, Br$^{\bullet}$ will function as an electrophile. If Br$^{\bullet}$ is generated in the presence of an alkene, one of the π-electrons in the C=C bond will move towards Br$^{\bullet}$ and form a C–Br bond, while the other π-electron will stay behind on other carbon and form a carbon radical. The C–Br bond will form at the less substituted alkene carbon, because the carbon radical will be more stable at the more substituted alkene carbon (the trend of carbon radical stability is the same as carbocations, see Lesson I.11). This carbon radical can then react with another molecule of HBr, abstracting H$^{\bullet}$ to form a C–H bond and regenerating the propagating species Br$^{\bullet}$.

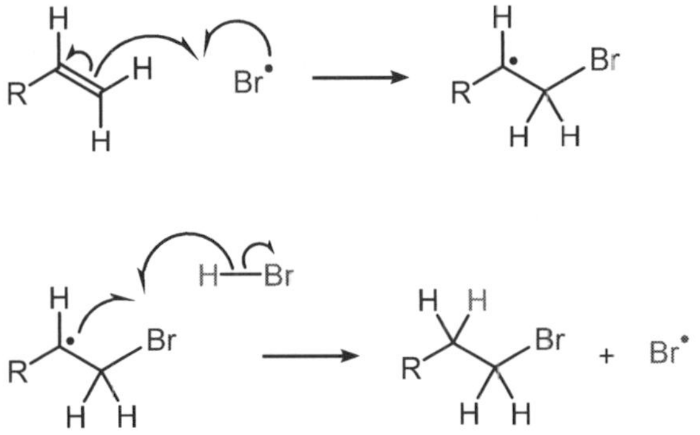

Example III.17.1

Provide an explanation for why $Br^{\bullet}$ reacts with the π-bond of an alkene instead of abstracting $H^{\bullet}$ from a C–H bond.

Solution III.17.1

The π-bond in an alkene is weaker and thus easier to break than a C–H σ-bond. Considering it from a slightly different perspective, even if we put in sufficient energy to break a C–H σ-bond, all of the $Br^{\bullet}$ would react with all of the C=C π-bonds first (it has a lower activation barrier).

Lesson III.17.3: Radical Termination

A reaction in which one or more radical species react and afford zero radical products is called a "radical termination reaction". There are several such reactions possible with peroxide-mediated alkene hydrobromination. Each radical intermediate can react with another molecule of itself or with one of the other radical intermediates present in the reaction. The possible products are shown below:

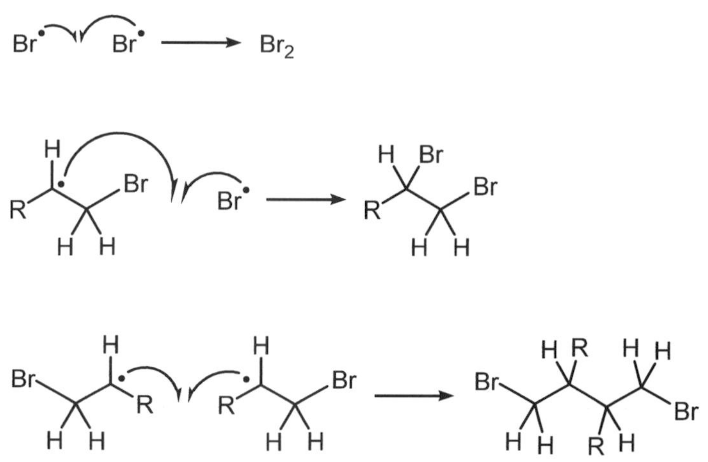

Lesson III.17.4: Regiochemistry and Stereochemistry

In Lesson I.11, we showed that the trend in carbon radical stability was 3° > 2° > 1° > CH_3, due to hyperconjugation and the greater electron donating ability of alkyl groups vs. hydrogen atoms. Unlike carbocations, however, carbon radicals do not rearrange! When $Br^{\bullet}$ reacts with the π-bond in an alkene, it will react in such a way that the most stable carbon radical is formed, which occurs when the C–Br bond is formed at the less substituted alkene carbon. Keep in mind that when an electrophile (i.e., $Br^{\bullet}$) adds to an alkene π-bond, it can do so from above or below the plane. Furthermore, a carbon radical is sp^2-hybridized, (a "missing electron" is more stable in an unhybridized *p*-orbital) and is planar, therefore it can abstract $H^{\bullet}$ from HBr from either above or below the plane. Peroxide-mediated hydrobromination thus exhibits anti-Markovnikov regiochemistry and is not stereoselective (a mixture of configurational isomers will form).

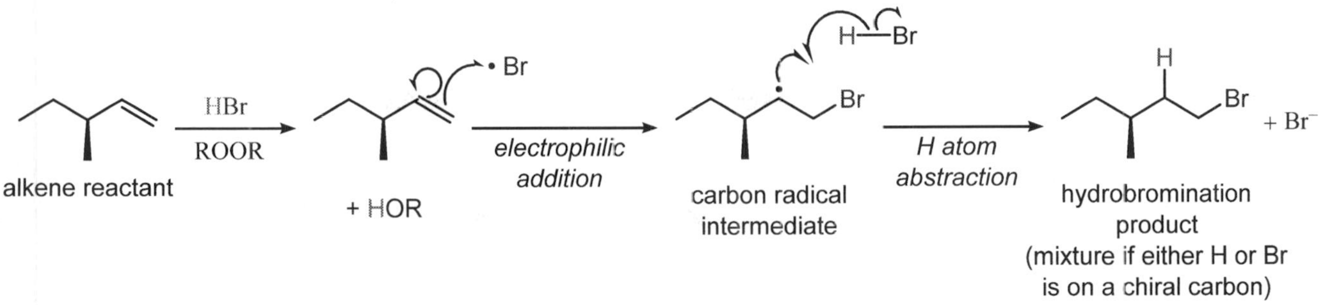

Example III.17.2

Draw the major product for the reaction shown below:

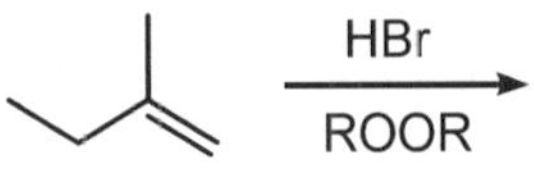

Solution III.17.2

An alkene reacts with hydrobromic acid/ROOR to give non-Markovnikov addition of H and Br. For this alkene, such an addition generates a chiral center, so we will get a 50:50 mixture of enantiomers, a racemic mixture:

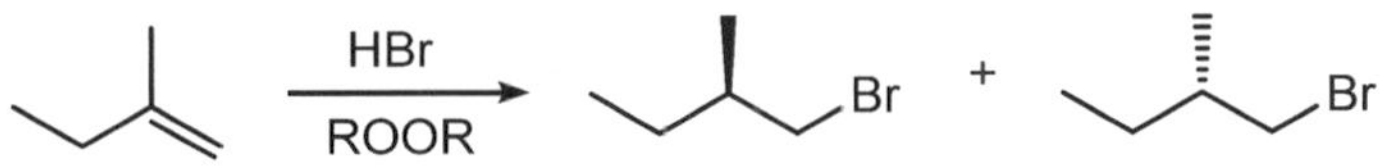

Additional help from "Organic Chemistry 1 Reactions and Practice Problems 2018" (Smith):

- After finishing Lesson III.17, you may want to review Reaction D.12 in the companion book. This is a quick review with key points and has a short self test with answers covering the reactions in this Primer Lesson.

Lesson III.18.1: Radical Initiation: Homolysis of the X–X Bond

The X–X bond in X_2 (X = F, Cl, Br, I) is relatively weak and can be broken homolytically via photoirradiation (which is typically represented with "hv"). Homolysis of the X–X bond generates two equivalents of X•, which is the radical propagating species.

$$X\text{—}X \xrightarrow{\ hv\ } 2\ X^{\bullet}$$

Lesson III.18.2: Radical Propagation: H-atom Abstraction by X•

Any atom without a complete octet will react as an electrophile. In the previous Lesson, Br• reacted with the π-bond of an alkene (remember: π-bonds are weaker than σ-bonds). What happens when X• is generated in the presence of an alkane? The only electrons available for X• to achieve an octet are those in C–H and C–C σ-bonds. In general, C–H σ-bonds are more easily broken than C–C σ-bonds, so when X• encounters an alkane molecule, it will break a C–H by abstracting an H•. This process forms HX and a carbon radical. The carbon radical then reacts with a molecule of X_2, breaking the X–X bond homolytically to form a C–X bond and regenerate the radical propagating species X•. Because the concentration of X• is usually low, these reaction conditions will typically only afford the monohalogenated product.

Keep in mind that a "missing electron" is like having a positive charge, so the relative stability of X• will be I• > Br• > Cl• > F•. It turns out that I• is so stable that it is not reactive enough to abstract H• from a C–H bond. Conversely, F• is so unstable that there are no conditions to generate it photolytically from F_2 without breaking alkane σ-bonds first. As a result, the **radical halogenation of alkanes is generally only synthetically useful when Cl_2 or Br_2 is used.**

Lesson III.18.3: Radical Termination

The radical termination reactions in the free radical halogenation of alkanes are shown below:

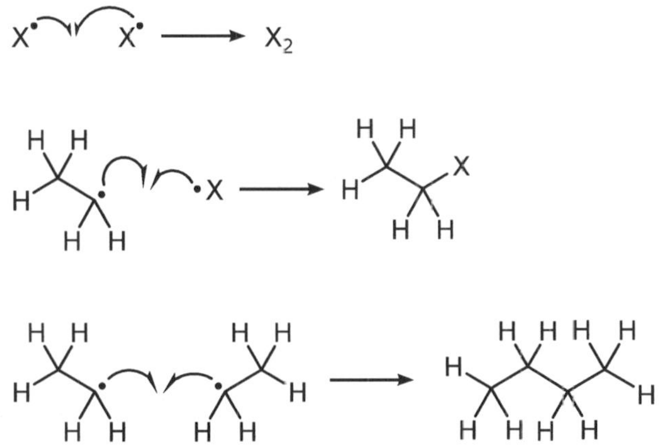

Lesson III.18.4: Regiochemistry and Stereochemistry

Remember that the radical halogenation of an alkane will only replace C–H bonds with C–X bonds, it will never break C–C bonds. So, the easiest way to draw all the possible products of this reaction is to identify all of the chemically unique C–H bonds in a given molecule. If our reactant is 2-methylbutane, there are 4 chemically unique C–H bonds, thus radical halogenation of this molecule will generate 4 different monohalogenated products (which are constitutional isomers of each other). To identify which will be the major product, we need to consider the relative stability of the radicals which led to each constitutional isomer. Abstraction of H$^{\bullet}$ from position (1) or (4) will yield a 1° radical, from position (2) will yield a 3° radical, and from position (3) will yield a 2° radical. Given that the stability of carbon radicals is 3° > 2° > 1°, intermediate (2) is the most stable, and thus we would expect the major product to be derived from that intermediate. When X = Br, product (2) is by far the most abundant. However, when X = Cl, products (1) and (4) are formed in nearly equal amount to product (2)! So, it is not only intermediate stability that is influencing product distribution. What is going on here?

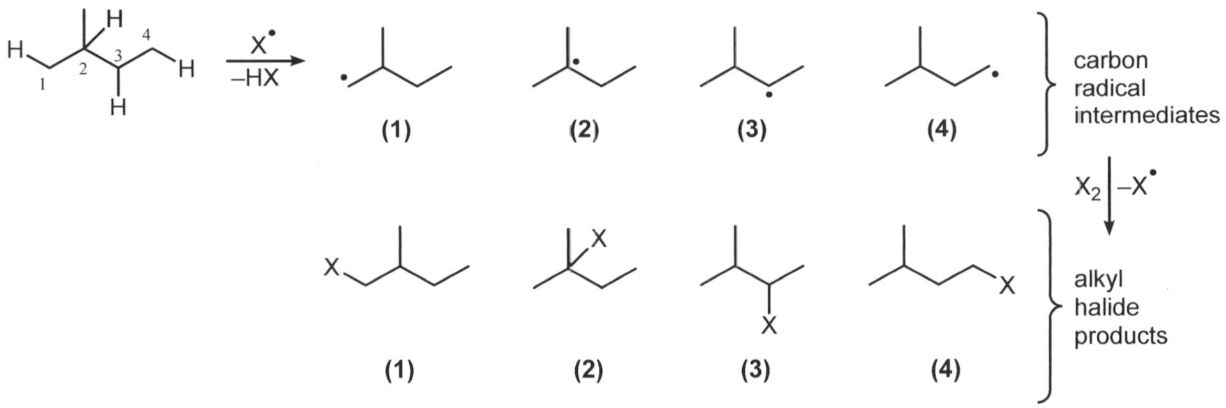

195

For a reaction between two molecules to occur, those two molecules must collide with each other, a phenomenon that depends on the probability of the collision and the relative orientation of the two molecules with respect to each other. Chlorine radicals are extremely reactive compared to bromine radicals. So, whenever a Cl˙ collides with an alkane near a C–H bond, it generally has enough energy to abstract H˙ to form HX and a carbon radical. Because of this reactivity, the chlorination reaction is statistically controlled; more H atoms of a particular type to be abstracted generally leads to the major product. The bromine radical, on the other hand, is less reactive than the chlorine radical. This means that the bromine radical will preferentially react with the more reactive C–H bonds that would give the most stable carbon radical. The major product of bromination is energetically controlled; the placement of Br where the most stable radical intermediate forms is the major product. The manner in which the different reactivity of Cl and Br radicals leads to different major products leads to a generally applicable concept: **more reactive = less selective**. For problems involving radical halogenation of alkanes, it is generally sufficient to draw all possible monohalogenation products and indicate which is the "energetically preferred" product and which is the "statistically preferred" product (and to know that probability plays a more important role in chlorination than in bromination). Consider the radical halogenation of 2-methylbutane:

6 C–H bonds can
give rise to radical (1)

(1)

most probable
radical to form

(1)

statistically preferred
product

major product if X = Cl

only 1 C–H bond can
give rise to radical (2)

(2)

least probable
radical to form...

...but most stable

(2)

energetically preferred
product

major product if X = Br

Example III.18.1

Draw the monohalogenated products for the reaction shown below. Indicate which is energetically preferred and which is statistically preferred. What is the major product in this case?

Solution III.18.1

On this reactant, 1,1,3,3,5,5-hexamethylcyclohexane, there are 18 H atoms on the primary sites (the methyl groups), compared to only 6 on the secondary sites. The statistical product is the one derived from replacing a H on a primary C. A secondary radical is more stable than a primary radical, so the energetically preferred product is the one in which the H on a secondary C is replaced by Br:

Because Br is less reactive, it is more selective for the energetically preferred product, so the energetically preferred product is the major product.

Additional help from "Organic Chemistry 1 Reactions and Practice Problems 2018" (Smith):

- After finishing Lesson III.18, you will be ready for Progress Check 3 in the companion book. Progress Check 1 is a practice exam covering materials from all of the Primer Lessons.

- You will also be ready for Progress Check 4, a 74-question multiple choice practice final exam that is broken down into sections so that you can determine where your weaknesses lie from the whole semester of material.

BONUS Material

The remaining Lessons appear in both the "Organic Chemistry 1 Primer 2018" and the "Organic Chemistry 2 Primer 2019" to account for flexibility with respect to what chapters instructors choose to teach in the first and second semester classes. These bonus Lessons are numbered in the same way that they are in the "Organic Chemistry 2 Primer 2019" so that the companion texts can be used with either Primer independently.

Bonus Lessons from Part IV: Properties and Reactions of Conjugated and Aromatic Molecules

Lesson IV.1: π-Bond Conjugation is Stabilizing and π-Bond Cumulation is Destabilizing

In Lessons III.1-10, we considered a variety of reactions typical for individual C=C double bonds in isolated alkene units. Next, we will consider the stability trends for molecules that have *more than one* C=C bond and then examine some reactions of dienes. Remember that π-bonds are made up of carbon *p*-orbitals. In 1,4-pentadiene, the two C=C bonds are separated by an sp^3-hybridized carbon, so the *p*-orbitals cannot overlap, so each of the π bonds is **isolated**:

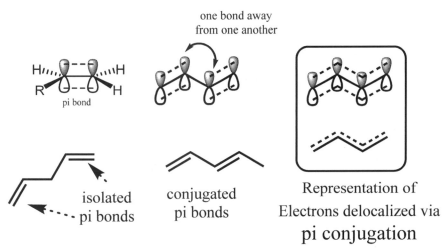

In *trans*-1,3-pentadiene, however, there are no sp^3-hybridized carbons separating the two C=C bonds, so all four of the *p*-orbitals involved in making π bonds can overlap with each other, and we classify this type of diene as **conjugated**. When two C=C bonds are conjugated, each of the 4 π-electrons can spread out over 4 positions, this delocalization is why **conjugation significantly stabilizes π-bonds**. Recall from Lesson III.2 that we measure alkene stabilities using heats of hydrogenation (ΔH_h). For 1-pentene and *trans*-2-pentene, the ΔH_h values are –30.1 and –28.6 kcal/mol, respectively. At first glance, we might expect the heat of hydrogenation for *trans*-1,3-pentadiene to be simply the sum of the values for 1-pentene and *trans*-2-pentene (–58.7 kcal/mol, because it has one monosubstituted alkene and one *trans* alkene). The experimentally observed ΔH_h for *trans*-1,3-pentadiene is –54.1 kcal/mol, which demonstrates that **conjugation of the two C=C bonds provides an extra 4.6 kcal/mol of stabilization:**

		ΔH_h (kcal/mol)
	1-pentene	−30.1
	trans-2-pentene	−28.6
	1,4-pentadiene	−60.8
	trans-1,3-pentadiene	−54.1
	1,2-pentadiene	−69.8

When two C=C bonds begin at the same carbon, we get a C=C=C unit, in which the C=C bonds are classified as **cumulated**. Note that the central carbon is *sp*-hybridized, so the *p*-orbitals used to make the C=C bond to the left carbon is orthogonal to those used to make the C=C bond to the right, and thus the two π-bonds cannot overlap. This is illustrated for H_2C=C=CH_2 here:

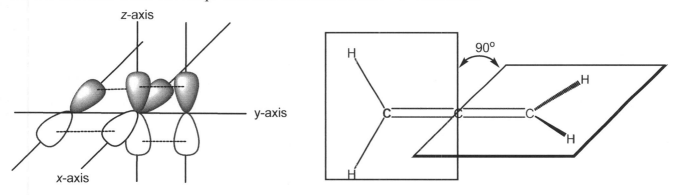

The diagram on the left shows the *p*-orbitals used to make the π-bonds (p_x for the left π bond and p_y for the right π-bond). The diagram on the right shows the geometry in a typical structural drawing.

When we measure the ΔH_h for such a C=C=C unit in 1,2-pentadiene, it is significantly higher than ΔH_h for 1,4-pentadiene (−69.8 vs. −60.8 kcal/mol, respectively), which indicates that **cumulated π-bonds are significantly less stable than isolated π-bonds**. This phenomenon is due to the fact that an *sp*-hybridized carbon is much more electronegative than an *sp²*-hybridized carbon, so a C=C bond between an *sp*-hybridized carbon and an *sp²*-hybridized carbon is more electron-deficient than a C=C bond between two *sp²*-hybridized carbons. Remember that alkene units are stabilized by inductive electron-donating groups like alkyl groups (*sp³* hybridized C atoms).

Example IV.1.1

Which of the following alkenes would have the higher heat of hydrogenation?

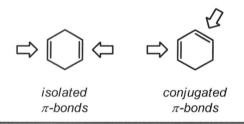

Solution IV.1.1

In the molecule on the left (1,4-cyclohexadiene), the two π-bonds are isolated, but in the molecule on the right (1,3-cyclohexadiene), the two π-bonds are conjugated. When π-bonds are isolated from each other by one or more *sp³*-hybridized carbons, they cannot interact with each other and thus cannot be stabilized or destabilized by each other. However, when π-bonds are conjugated with each other, the π-electrons are able to delocalize over a greater number of positions, which increases stability. As a result, 1,3-cyclohexadiene will be more stable than 1,4-cyclohexadiene, which means that 1,3-cyclohexadiene will release less energy upon hydrogenation of its C=C bonds. Thus, a higher heat of hydrogenation will be observed with 1,4-cyclohexadiene.

isolated
π-bonds

conjugated
π-bonds

Lesson VI.2.1 Introduction to Addition Reactions of Conjugated Dienes

We saw in Lesson III.5 that reaction of one equivalent of HX (X = Cl, Br or I) to a C=C bond will produce the more substituted alkyl halide as the major product (Markovnikov's Rule). However, two products are possible when one equivalent of HX reacts with a 1,3-diene:

Electrophilic Additions of HX:

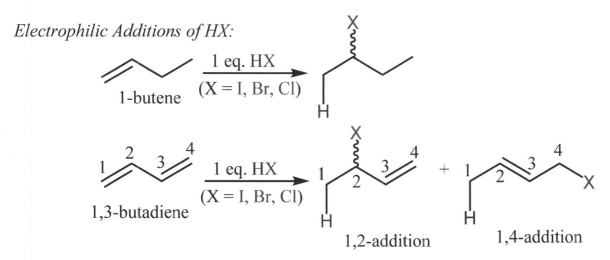

The **1,2-product** (also called the **direct addition** product) and **1,4-product** (also called the **conjugate addition** product) are possible because the carbocation formed by electrophilic addition of the proton to the C1 end of the C=C bond leads to a resonance-stabilized carbocation having δ+ character on both C2 and C4:

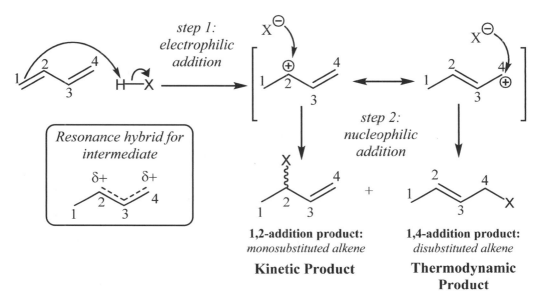

The major product isolated from these reactions depends on the conditions of the reaction.

Both 1,2- and 1,4-addition products have the first mechanistic step: electrophilic addition of the proton to one of the C=C bonds. The second step of the 1,2-addition is coordination of the bromide to C2, whereas the second step of 1,4-addition is coordination of bromide to C4. In the case of addition of HX to 1,3-butadiene, the product of 1,2-addition is a monosubstituted alkene, whereas the product of 1,4-addition is a disubstituted alkene. The 1,4-addition produces the more stable alkene (the **thermodynamic product**). The 1,2-addition is faster (lower energy of activation, $E_{a1,2}$ in the figure below), however, because the bromide is closer to C2 when it is produced in the electrophilic addition step. This is known as a **proximity effect**, and the result of this is that the 1,2-addition product is formed faster – it is the **kinetic product**. The qualitative reaction coordinate diagram below illustrates the energetics of these processes:

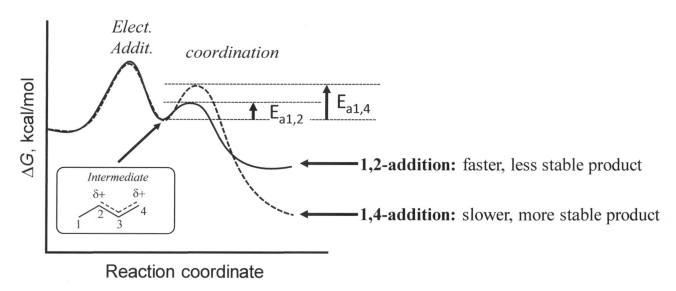

The 1,2-addition is faster, but the 1,4-addition produces the more stable product in this case. So, how to we determine which is the major product? A fundamental property of chemical reactions is that **the major product of irreversible reactions is the kinetic product** (the one formed at a higher rate). For a reaction **at equilibrium (reversible), the major product is the thermodynamic product** (the more stable product). We can control which product is the major product by controlling the reaction conditions. **At low temperature (below ~20 °C for these reactions) the reaction is irreversible** because there is not enough energy to overcome the larger energy barrier for the reverse reaction, so the kinetic product is the major product, and the reaction is said to be under **kinetic control**.

At higher temperature (above ~50 °C for these reactions), the reaction is reversible because there is enough energy to overcome the energy barrier to the reverse reaction, so the thermodynamic product is the major product, and the reaction is said to be under **thermodynamic control**.

The 1,2-product is always the kinetic product due to the proximity effect. The thermodynamic product is always the more stable alkene, which may be either the 1,2- or 1,4-addition product depending on the substitution pattern. For example, consider addition of HBr to 2,5-dimethyl-2,4-hexadiene:

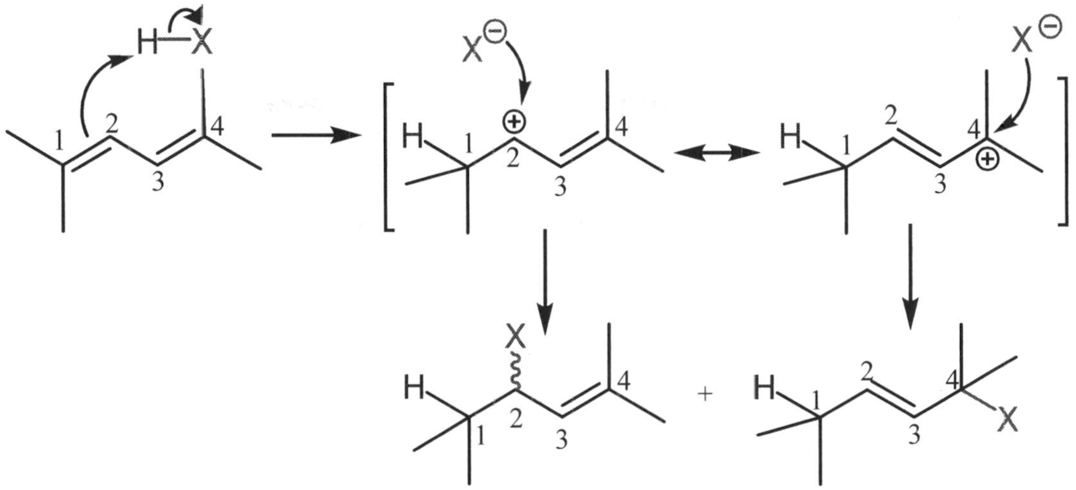

1,2-addition product:
trisubstituted alkene

1,4-addition product:
disubstituted alkene

Kinetic product
and
Thermodynamic product

In this case, the 1,2-addition product is *both* the kinetic product *and* the thermodynamic product.

To approach these problems effectively, follow this procedure:

1. Number the π-conjugated part 1–4.
2. Add H^+ to C1
3. Draw both resonance contributors for the cation you get
4. Place the X- on each cation to get your final products
5. The 1,2-product is the kinetic product
6. The most substituted alkene is the thermodynamic product

Example IV.2.1

Provide the major product for each reaction. Label each reaction as favoring either the kinetic or thermodynamic product.

205

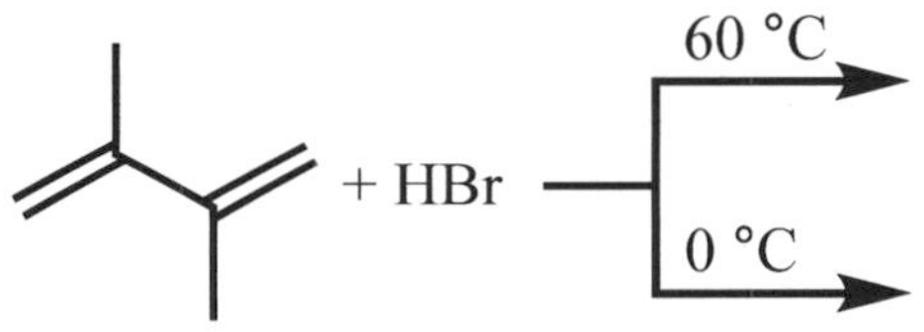

Solution IV.2.1

First, we consider what the 1,2- and 1,4-addition products would be:

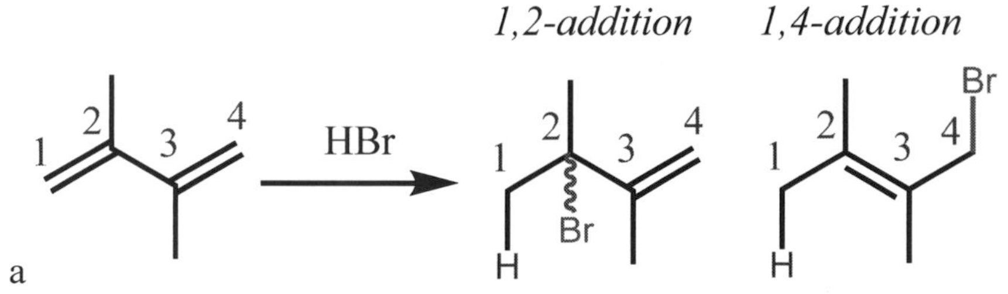

At 60 °C, the thermodynamic product is favored. This will be the most stable alkene. In this case, that is the 1,4-addition product, a tetrasubstituted alkene.

At 0 °C, the kinetic product is favored. This will always be the 1,2-addition product, due to the proximity effect.

IV.3.1: Introduction to the Diels-Alder Reaction

The Diels-Alder reaction is a [4 + 2] **cycloaddition reaction** of a diene and an alkene to form a cyclohexene ring. The Diels-Alder reaction is one of the most widely-used reactions in synthesis. The reaction takes place between a diene, which acts as a nucleophile and an alkene which acts as an electrophile (often referred to in this reaction as a **dienophile**). For the most effective Diels-Alder reactions, the diene is electron-rich and the dienophile is electron poor. The scheme below shows the general mechanism of the reaction:

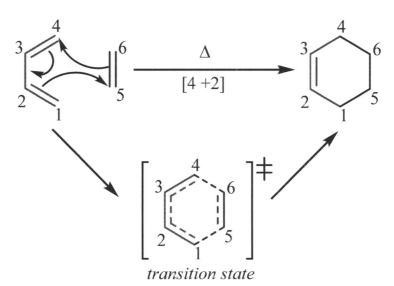

transition state

The Diels-Alder reaction is an example of a **pericyclic reaction**: a concerted, cyclic flow of π electrons within a cyclic transition state structure. The π bond between carbons 1 and 2 breaks and these electrons form a new σ bond between carbons 1 and 5, causing the π bond between carbons 5 and 6 to flow into a σ-bonding orbital between carbons 6 and 4, which in turn breaks the π bond between carbons 4 and 3, pushing those electrons to make a π bond between carbons 3 and 2.

The diene of the Diels-Alder reaction has to be a s-cis configuration for the cycloaddition to take place in a concerted mechanism. Even if the diene in the starting material is in the thermodynamically more stable configuration (s-trans), the added heat to the reaction will promote the rotation of the C—C σ bond to form the less stable configuration for the reaction to take place as the figure below shows.

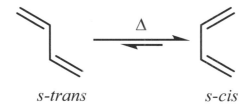

s-trans   *s-cis*

The Diels-Alder reaction proceeds best when the dienophile has an electron-withdrawing group (an electronegative atom, or an atom with a δ+ on it) attached to carbon 6. The presence of an electron-withdrawing group such as carbonyl groups (C=O), nitro groups (–NO_2) or nitrile groups (–C≡N) creates a dipole through resonance, placing +δ and –δ charges on carbons 5 and 6 respectively:

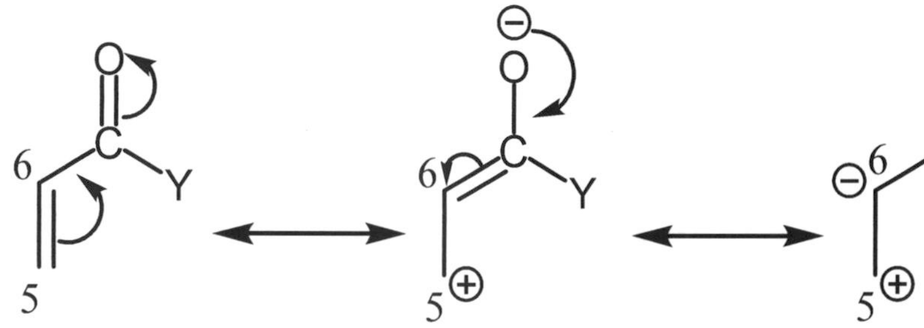

The Diels-Alder reaction is a stereoselective reaction: a cis- alkene (dienophile) will produce a cis-cyclohexene and a trans-alkene will produce a trans-cyclohexene as the following figure shows.

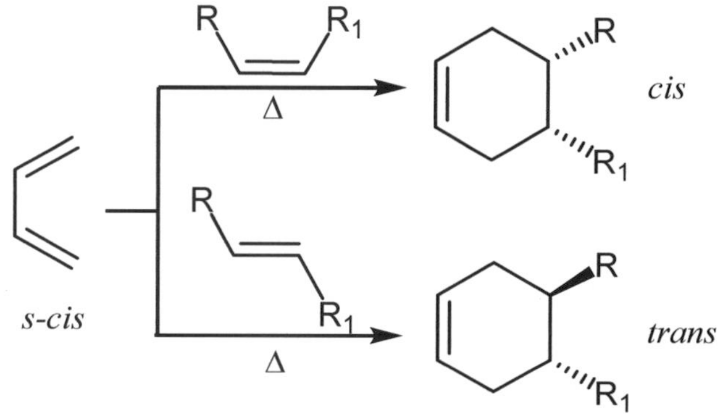

Example VI.3.1

Give the final product of the following Diels-Alder cycloaddition

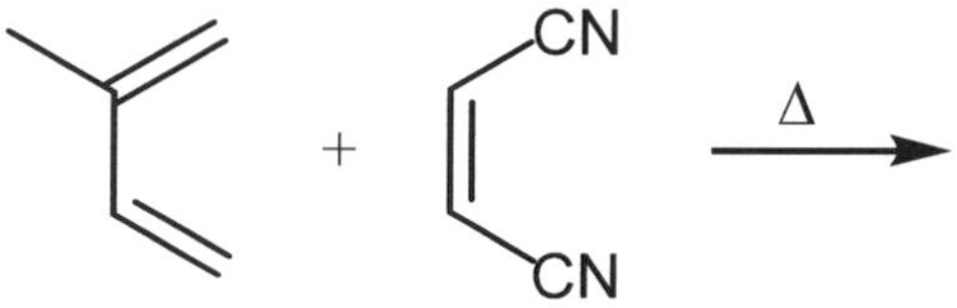

Solution VI.3.1

To give the product of this reaction, we number the reactants in a sequence of 1 to 4 on the diene and 5 and 6 on the dienophile to figure out where the new bonds are formed and the bonds are broken. Then we give the cyclohexene, the double bond is always formed between carbons 2 and 3. Then we add the substituents, the methyl group on carbon 3 and two –CN groups on carbons 5 and 6, since the alkene is a *cis* alkene then two nitrile groups are going to be *cis* in configuration. As we can see the product has two chiral centers (marked by asterisk), this will result in a racemic mixture of two enantiomers:

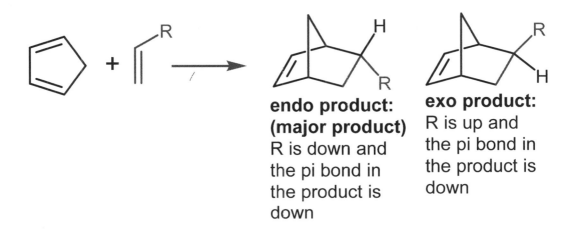

+ enantiomer

IV.3.2: The Endo- and Exo- Products

When you have a cyclic diene, you sometimes have a choice between two products that differ only in the position of the new π bond in the product relative to the substituent that came from the dienophile. In the endo product, the substituent points towards the same direction as the pi bond. In the exo product, the substituent points away from the π bond. The rule is that if the substituent R has a π bond in it itself, the endo product is the major product.

endo product:
(major product)
R is down and
the pi bond in
the product is
down

exo product:
R is up and
the pi bond in
the product is
down

Bonus Lessons from Part VII: Methods for Determining the Structure of Organic Compounds

Lesson VII.1.1: The Electromagnetic Spectrum

The electromagnetic spectrum stretches from small wavelength gamma rays to long wavelength radio waves. Different wavelengths of light interact with matter in different ways. The region of the electromagnetic spectrum with which we are most familiar is the visible region because light in this range is detectable by our unaided eyes. At longer wavelengths than visible light is **infrared (IR) light**, which we can feel as heat. At shorter wavelengths than visible light is **ultraviolet (UV) light**, which we (unintentionally) detect as sunburned skin and other damage to our tissues. In the next few lessons, we will learn how we can gain structural information about molecules by studying how they interact with electromagnetism in the UV, visible, IR, and radio frequency ranges of the electromagnetic spectrum. These regions of the electromagnetic spectrum are shown in terms of relative energies below:

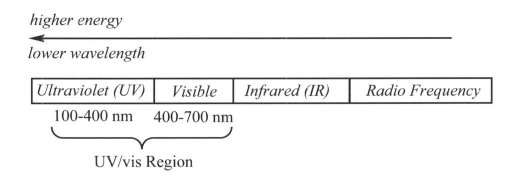

In this lesson, we will focus on how UV and visible light, collectively abbreviated **UV–visible (UV/vis) light**, interact with organic molecules. The UV/vis part of the spectrum we will consider spans a wavelength range from ~100–700 nm.

Lesson VII.1.2: UV and Visible Light Cause Electronic Transitions in Molecules

Each covalent bond in an organic compound consists of two electrons shared between the nuclei joined by the bond. When a molecule absorbs UV/vis radiation of an appropriate energy, it causes one of the electrons to undergo an **electronic transition** to a higher-energy orbital that. In terms of energy, the **highest occupied molecular orbital** (abbreviated HOMO) is commonly the orbital holding the electron that is promoted to higher energy upon absorption of light energy. The **lowest unoccupied molecular orbital** is abbreviated LUMO. Here, "occupied" and "unoccupied" refer to whether or not the orbitals contain electrons in them before energy absorption. Energy absorption (in the form of a photon) can promote an electron from the HOMO to the LUMO. The orbital that contains a pair of bonding electrons is called a **bonding orbital**. If the bonding orbital holds electrons in a σ-bond, the orbital is given the symbol σ, whereas if the bonding orbital holds electrons in a π-bond, it is given the symbol π. Upon absorption of an appropriate energy photon of UV/vis light, a σ-bonding electron will generally be promoted to a σ-**antibonding orbital**, given the symbol σ*:

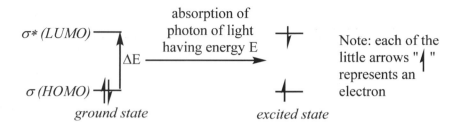

This type of transition is called a **σ→σ* transition** (read "sigma to sigma star transition"). Similarly, a π-bonding electron generally gets promoted to a π-antibonding orbital, given the symbol π*:

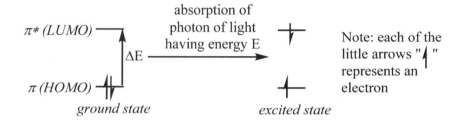

This type of transition is called a **π→π* transition** (read "pi to pi star transition").

Regardless of it is a σ→σ* transition or a π→π* transition, the energy of the photon must be identical to the energy gap between the electronic energy levels (ΔE in the figures above) for the photon to be absorbed and cause the electronic transition to occur. Longer wavelength light – towards the visible end of the UV/vis range – can only cause transitions requiring less energy. The lower energy transitions in organic molecules are usually π→π* transitions. By measuring the wavelength of UV/vis light that is absorbed by the sample, some knowledge about the bonding in the sample molecule can be inferred. The types of information we can gain by measuring absorption of UV-vis light are detailed in Lesson VII.2.

Example VII.1.1

Which of these molecules will have a lower-energy electronic transition? What type of transition would the HOMO–LUMO transition represent in each?

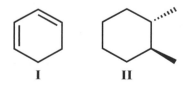

I   **II**

Solution VII.1.1

The lower-energy transitions in organic molecules tend to be π–π* transitions, so molecule **I**, which has a π-bond, would be expected to have a lower energy (longer wavelength) transition than would molecule **II**. The transition observed in the UV-vis spectrum of molecule **I** will be a π–π* transition, while the transition observed for molecule **II** would be a σ–σ* transition.

Lesson VII.1.3: Comparing σ→σ to π→π* Transitions, and the Effect of π-Conjugation*

Because σ-bonding electrons lie nearer the nuclei than π-bonding electrons, they are held more tightly by Coulombic attraction to the nucleus than are π-bonding electrons. It therefore takes more energy (ΔE_2 in the figure below) to pull an electron out of a σ orbital to promote it to a σ*-orbital than it does to promote a π-bonding electron to a π*-orbital (requiring ΔE_1 in the figure below). A qualitative diagram showing both the σ→σ* and the π→π* transitions in a molecule that has both types of bonds will consequently look like this:

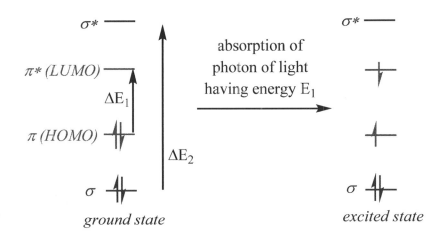

Figure: σ* ——   π* (LUMO) ΔE_1 π (HOMO) ΔE_2 σ — *ground state*; absorption of photon of light having energy E_1; σ* ——   σ — *excited state*

What if a molecule has more than one π-bond? The answer depends on whether the π-bonds in the molecule are isolated or conjugated (see Lesson IV.1). If the two π-bonds are isolated, they will not interact with one another, so the π-orbitals lie at similar energies. This results in an electronic transition at about the same energy as if there were only one π-bond. However, two photons will be needed per molecule to cause both to promote both the π→π* transitions (i.e., a molecule with two isolated π-bonds will absorb twice as much light as a molecule with only one π bond). The amount of light absorbed per mole of a sample is called the **molar absorptivity** or **molar extinction coefficient**.

We also know that conjugated π-bonds are more stable than isolated π-bonds. It takes less energy to cause an electronic transition of an electron in a conjugated π-system than it does to cause the transition in an isolated π-bond. One reason for this is that the single electron that is left in the bonding orbital – which we can think of as a radical – has resonance stabilization, so it takes less energy to form than it would take to form the radical resulting from an isolated π-bond that lacks resonance

213

stabilization. In fact, **the longer the π conjugated system, the lower the energy of the photon needed to promote the π→π* transition.** The energy of UV-vis light absorbed and the number of photons absorbed at that energy allow us to assess the relative number of π-bonds in a compound and the extent to which these π-bonds are conjugated.

Example VII.1.2

Which of these molecules will have a lower-energy electronic transition? Which would have the highest molar absorptivity?

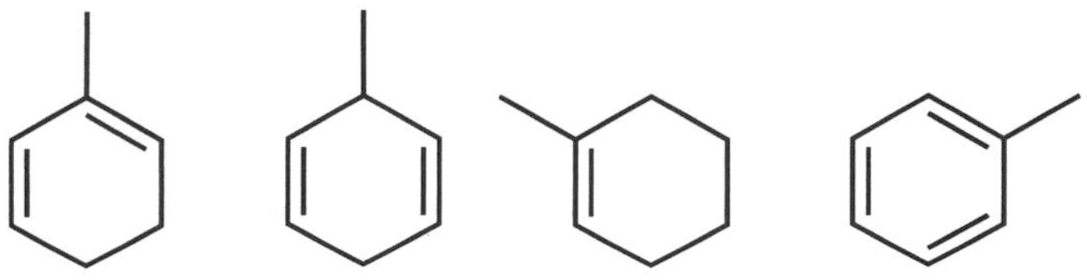

I II III IV

Solution VII.1.2

The lowest-energy transition will occur for the molecule with the most-extended π-conjugated system. In molecules **II** and **III** have only isolated alkenes. Molecule **I** has a π-conjugated system of two π-bonds, whereas molecule **IV** features a π-conjugated system of three π bonds. This analysis suggests that molecule **IV** will have the lowest-energy (highest wavelength) band in its UV-vis spectrum. Molecule **IV** is also expected to have a higher molar absorptivity because it has the greatest number of π bonds per molecule as well.

Lesson VII.2.1: The UV/vis Spectrum

In Lesson VII.1, we learned that an electronic transition occurs when a molecule absorbs UV-vis light of an appropriate energy. In the current lesson, we will learn how scientists have developed a technique, called **UV/vis spectroscopy**, that correlates the absorption of light at a given wavelength with molecular properties, intermolecular forces, and chemical reactions. The operating principle of a typical UV-vis spectrometer is illustrated as follows:

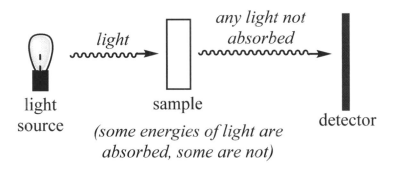

The light source generates a beam of light, which is directed through the sample. The source provides one specific wavelength at a time, scanning over the range of wavelengths that is set by the experimentalist. The detector, located on the opposite side of the sample relative to the source, detects the intensity of the light that passes through the sample relative to the amount of light emitted by the source. If the sample absorbs light at a particular wavelength, the detector will detect a decrease in light coming through at that wavelength. The computer system then provides the user with a plot of how much light was absorbed versus the wavelength at which it was absorbed. A sample that has electrons in bonds that undergo an electronic transition at 220 nm, for example, might produce a UV-vis spectrum like this:

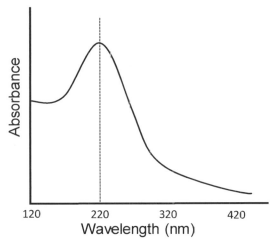

Lesson VII.2.2: Information Provided by the UV-vis Spectrum: Concentration and Reaction Rates

A few things should be noted at this point. If we increase the **concentration** (*c*) of the compound in the sample cell that is absorbing light at 220 nm, then more light will be absorbed. If we increase the size of the sample cell (the **pathlength**, *b*), then then more light will be absorbed. For a certain concentration and a certain pathlength, the amount of light absorbed will be a constant for a given electronic transition. This constant that relates the absorbance to the concentration and the pathlength is called the **absorptivity**, or the **extinction coefficient**, and it is given the symbol ε. The **Beer-Lambert Law** provides an equation relating the absorbance (*A*), pathlength (*b*), concentration (*c*) and extinction coefficient (ε):

$$A = \varepsilon bc$$

The UV-vis spectra shown below illustrate the Beer-Lambert Law:

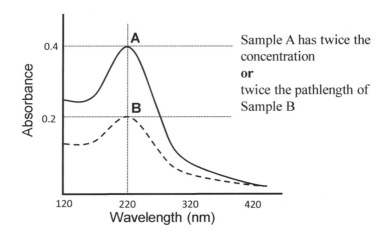

Usually, a sample cell with a pathlength of 1 cm is used, which simplifies the relationship between absorbance and concentration. The well-defined way that absorbance relates to concentration for a given pathlength allows us to measure the concentration of a molecule as a function of time with very high accuracy and sensitivity. As a result, **UV-vis spectroscopy is an excellent way to quantify reaction rates**. Let us consider, as an example, a sample that contains 1 mole each of reactants **A** and **B**, where **B** is the only species that absorbs at 500 nm, and you experimentally measure an absorbance of 0.6. After 1 h has elapsed, you measure the absorbance at 500 nm and now obtain a value of 0.3, which allow you to deduce that the reaction between **A** and **B** has proceeded at a rate of 0.5 moles h^{-1} during this time period.

216

Lesson VII.3.1: Infrared Radiation Causes Vibrational Transitions in Molecules

In Lessons VII.1–2, we saw how UV-vis light interacted with organic molecules to cause electronic transitions. In this lesson, we will learn what happens when lower-energy IR light interacts with organic molecules. Unlike UV-vis light, infrared light does not have enough energy to cause an electron to be promoted to a higher electronic level in the majority of organic molecules. Instead, molecules undergo **vibration** upon interaction with IR light. The wavelength of light that is most commonly used to study the vibrational modes of organic molecule runs from about 2500-20,000 nm. There are several modes of molecular vibration that result when a molecule absorbs infrared energy. Molecular vibrational modes can be broadly divided into **stretching** and **bending** modes. Stretching modes involve changes in the bond lengths. Bending modes involve changes in bond angles. Bond stretching and bond bending in molecules occurs in well-defined combinations at specific energies. Let us begin by looking at the stretching modes. Consider how the C–H bonds in a CH_2 unit might undergo stretching in a molecule:

Symmetric stretch:
bonds lengthen
and shorten at the
same time

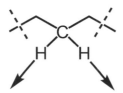

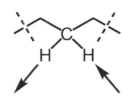

Asymmetric stretch:
One bond lengthens
as the other shortens

There are more possibilities for bending modes. Not only may a given bending mode be symmetric or asymmetric, but the different bending modes may involve the atoms remaining coplanar as they bend, or they may bend in a way that they are no longer coplanar:

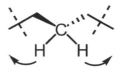

Symmetric in-plane bending:
Both angles increase or
decrease at the same time by
bending in the plane of the page

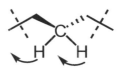

Asymmetric in-plane bending:
One angle increases as the
other decreases by bending in
the plane of the page

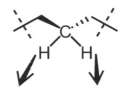

Symmetric out-of-plane bending:
Both angles increase or decrease
at the same time by bending out of
the plane of page (here, both
shown bending towards the viewer)

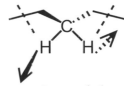

Asymmetric out-of-plane bending:
One angle increases as the other
decreases by bending out of the
plane of page (here, one bending
towards, one away from the viewer)

Lesson VII.3.2: Different Types of Bonds Absorb IR Radiation at Different Energies

Bonds can be thought of as springs. The strength of a spring is reflected in how much energy it takes to stretch and compress it. Likewise, the energy at which a bond stretches depends on the strength of the bond. A stronger bond requires more energy to stretch than does a weaker bond. This means that a set of strong bonds absorbs a higher energy of IR light than does a set of weaker bonds. This means that a vibrational mode involving a set of strong bonds will absorb higher energy light than a set of weaker bonds. This phenomenon is invaluable for determining the chemical identity of bonds present in a given sample based on what energies of IR light the sample absorbs.

In addition to the energy of the IR light absorbed, the *amount* of light absorbed per molecule can also provide us with information about the bonds present. Due to some considerations that are outside the scope of this course, one result of how light and charged species interact is that the more polar bonds in a sample absorb more of the IR energy to which the sample is exposed than do less polar bonds. The next lesson will illustrate how the interaction of a molecule with IR light can be used to infer structural information about that molecule.

Lesson VII.4.1: The IR Spectrum

In Lesson VII.3, we learned that a molecule absorbs IR light of an appropriate energy to excite vibrational modes for specific sets of bonds in that molecule. In the current lesson, we will learn how scientists have developed a technique that allows us to use this property of matter to gain a wide range of knowledge about molecules and reactions. The infrared spectrometer instrument setup is very similar to the UV-vis spectrometer we saw in Lesson VII.2, but using IR radiation in place of UV-vis wavelength light:

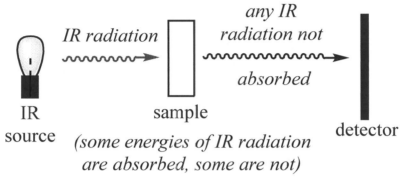

A typical IR spectrum provided by the IR spectrophotometer is a plot of transmittance (the % of light that is **not absorbed** by the sample) versus the energy of light (in units of **wavenumbers**, cm⁻¹). A higher wavenumber value corresponds to higher energy. If a sample absorbs all of the IR radiation from the IR source, the transmittance would be zero and a downward peak would extend all the way to the bottom of the spectrum:

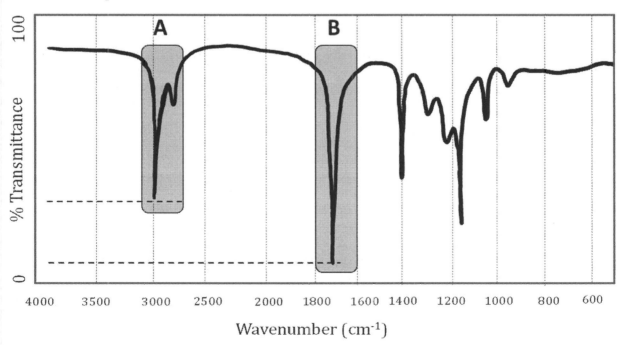

The above spectrum shows the typical *x*-axis range of 4000–500 cm^{-1} (high energy to low energy). Two bands are highlighted. Band **A** corresponds to a set of bonds that absorbs ~75% of the IR light at 3000 cm^{-1} emitted by the source (i.e., 25% transmittance), whereas band **B** corresponds to a set of bonds that absorbs nearly 95% of the IR light at 1750 cm^{-1} (i.e., 5% transmittance).

Lesson VII.4.2: Information Provided by the IR Spectrum

The infrared spectrum of a compound can provide information about the types of bonds, and therefore the functional groups, that are present in a given compound. IR spectra are usually less cluttered at the higher-energy region of the IR spectrum (4000–1500 cm^{-1}), which is referred to as the **functional group region**. The lower-energy region of the IR spectrum of the spectrum (1500–500 cm^{-1}) is referred to as the **fingerprint region**, because the peaks there are characteristic to each given molecule. However, the fingerprint region is significantly more cluttered and is thus more difficult to assign specific transitions. The characteristic peaks for the common functional groups encountered in an undergraduate organic chemistry course are provided below:

Bond	Energy (cm^{-1})	Intensity
N≡C	2255-2220	m-s
C≡C	2260-2100	w-m
C=C	1675-1660	m
N=C	1650-1550	m
⬡	1600 **AND**	w-s
	1500-1425	
C=O	1775-1650	s
C—O	1250-1000	s
C—N	1230-1000	m
O—H	3650-3200	s (br)
O—H	3300-2500	s (br)
N—H	3500-3300	m (br)
C—H	3300-2725	m

C-H Bond (Stretch)	Energy (cm^{-1})
C≡C—H	3300-ish
C=C—H	3100-3000
C—C—H	2950-2850
(aldehyde)	2820-ish and 2720-ish

C-H Bond (Bending)

—CH$_3$
—CH$_2$—
—C— } 1450-1400

980-960
trans

730-670
cis

840-800
trisubstituted

990 and 910
monosubstituted

890
disubstituted terminal

220

Lesson VII.4.3: Interpreting IR Spectra for Simple Molecules

Knowing the energy at which each of the common organic functional groups absorbs in the IR spectrum, we are now able to look at an IR spectrum and identify what specific functional groups are present or absent. The following examples demonstrate the method by which one deduces the possible structure of a compound from its IR spectrum. Numerous examples to illustrate how IR spectra can be used to gain structural information are provided in Part VIII.

Lesson VII.4.4: Influence of Resonance and Pi-Conjugation on IR Band Energies

We know that the resonance hybrid structure is a better representation of the "real" structure of a molecule. The resonance hybrid reflects the fact that the "real" bond order in the hybrid structure is different from that in any of the individual resonance contributors. Consider, for example, the resonance hybrid for a carboxamide that takes into account the two contributors:

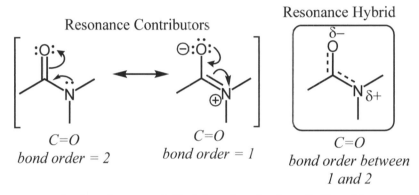

One result of the resonance is that the actual C–O bond order is < 2. For this reason, the C=O bond in a carboxamide is weaker than a C=O bond that does not participate in resonance delocalization, and will thus have an IR band at a lower wavenumber (~1680 cm⁻¹). As a rule of thumb, a C=O bond that can engage in resonance delocalization with an adjacent C=C bond will have a peak at ~20 cm⁻¹ lower in energy than a C=O bond that does not participate in resonance. Resonance effects can also be observed in the IR absorptions by C=C bonds. Notice in the table of IR absorptions in Lesson VII.4.2 that a C=C bond in a typical alkene absorbs in the 1660–1675 cm⁻¹ range, whereas a C=C bond in an arene absorbs at energies below 1600 cm⁻¹. This reflects the resonance delocalization of π-bonds in arene rings, whose highest C–C bond order is 1.5, rather than the 2 for a typical alkene.

Lesson VII.5.1: Behavior of Nuclei in a Magnetic Field

Although chemistry primarily focuses on electrons, the behavior of some nuclei can provide useful information about the bonding within a molecule. This information can be obtained due to the fact that some nuclei have *magnetic* dipoles (not to be confused with dipoles in polar molecules). Not all elements and not all isotopes of a single element have a nuclear magnetic dipole, but fortunately many of the elements present in common organic molecules do have isotopes whose nuclei have magnetic dipoles: hydrogen-1 (^{1}H), carbon-13 (^{13}C), phosphorus-31 (^{31}P), and fluorine-19 (^{19}F). Nuclei such as these that have magnetic dipoles are called **NMR active** nuclei and can be observed by **Nuclear Magnetic Resonance (NMR) spectrometry**. Under typical conditions, the magnetic dipole vectors for the nuclei in a sample will be oriented in random directions. If an external magnetic field is applied, however, these magnetic vectors will align such that they are pointing in either the same direction (parallel) or opposite direction (antiparallel) of the applied field:

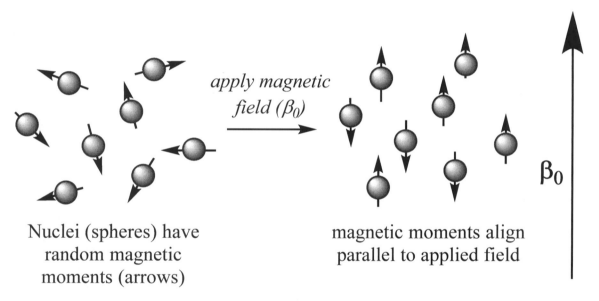

apply magnetic field (β_0)

β_0

Nuclei (spheres) have random magnetic moments (arrows)

magnetic moments align parallel to applied field

Nuclei that are aligned parallel with a magnetic field will have a lower energy than nuclei aligned antiparallel. The stronger the applied field, the greater the energy difference (ΔE) between these two spin states. In the magnetic field strength used in NMR spectroscopy, the energy difference between these two spin states is comparable to the energy of a photon in the radio frequency range (usually 60–1000 MHz). When **radio frequency (RF) radiation** is transmitted into the sample at an energy that matches ΔE, these photons will be absorbed and will promote nuclei from the lower-energy parallel spin state to the higher-energy antiparallel spin state:

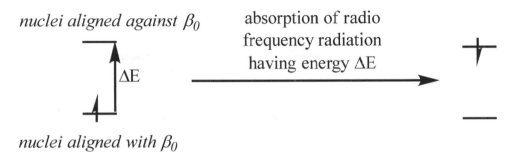

nuclei aligned against β₀

absorption of radio
frequency radiation
having energy ΔE

nuclei aligned with β₀

The detector in an NMR spectrometer measures the absorption of the RF energy and can thus report the energy between states for each nucleus in a sample.

Lesson VII.5.2: The NMR Spectrum

An NMR spectrometer subjects a sample to a strong magnetic field. A coil around the sample detects absorption of RF photons applied by the instrument. Each instance of the absorption of RF radiation is detected and reported to a computer, whereby this energy absorption is represented as an upwards-pointing peak (also known as a **signal**). The particular magnetic field and radio frequency range required depend on the specific type of nucleus that is being detected. A ¹H NMR spectrum will have an appearance like this:

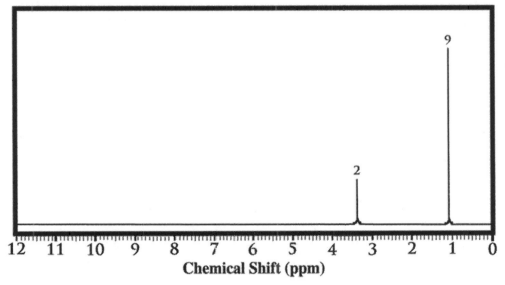

This example features two signals: one at 1.1 ppm and one at 3.3 ppm on the *x*-axis. The units of the *x*-axis are **parts per million (ppm)** and correspond to **chemical shift**, which correlates with energy. In the rest of this Lesson, we will discuss how the chemical shifts of the different nuclei are influenced by (1) the other nuclei and (2) the electrons in the sample. In the few lessons that follow this one, we will study how NMR spectrometry (¹H and ¹³C NMR in particular) can be used to elucidate organic molecule structure.

Lesson VII.5.3: Factors Influencing the Energy Between Spin States

Not all nuclei in a molecule exhibit the same ΔE between spin states, because (1) the electrons in a molecule affect how the various nuclei "experience" β_0 and (2) the electronic environment varies for each nucleus according to its chemical environment. For example, there will be more electron density near a nucleus at the δ^- end of a polar bond than at the δ^+ end. How does this influence the effective magnetic field strength at a given nucleus? Well, not only does β_0 applied by the NMR spectrometer interact with the magnetic spin of nuclei, it also interacts with the magnetic spin of electrons. As a result, the electrons generate their own localized magnetic field that opposes β_0. Thus, as the electron density that surrounds a nucleus increases, the opposing magnetic field those electrons create also increases, which decreases the β_0 that particular nucleus experiences, and consequently it takes less energy to promote that nucleus to a higher spin state. As a result, **electrons shield the nuclei from the applied magnetic field.**

The NMR spectrometry experiment operates on a timescale slower than the rate of σ-bond rotation and slower than the rate of molecular diffusion or rotation. This means that all nuclei that interconvert by free bond rotation or that can be interconverted by molecular rotation are **magnetically equivalent** and will be promoted at identical energies. On the other hand, nuclei that cannot be interconverted by σ-bond or molecular rotation will have slightly different electron densities around them and will thus require a slightly different energy to be promoted. **Each set of magnetically-inequivalent nuclei will give a signal at a different energy in the NMR spectrum**.

Lesson VII.5.4: Effect of Neighboring Nuclei on NMR Energies

As we learned in Lesson VII.5.1, each nucleus has a magnetic dipole that aligns either parallel or antiparallel with the applied magnetic field of an NMR spectrometer. However, just as the magnetic spin of the electrons surrounding a nucleus can affect the β_0 it "experiences", so too can the magnetic spin a neighboring nucleus. This means that, depending on the direction of nucleus A's magnetic field, nucleus A may shield or reinforce the magnetic field experienced by its neighboring nucleus B:

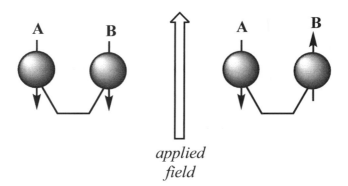

applied field

For a nucleus having one nearby nucleus, then, there are two slightly different energies needed to promote the nucleus. The difference in energies is very slight in cases we will encounter in this book, so the result is that the peak for the nucleus is "split" into two peaks. The peak looks like this:

This peak shape is called a doublet. As more and more nuclei are present on neighboring sites, the number of smaller signals into which a signal splits increases, as does the complexity of the peak shape. The number of peaks into which a signal splits is called the **multiplicity** (*m*). For the nuclei studied in organic chemistry, $m = n+1$, where *n* is the number of nuclei (only counting those capable of causing splitting) on adjacent C atoms. In common organic molecules, a signal that is well-defined will generally not have a multiplicity greater than seven (six splitting atoms on adjacent C atoms). Those signals having a higher multiplicity generally are too broad to readily see the splitting on the strength of spectrometers in common use. The following schematic shows the typical shape of simple **multiplets**:

Type of peak		Ratio of heights
singlet		1
doublet		1:1
triplet		1:2:1
quartet		1:3:3:1
quintet		1:4:6:4:1
sextet		1:5:10:10:5:1
septet		1:6:15:20:15:6:1

Lesson VII.6.1: The NMR Spectrum

In the current Lesson, we will learn how a ^{13}C NMR spectrum can reveal structural information about a molecule. In the previous Lesson, we learned about nuclear magnetic resonance and that the energy at which a nucleus absorbs energy is influenced by its electronic environment. This means that the chemical shifts at which peaks appear in a ^{13}C NMR spectrum reveals the types of carbons in the molecule. The diagram below is a representative sample of a ^{13}C NMR spectrum:

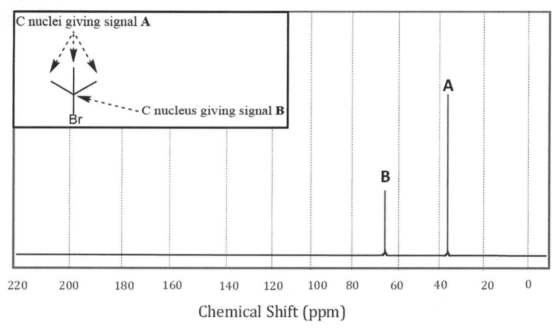

In this spectrum, each ^{13}C nucleus (or set of magnetically inequivalent ^{13}C nuclei) has a resonance that produces an upward-pointing peak.

Lesson VII.6.2: Avoiding Splitting in ^{13}C NMR spectra

We saw in Lesson VII.5 that the interaction of one nuclear magnetic dipole with another can cause an NMR signal to split into a multiplet. This phenomenon can make spectra substantially more difficult to interpret than if each peak was just a singlet. Most ^{13}C NMR spectra typically contain only singlets. Why is this? The first reason is that, although a carbon-13 nucleus is NMR-active, 99% of all carbon atoms in the universe are the carbon-12 isotope which is not NMR-active. It is therefore statistically very unlikely for one ^{13}C atom to be bonded directly to another ^{13}C atom (i.e., 0.01% probability), so C–C splitting is rarely observed. Most organic molecules feature multiple H atoms attached to C. Protons (^1H) are NMR-active nuclei, so the fact that each ^{13}C atom has one or more ^1H atom would produce a lot of splitting in a ^{13}C NMR spectrum and render interpretation nearly impossible. To prevent the splitting of ^{13}C NMR signals by ^1H nuclei, the ^{13}C NMR spectrometer is typically run in **proton-**

decoupled mode. In this mode, the spectrometer suppresses the ^1H splitting effect so that each ^{13}C nucleus in a molecule appears as a single, unsplit peak in the ^{13}C NMR spectrum.

Lesson VII.6.3: Carbon-13 NMR Spectra Provide Information on Types of C in a Sample

We know that the electronic environment around an atom differs based on its chemical environment (number and types of bonds). These differences produce predictable shifts in ^{13}C NMR resonances depending on what substituents the C atoms carry. Chemical shifts for ^{13}C nuclei in the bonding environments most frequently encountered in organic molecules are listed below:

Carbon (Shown)	Chemical Shift	Carbon (Shown)	Chemical Shift
Si(CH₃)₄	0	O—C	50-80
—CH₃	10-35	N—C	40-60
—CH₂—	15-50	C—X	X = I 0-35
—C(H)—	20-60		X = Br 20-65
			X = Cl 35-80
—C—	30-40		
=C<	100-150	(C=O)—Y	Y = H 190-200
			R 200-220
			OR 160-180
			OH 175-185
			NR₂ 165-175
Ph—C—H	110-175		
≡C—	60-85		

Examining the peaks in a ^{13}C NMR spectrum and comparing the chemical shifts therein to this table can provide significant insight into the structure of the molecule. In the ^{13}C NMR spectrum of 2-bromo-2-methylpropane on the previous page, the three magnetically-equivalent methyl carbons produce peak **A** at 35 ppm, which falls within in the range (10–35 ppm) suggested in the table above. The quaternary C attached to the bromine produces a peak at 65 ppm, again within the typical range for carbons bearing Br substituents in the table (20–65 ppm). Even if we were not provided with the structure and only had the spectrum, we could easily conclude that the sample molecule contains no alkenes, carbonyls, alkynes, or aromatics because no ^{13}C resonances characteristic for these functional groups appear in the spectrum.

Lesson VII.7.1: Chemical Shifts in ^{1}H NMR Spectra

In Lesson VII.6, we saw that ^{13}C NMR spectra can provide significant insight into the structures of organic molecules. We can gain even more information from a ^{1}H NMR spectrum, which will look like the following:

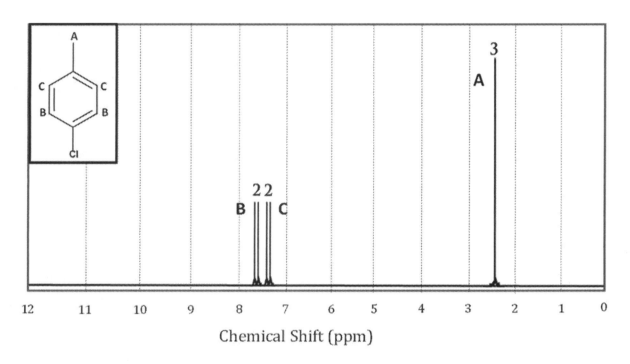

One notable difference between ^{13}C NMR spectra and ^{1}H NMR spectra is that the chemical shift scale for ^{1}H signals in typical organic samples fall in the range of about 0–12 ppm (cf. 0–220 ppm for ^{13}C NMR). Another difference is that ^{1}H NMR spectra often contain multiplets, whereas ^{13}C NMR spectra (by experimental design) only contain singlets.

Although not present in the example above, many ^{1}H NMR samples include tetramethylsilane (TMS) in addition to the molecule of interest, because the TMS speak is set to be 0 ppm as a common reference point for all ^{1}H NMR chemical shifts. Another common reference peak is $CHCl_3$ (7.28 ppm) because chloroform is one of the most commonly used solvents for NMR samples.

Chemical shifts for ^{1}H nuclei in the bonding environments most frequently encountered in organic molecules are listed below:

Protons (Shown)	Chemical Shift	Protons (Shown)	Chemical Shift
$Si(CH_3)_4$	0	$R-OCH_3$	3.3
$-CH_3$	0.9	(vinyl =CH with H)	4.5-5.5
$-CH_2-$	1.2		
$-\overset{H}{\underset{|}{C}}-$	1.4	$H-\overset{|}{\underset{|}{C}}-X$ $\begin{array}{l} X = I \\ X = Br \\ X = Cl \\ X = F \end{array}$	$\begin{array}{l} 2.5\text{-}4 \\ 2.5\text{-}4 \\ 3\text{-}4 \\ 4\text{-}4.5 \end{array}$
(allylic $-CH_3$)	1.7		
$\overset{O}{\overset{\|}{C}}-CH_3$	2.1	(phenyl$-H$)	6.5-8.0
(phenyl$-CH_3$)	2.3	$-\overset{O}{\overset{\|}{C}}-H$	10
$\equiv\!\!-H$	2.4		

Lesson VII.7.2: Integration of Proton Nuclear Magnetic Resonance Signals

In a ^{1}H NMR spectrum, the area under each peak (the **integration or integral**) is proportional to the number of protons that absorb at that energy (the number of protons in that set of magnetically equivalent protons in that group in the sample). The same is not true for a proton-decoupled ^{13}C NMR spectrum. There are several ways to indicate the integration for a given peak in a ^{1}H NMR spectrum. In this book, the integration will be provided as a number printed above the peak. For the spectrum of 4-chlorotoluene (shown in Lesson VII.7.1), the integration of peak **A** is 3, the integration of peak **B** is 2, as is the integration of **C**. The integrations can be very useful in figuring out what type of units are present in a molecule based on NMR data.

In practical settings, the spectrometer does not have a way to know how many protons give a signal, it can only measure the relative integration of one peak with respect to another. As a result, the spectrometer might automatically and arbitrarily provide integrations of 0.60, 0.40 and 0.40 for peaks **A**, **B** and **C** in the spectrum of 4-chlorotoluene. The ratio, 2:2:3, must then be calculated by the user (or software used with the spectrometer) to get the values displayed in the spectrum as shown in this book.

Lesson VII.7.3: Splitting in ^{1}H NMR Spectra

In Lesson VII.5, we saw that the magnetic spin of one nucleus can split the energy of absorption at nearby nuclei. In ^{1}H NMR spectra, the signal for a proton on carbon "X" is notably split into *n+1* subpeaks, where *n* is the total number of H atoms on the carbons directly adjacent to carbon "X". If the directly adjacent atoms are not carbon (i.e., oxygen or nitrogen), the H atoms on these directly adjacent atoms typically do not produce observable splitting. This property allows us to tell **how many H are on C atoms directly adjacent to the carbon bearing the ^{1}H nucleus (or set of ^{1}H nuclei) that produces a particular signal** in a ^{1}H NMR spectrum. If a particular signal is a triplet ($m = 3$), for example, we know that the protons giving rise to this signal are attached to a carbon which has carbons directly adjacent to it carrying a total of 2 protons among them. Numerous examples to illustrate how the chemical shift, integration and multiplicity of resonances in a ^{1}H NMR spectrum can be used to gain structural information are provided in Part VIII.

Bonus Lessons from Part VIII. Spectroscopy Practice with Solutions

Lesson VIII.1.1: Typical Wavenumbers in IR Spectra

This table provides some useful general ranges for where certain types of bonds are likely to show up in IR spectra.

Bond	Energy (cm^{-1})	Intensity
N≡C	2255-2220	m-s
C≡C	2260-2100	w-m
C=C	1675-1660	m
N=C	1650-1550	m
⬡	1600 **AND**	w-s
	1500-1425	
C=O	1775-1650	s
C—O	1250-1000	s
C—N	1230-1000	m
O—H	3650-3200	s (br)
O—H	3300-2500	s (br)
N—H	3500-3300	m (br)
C—H	3300-2725	m

C-H Bond (Stretch)

	Energy (cm^{-1})
C≡C—H	3300-ish
C=C—H	3100-3000
C—C—H	2950-2850
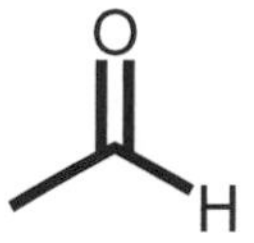 aldehyde C—H	2820-ish and 2720-ish

C-H Bond (Bending)

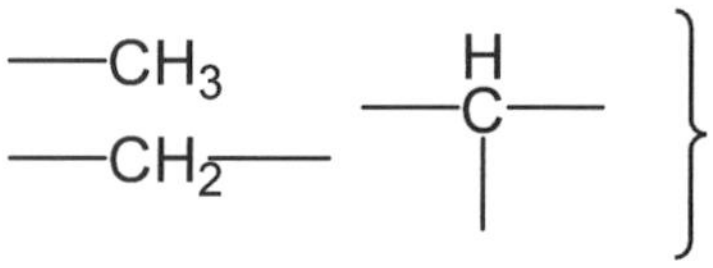

—CH$_3$
—CH$_2$—   —C—   } 1450-1400

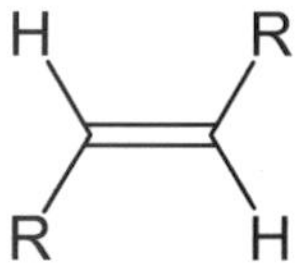

980-960
trans

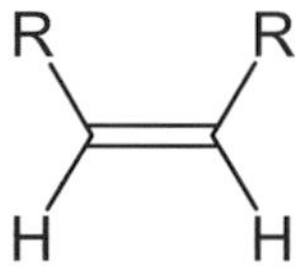

730-670
cis

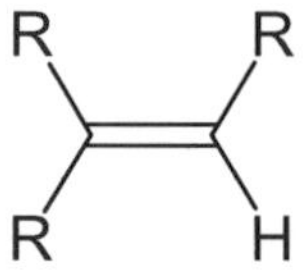

840-800
trisubstituted

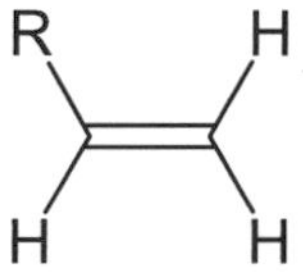

990 and 910
monosubstituted

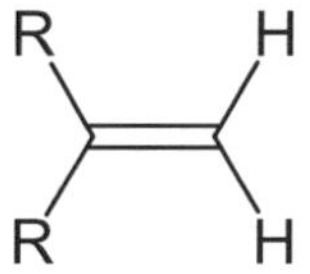

890
disubstituted terminal

Lesson VIII.1.2: Flowchart for Determining Functional Groups Present in Monofunctional Compounds

If only one functional group is present in a particular compound, the following simplified flowchart is a good starting point for determining which functional group it is:

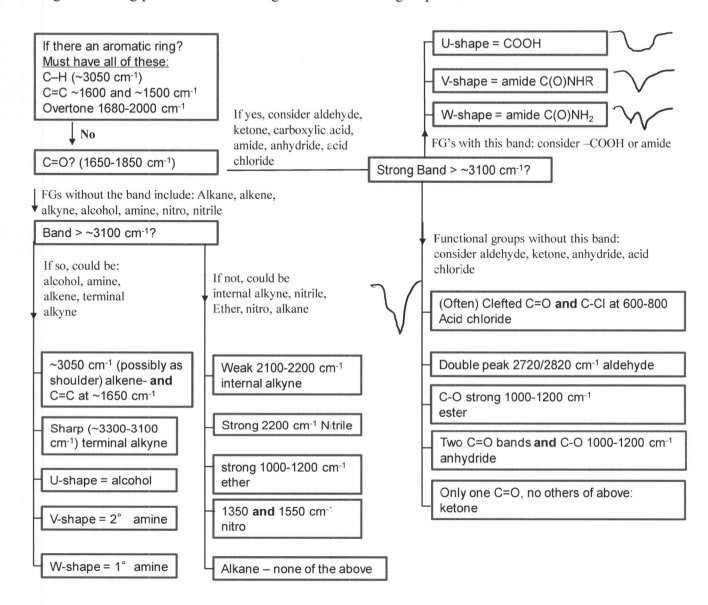

If there an aromatic ring?
<u>Must have all of these:</u>
C–H (~3050 cm^{-1})
C=C ~1600 and ~1500 cm^{-1}
Overtone 1680-2000 cm^{-1}

↓ **No**

C=O? (1650-1850 cm^{-1})

If yes, consider aldehyde, ketone, carboxylic acid, amide, anhydride, acid chloride

U-shape = COOH

V-shape = amide C(O)NHR

W-shape = amide C(O)NH$_2$

FG's with this band: consider –COOH or amide

Strong Band > ~3100 cm^{-1}?

FGs without the band include: Alkane, alkene, alkyne, alcohol, amine, nitro, nitrile

Band > ~3100 cm^{-1}?

If so, could be: alcohol, amine, alkene, terminal alkyne

If not, could be internal alkyne, nitrile, Ether, nitro, alkane

Functional groups without this band: consider aldehyde, ketone, anhydride, acid chloride

(Often) Clefted C=O **and** C-Cl at 600-800 Acid chloride

~3050 cm^{-1} (possibly as shoulder) alkene- **and** C=C at ~1650 cm^{-1}

Weak 2100-2200 cm^{-1} internal alkyne

Double peak 2720/2820 cm^{-1} aldehyde

Sharp (~3300-3100 cm^{-1}) terminal alkyne

Strong 2200 cm^{-1} Nitrile

C-O strong 1000-1200 cm^{-1} ester

U-shape = alcohol

strong 1000-1200 cm^{-1} ether

Two C=O bands **and** C-O 1000-1200 cm^{-1} anhydride

V-shape = 2° amine

1350 **and** 1550 cm^{-1} nitro

Only one C=O, no others of above: ketone

W-shape = 1° amine

Alkane – none of the above

This diagram gives you a good idea for determining the general functional groups present in a sample from the observed ^{13}C NMR chemical shifts:

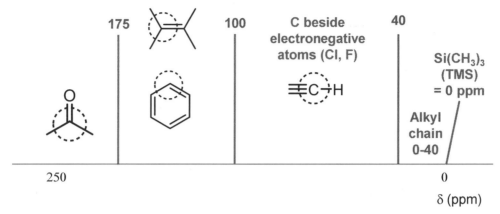

For more fine-tuned determinations than are possible with the above diagram, this table provides useful information on the commonly-observed ^{13}C NMR chemical shifts for different types of carbons:

Carbon (Shown)	Chemical Shift	Carbon (Shown)	Chemical Shift
Si(CH$_3$)$_4$	0	O—C	50-80
—CH$_3$	10-35	N—C	40-60
—CH$_2$—	15-50		
—CH—	20-60	C—X	X = I 0-35
			X = Br 20-65
			X = Cl 35-80
—C—	30-40		
=C<	100-150	C(=O)—Y	Y =
			H 190-200
			R 200-220
			OR 160-180
			OH 175-185
			NR$_2$ 165-175
⬡C—H	110-175		
≡C—	60-85		

Additional note:

Many common ^{13}C NMR spectra also have a peak at 0.00 ppm due to the presence of tetramethylsilane, Si(CH$_3$)$_4$, a standard, as well as a usually intense triplet at 77 ppm due to the presence of deuterated chloroform, CDCl$_3$, a solvent often used for NMR spectra.

This diagram gives you a good idea for determining the general functional groups present in a sample from the observed ^1H NMR chemical shifts:

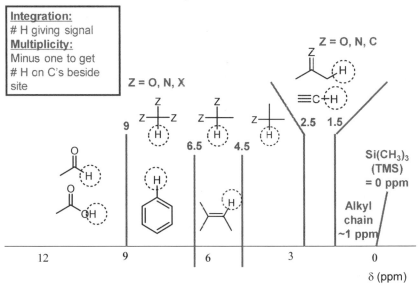

For more fine-tuned determinations than are possible with the above diagram, this table provides useful information on the commonly-observed ^1H NMR chemical shifts for different types of protons:

Protons (Shown)	Chemical Shift	Protons (Shown)	Chemical Shift
$Si(CH_3)_4$	0	R—OCH_3	3.3
—CH_3	0.9		4.5-5.5
—CH_2—	1.2		
—C— (H)	1.4		X = I 2.5-4
		H—C—X	X = Br 2.5-4
CH_3	1.7		X = Cl 3-4
C(=O)—CH_3	2.1		X = F 4-4.5
		—H	6.5-8.0
—CH_3	2.3		
		C(=O)—H	10
≡—H	2.4		

Additional note:

Many common ^1H NMR spectra also have a peak at 0.00 ppm due to the presence of tetramethylsilane, $Si(CH_3)_4$, a standard, as well as at 7.28 ppm due to the presence of chloroform, $CHCl_3$, present in the deuterated chloroform that is a solvent often used for NMR spectra.

Lesson VIII.2. Infrared Spectroscopy Practice Problems

For each of the following, determine which of the potential structures is most likely to have produced the provided IR spectrum.

Problem 1:

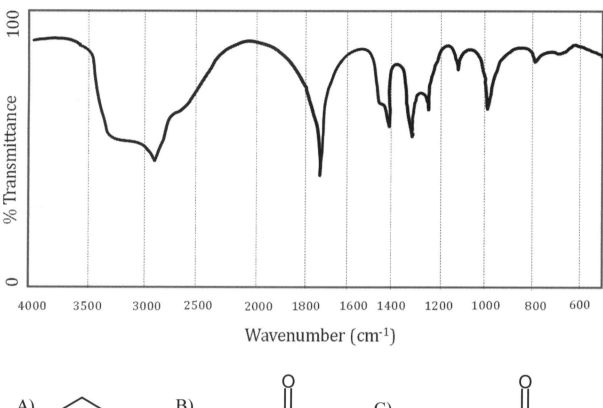

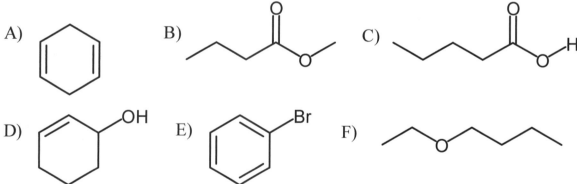

Problem 2:

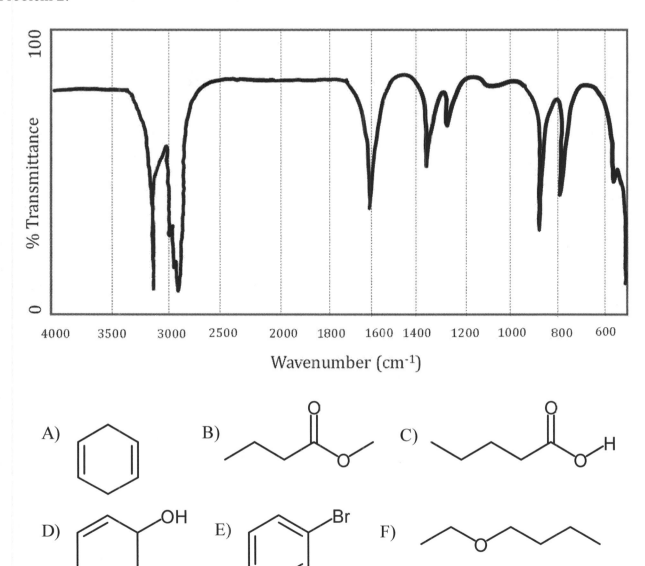

A)

B)

C)

D)

E)

F)

Problem 3:

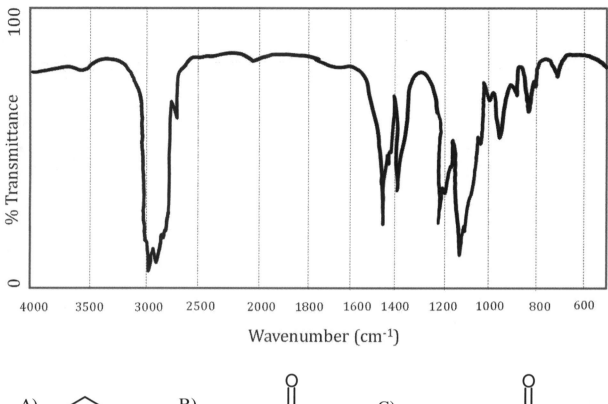

Wavenumber (cm⁻¹)

A)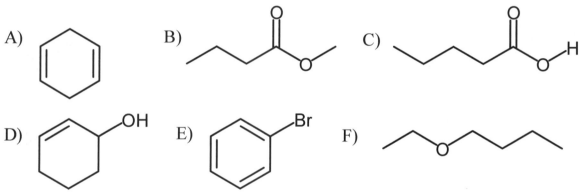

Problem 4:

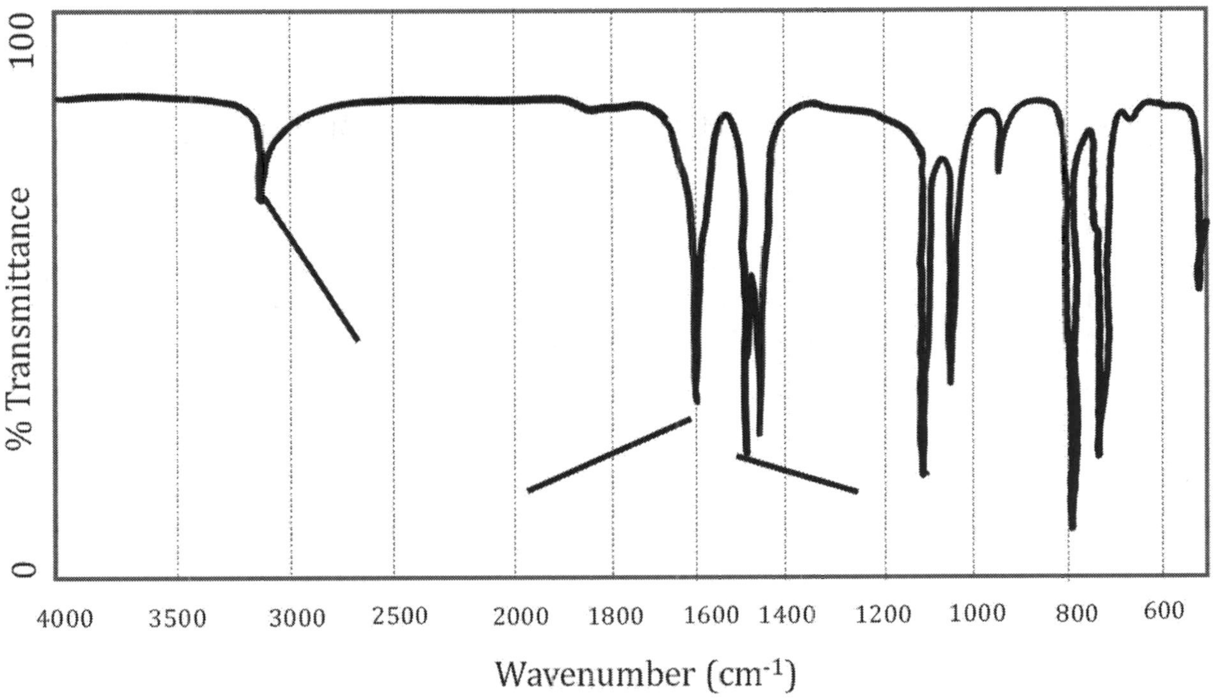

A) 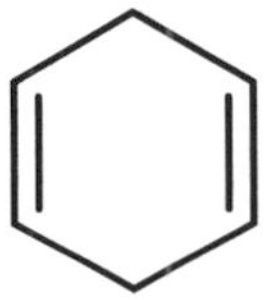

B) 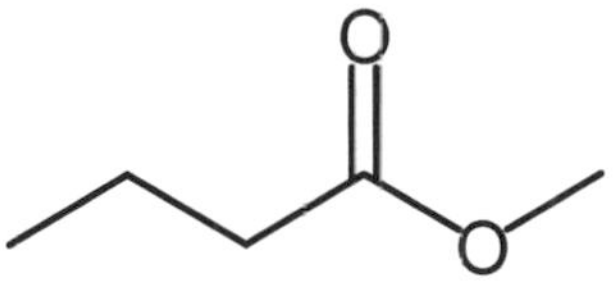

C) 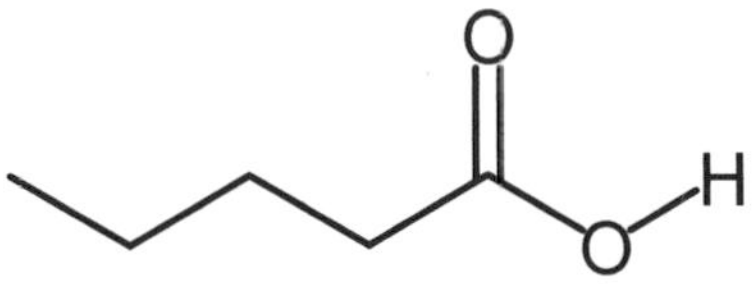

D) 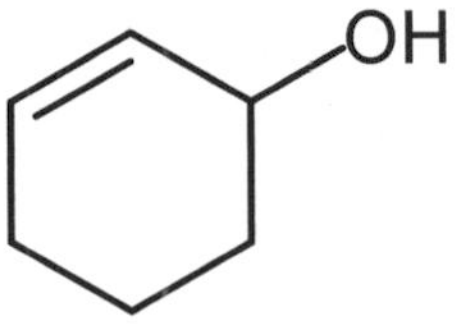

E) 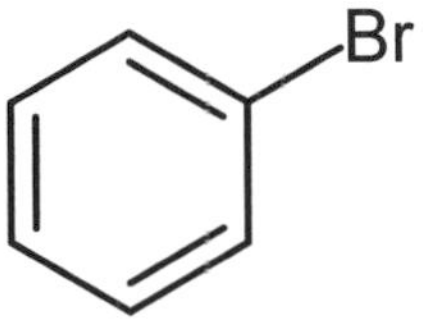

F) 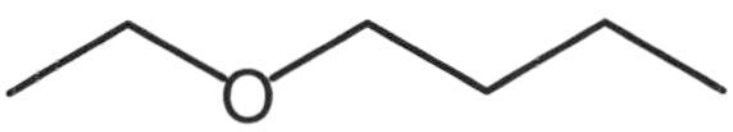

Problem 5:

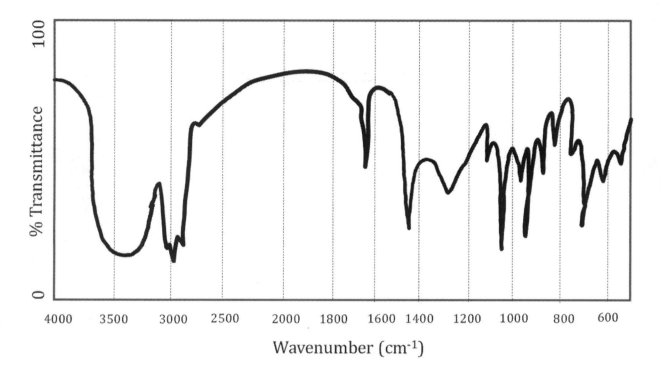

Wavenumber (cm⁻¹)

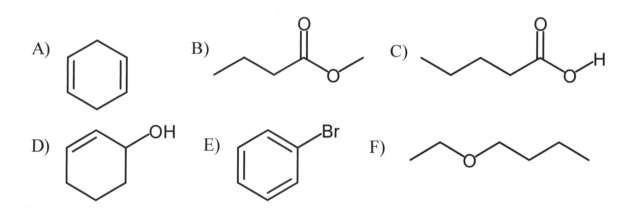

A)

B)

C)

D)

E)

F)

Problem 6:

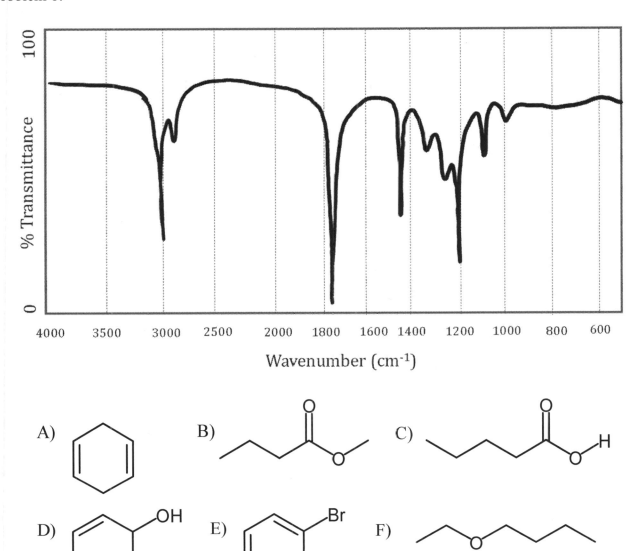

A)

B)

C)

D)

E)

F)

Problem 7:

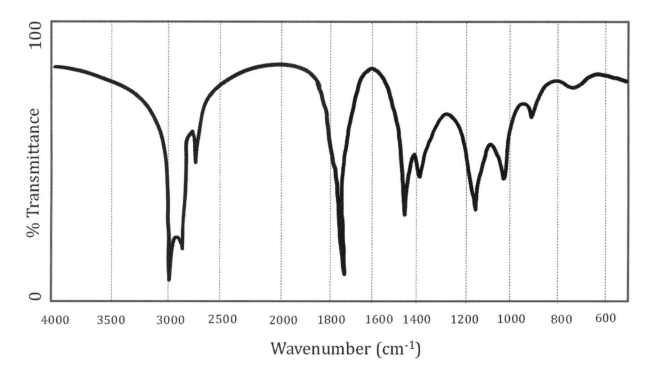

A)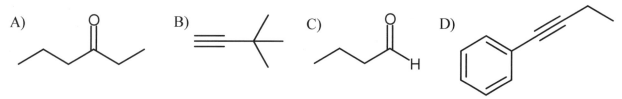

B)

C)

D)

Problem 8:

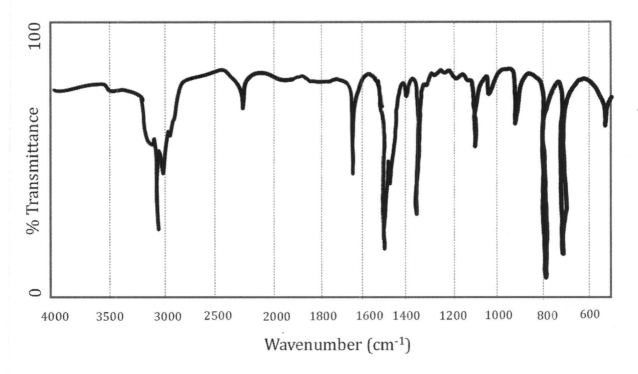

A)

B)

C)

D)

Problem 9:

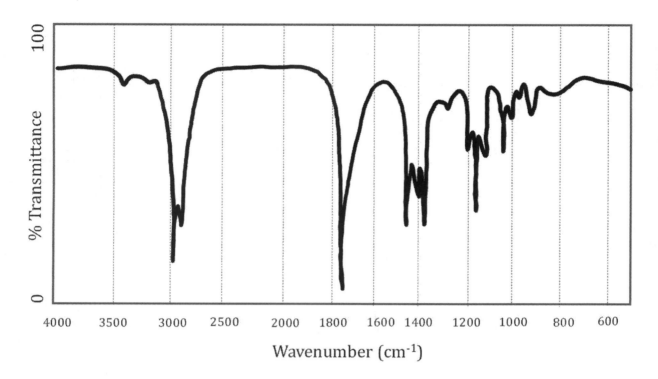

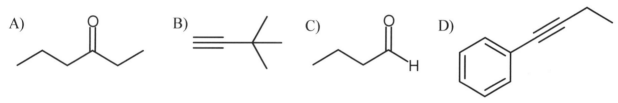

A)

B)

C)

D)

244

Problem 10:

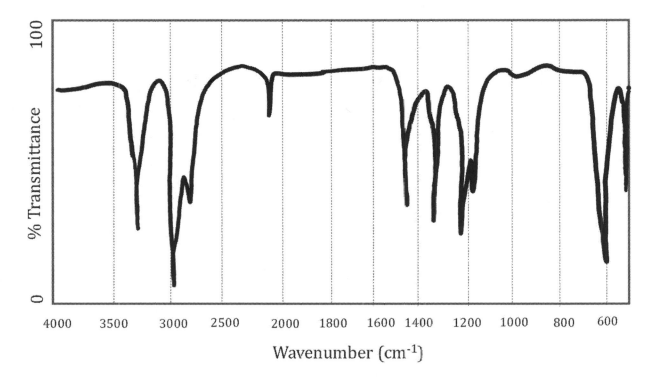

Wavenumber (cm⁻¹)

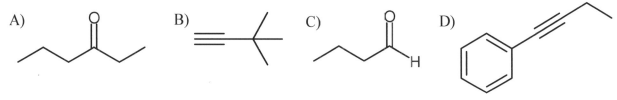

A)

B)

C)

D)

Problem 11:

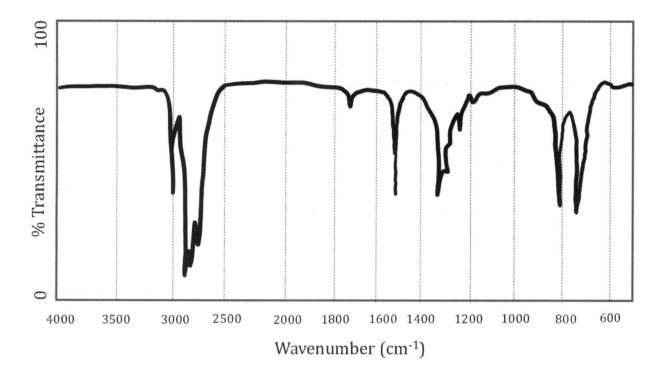

A)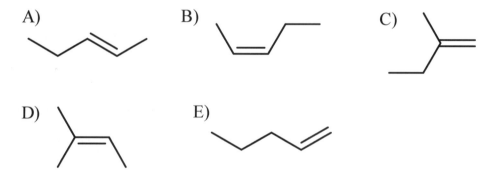

B)

C)

D)

E)

246

Problem 12:

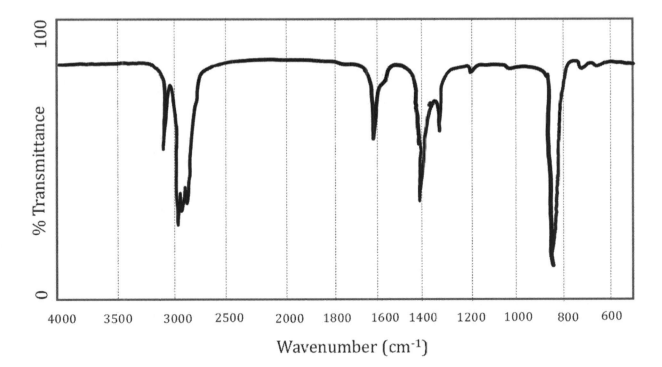

A)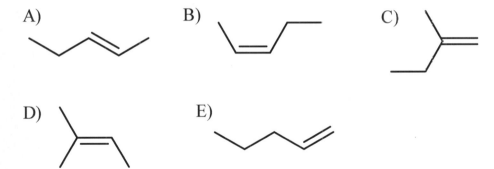

B)

C)

D)

E)

247

Problem 13:

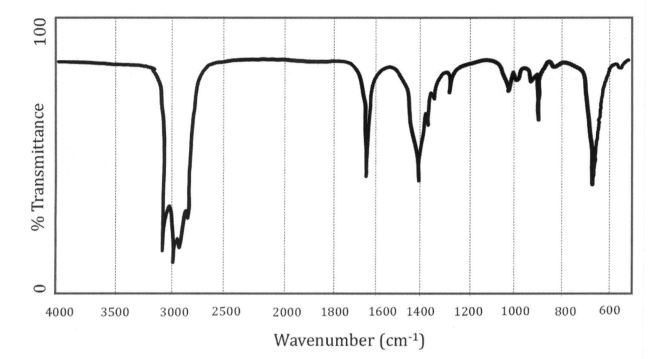

A)

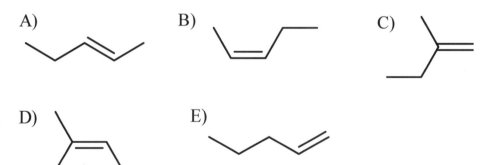

B)

C)

D)

E)

Problem 14:

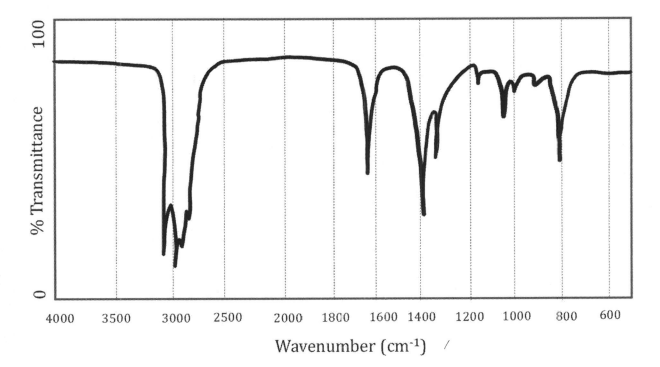

Wavenumber (cm⁻¹)

A)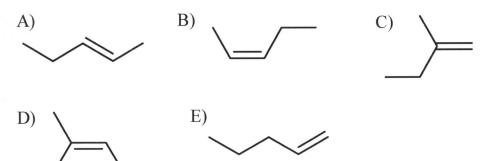

B)

C)

D)

E)

Problem 15:

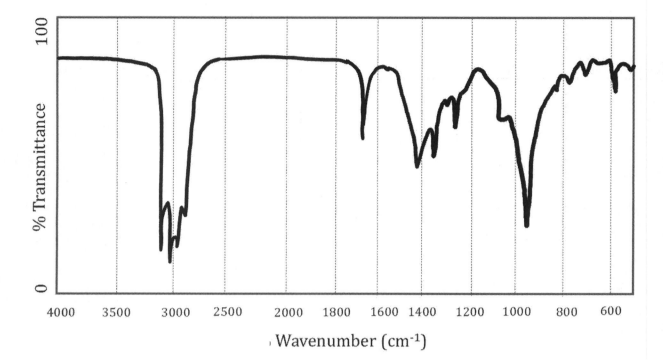

Wavenumber (cm⁻¹)

A)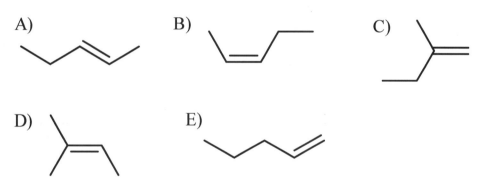

B)

C)

D)

E)

Answer to Problem 1:

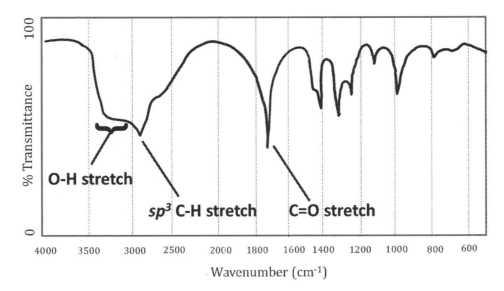

Answer to Problem 2:

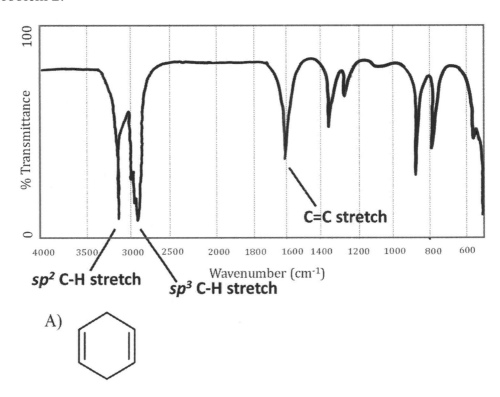

Answer to Problem 3:

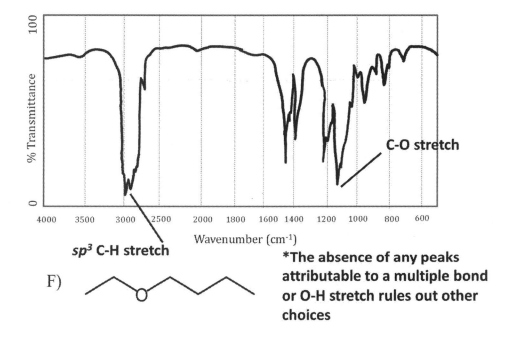

sp³ C-H stretch

C-O stretch

F)

*The absence of any peaks attributable to a multiple bond or O-H stretch rules out other choices

Answer to Problem 4:

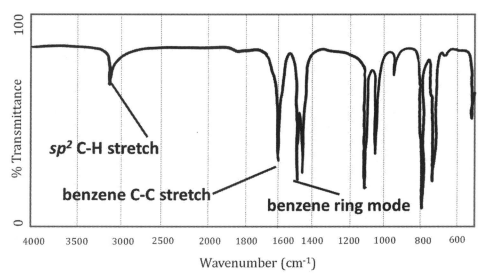

sp² C-H stretch

benzene C-C stretch

benzene ring mode

E)

Answer to Problem 5:

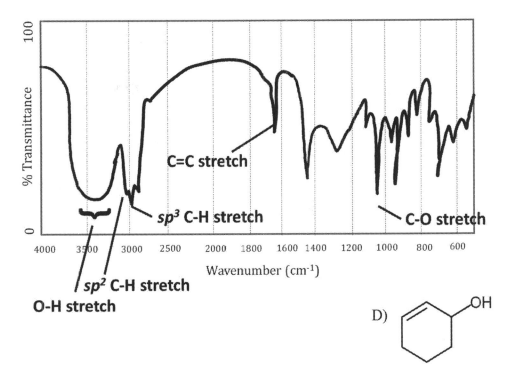

Answer to Problem 6:

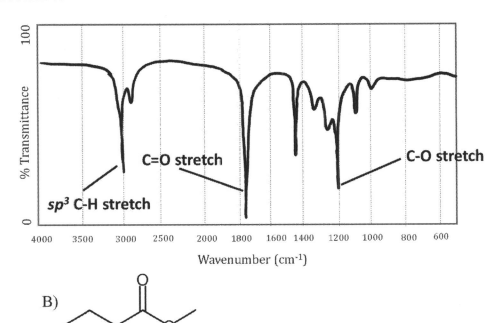

Answer to Problem 7:

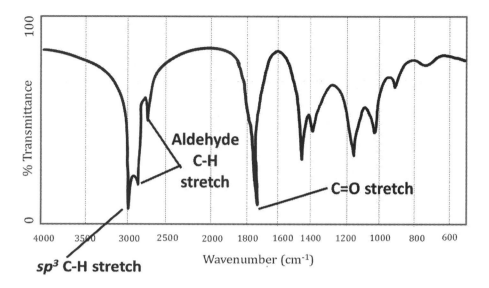

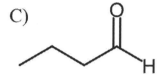

Answer to Problem 8:

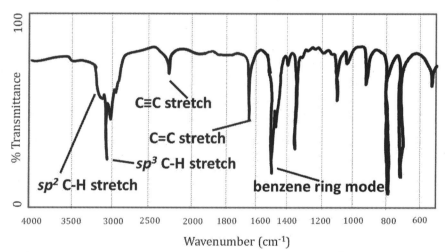

*The absence of an *sp* C-H stretch at 3300 cm⁻¹ rules out a terminal alkyne

Answer to Problem 9:

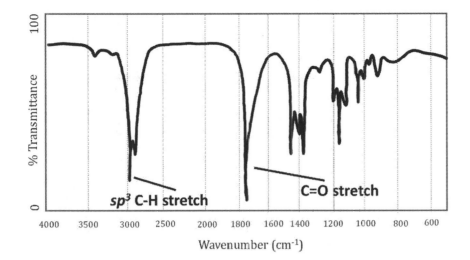

A)

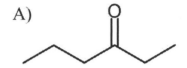

Answer to Problem 10:

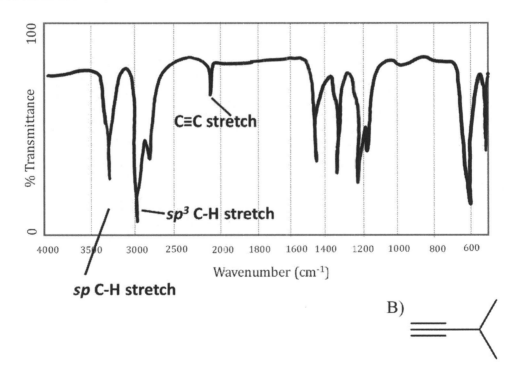

B)

Answer to Problem 11:

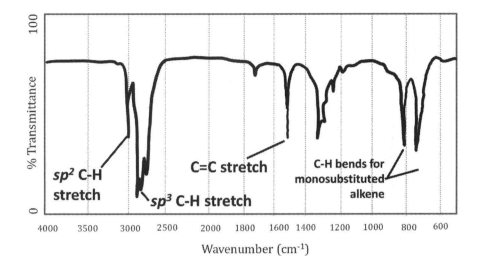

E)

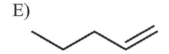

Answer to Problem 12:

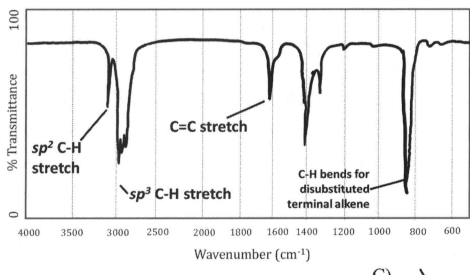

C)

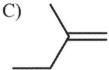

Answer to Problem 13:

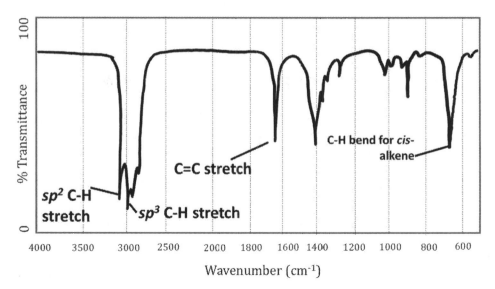

B)

Answer to Problem 14:

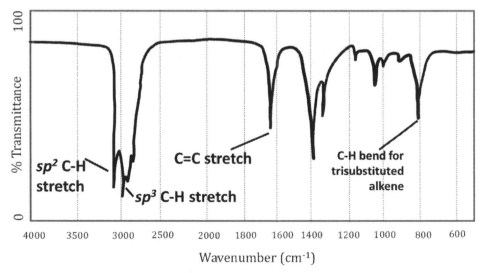

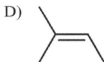

D)

Answer to Problem 15:

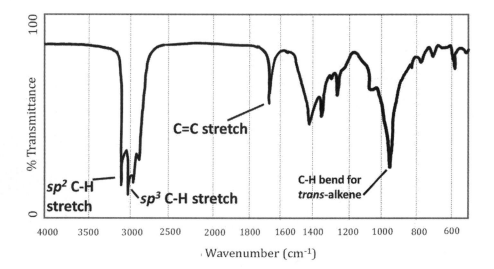

A)

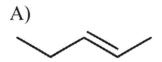

For each of the following, deduce the structure having the provided molecular formula that is most likely to have produced the accompanying ^{1}H NMR spectrum.

Problem 1

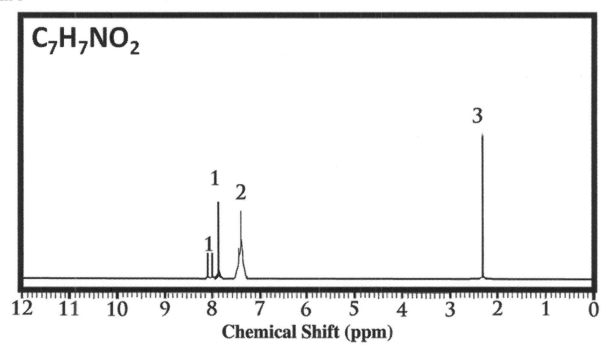

Problem 2

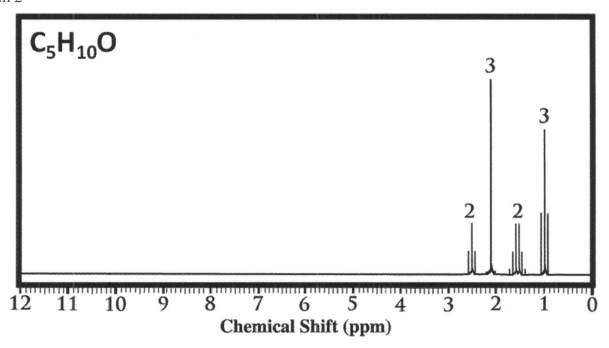

Problem 3

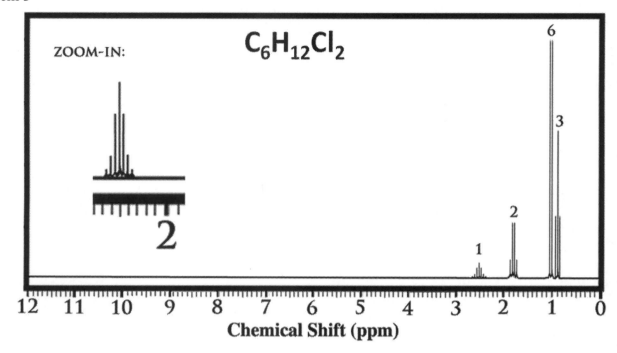

Problem 4

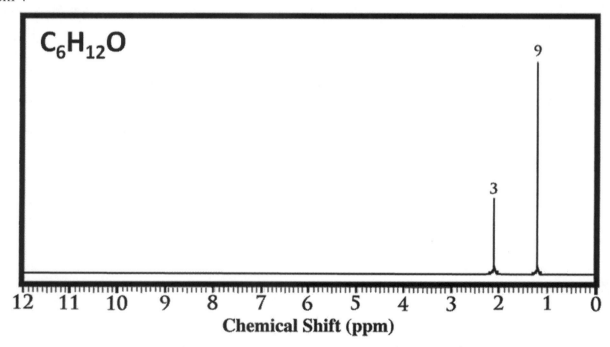

260

Problem 5

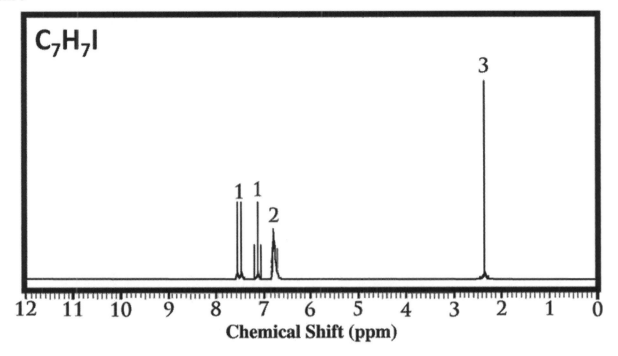

Problem 6

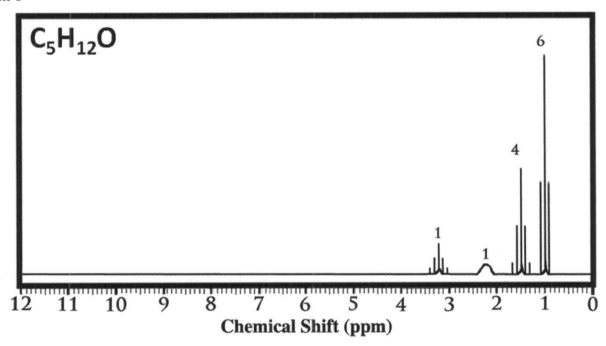

Problem 7

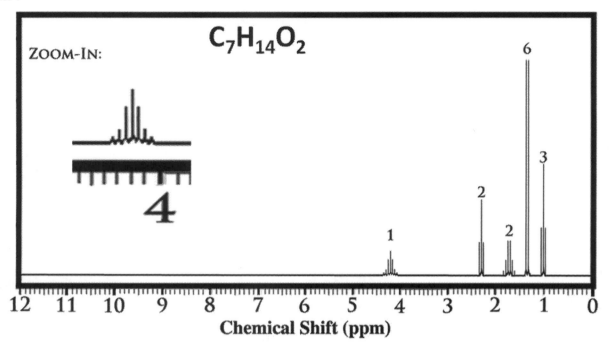

Problem 8

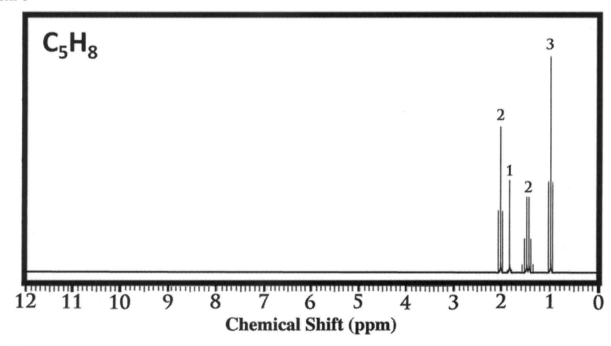

Problem 9

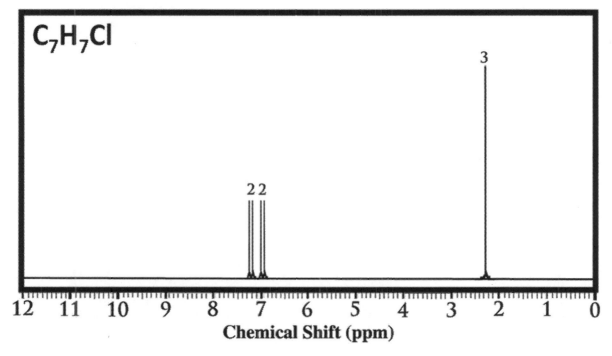

C_7H_7Cl

Problem 10

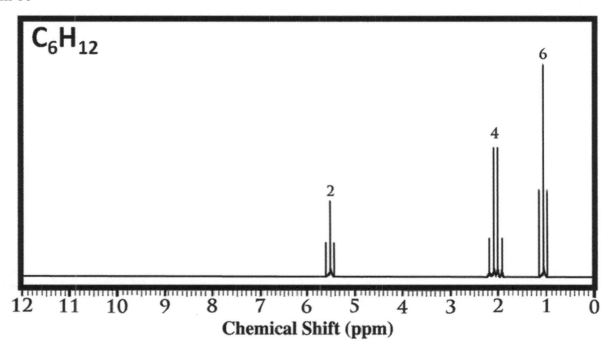

C_6H_{12}

Problem 11

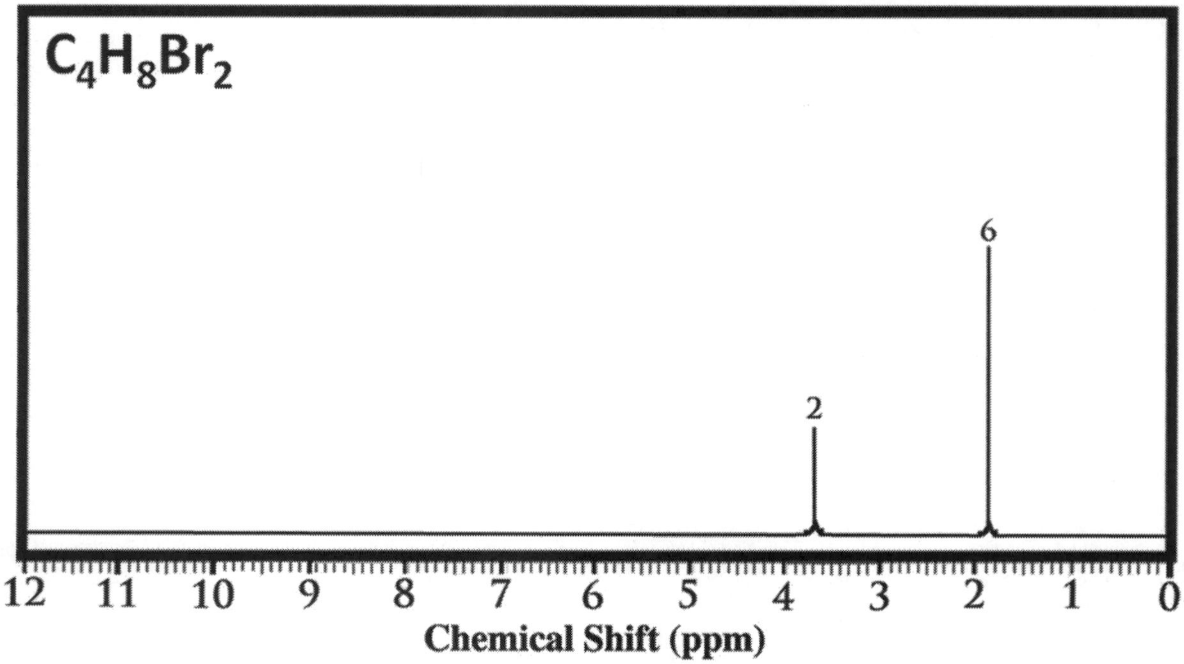

Problem 12

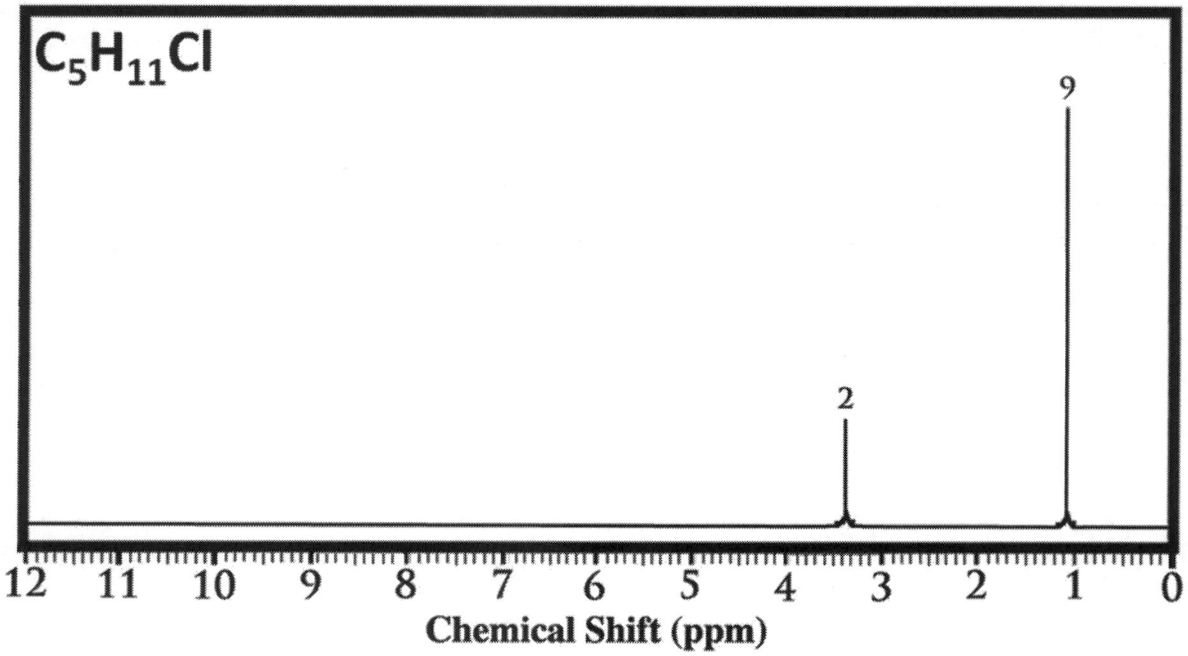

Problem 13

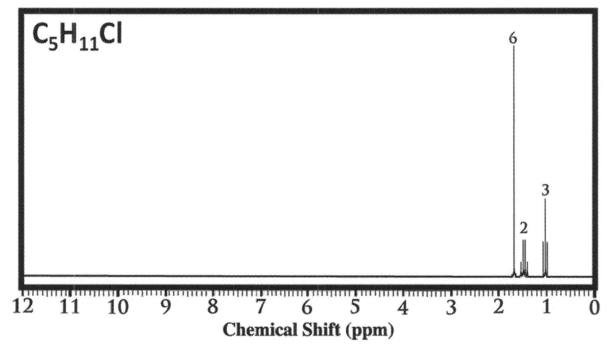

Problem 14

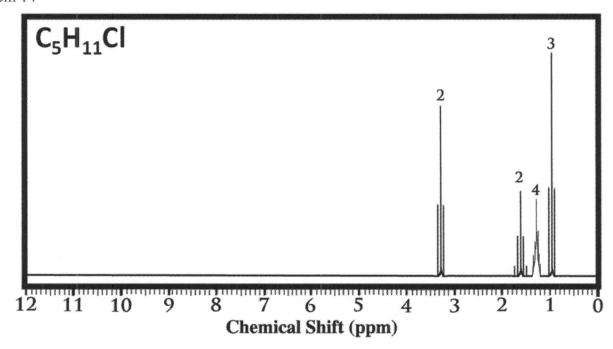

Problem 15

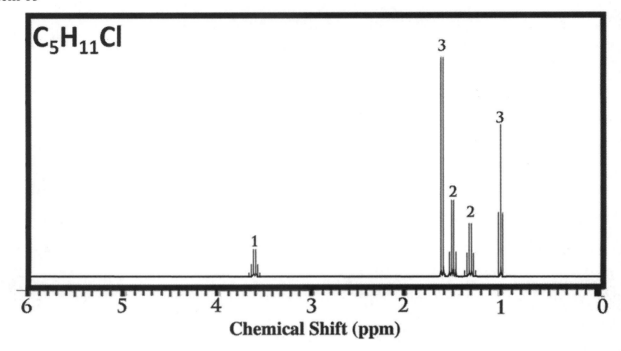

C_5H_11Cl

Answer to NMR Problem 1

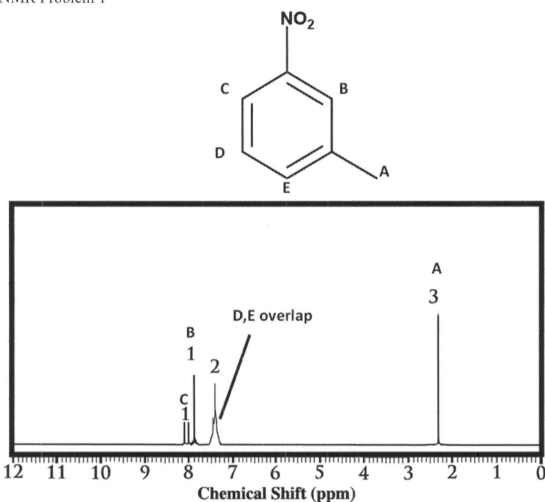

Answer to NMR Problem 2

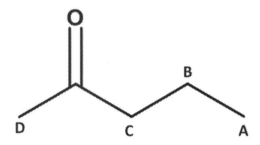

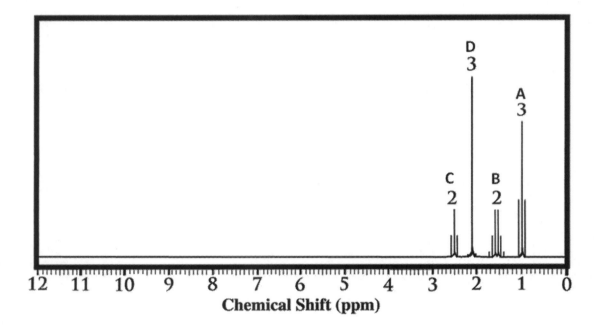

Chemical Shift (ppm)

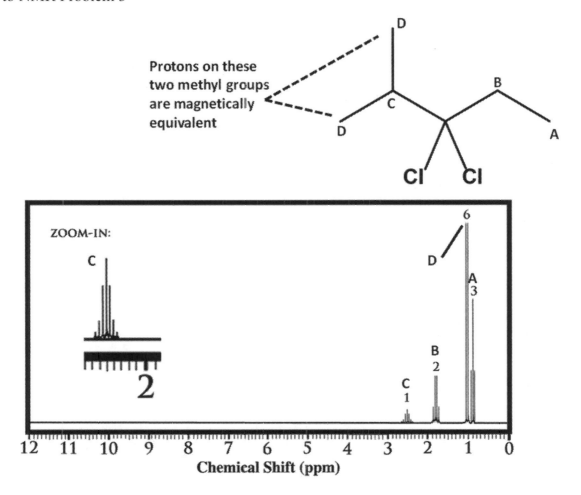

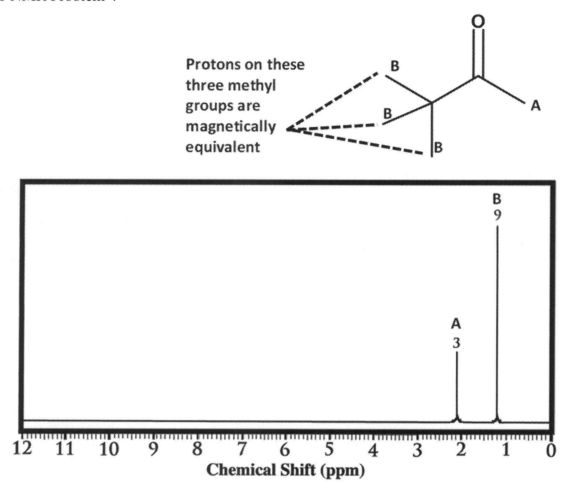

Protons on these three methyl groups are magnetically equivalent

Chemical Shift (ppm)

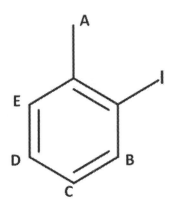

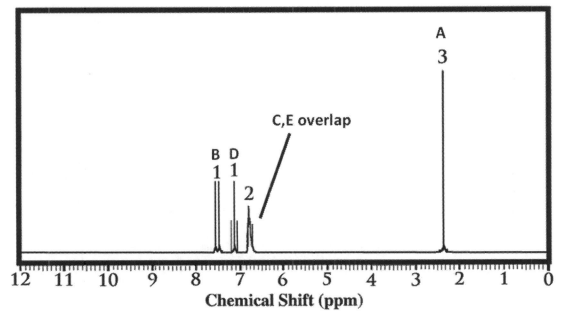

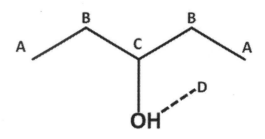

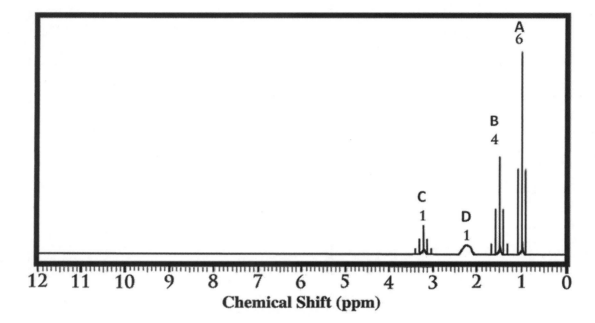

Answer to NMR Problem 7

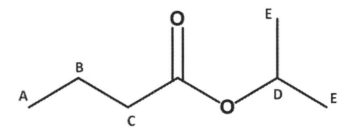

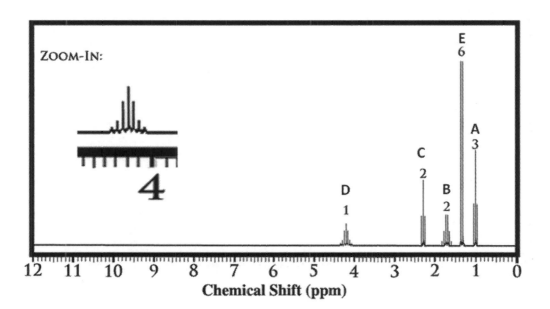

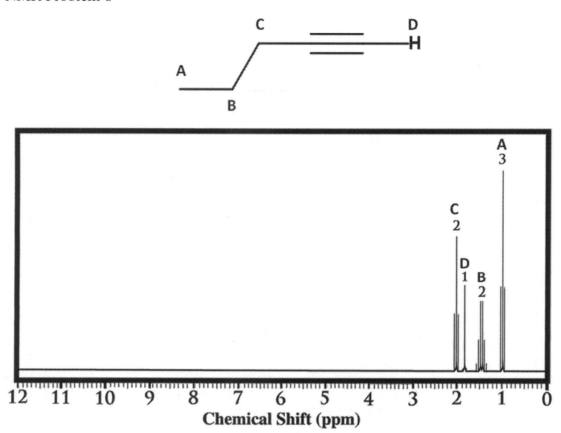

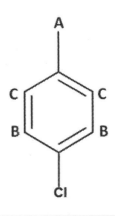

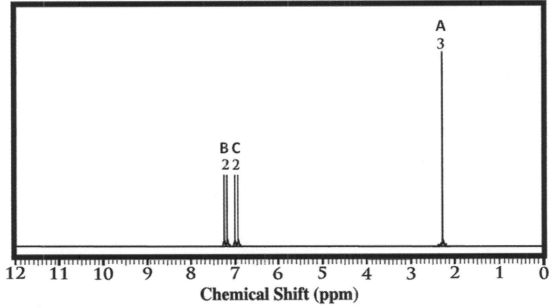

Chemical Shift (ppm)

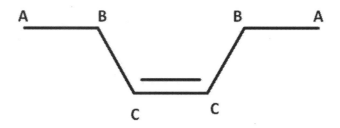

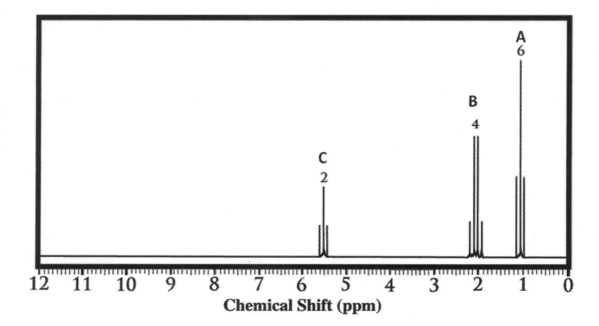

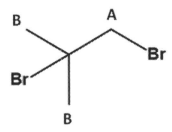

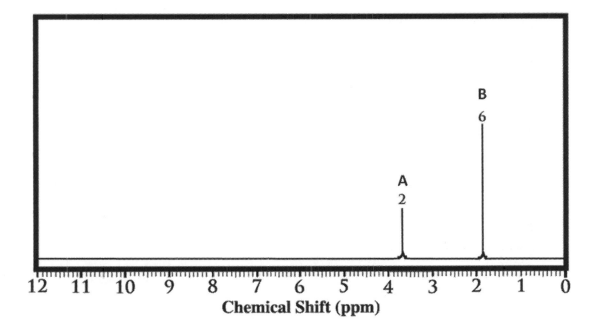

Chemical Shift (ppm)

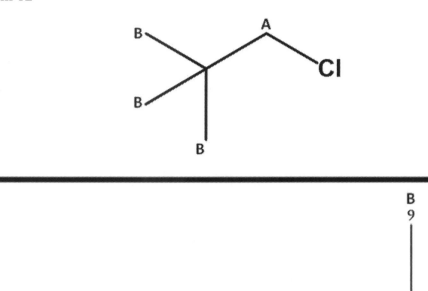

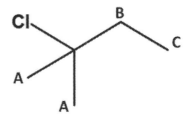

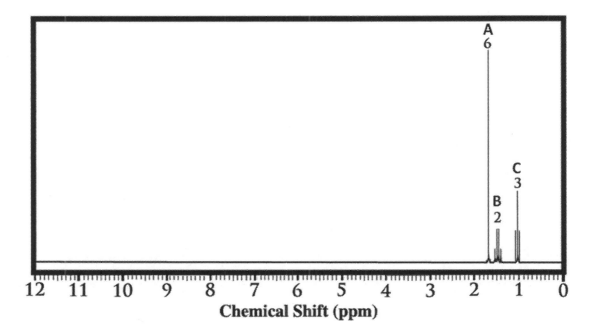

Chemical Shift (ppm)

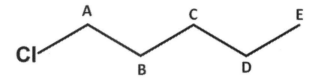

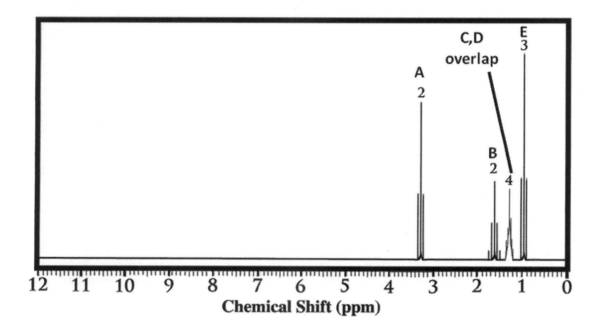

Chemical Shift (ppm)

Answer to NMR Problem 15

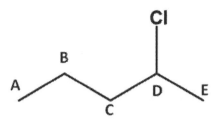

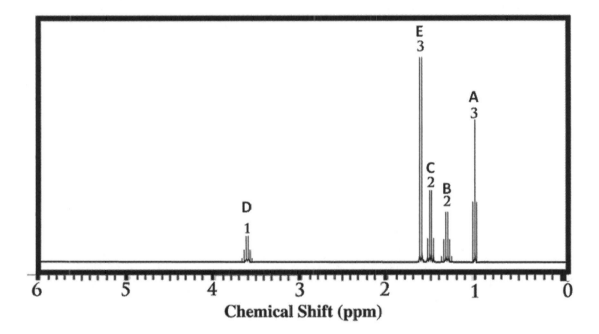

Chemical Shift (ppm)

INDEX

Made in United States
Orlando, FL
16 May 2022

17923537R00157